A&P TECHNICIAN
GENERAL
TEST GUIDE WITH ORAL AND
PRACTICAL STUDY GUIDE

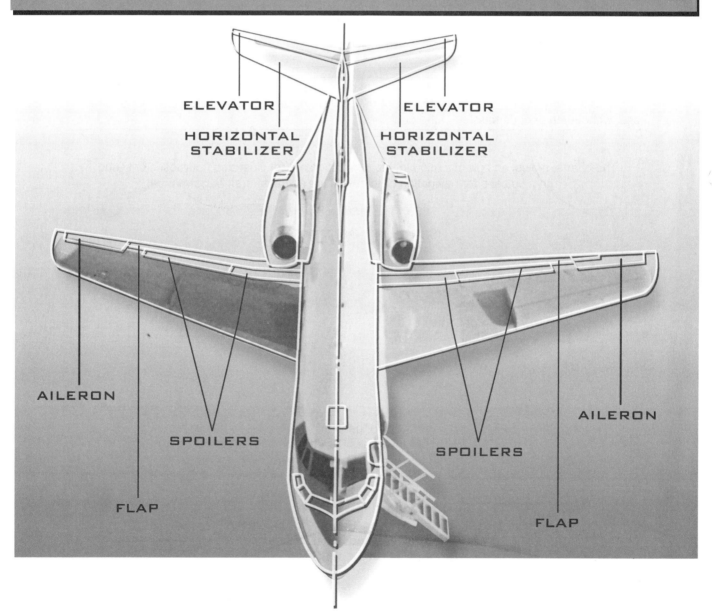

ISBN-13: 978-0-88487-058-6

Jeppesen
55 Inverness Drive East
Englewood, CO 80112-5498
Web Site: www.jeppesen.com
Email: Captain@jeppesen.com
Copyright © Jeppesen
All Rights Reserved. Published 2004-2014
Printed in the United States of America

10002000-007

WELCOME TO THE JEPPESEN
A&P INTEGRATED TRAINING SYSTEM

Our general, airframe, and powerplant mechanic course materials are fully integrated, providing a complete and systematic training program. Textbooks and test guides are written in a simple to understand format, delivering all the necessary information for you to obtain your aircraft maintenance certificate and ratings. Course materials are organized into the same chapter and section formats to integrate study as you progress through each subject area. FAA Learning Statement Code topics are fully covered and cross-referenced in test guide materials.

TEXTBOOKS

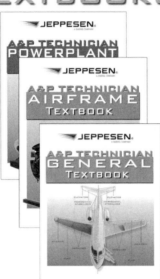

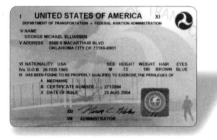

TEST
GUIDES
WITH ORAL AND PRACTICAL STUDY GUIDES

REFERENCE
BOOKS

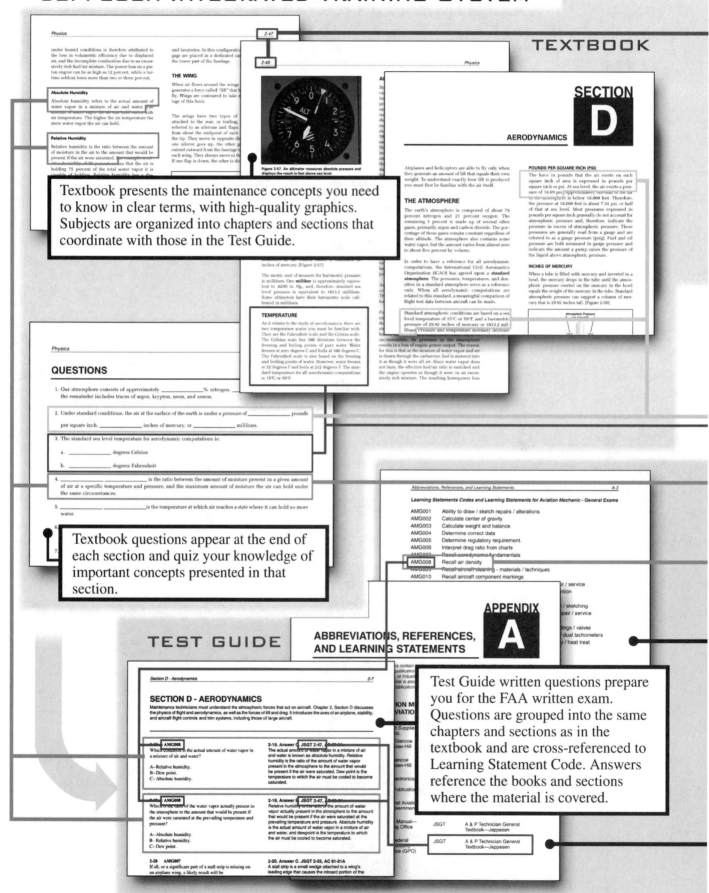

JEPPESEN INTEGRATED TRAINING SYSTEM

TEXTBOOK

Textbook presents the maintenance concepts you need to know in clear terms, with high-quality graphics. Subjects are organized into chapters and sections that coordinate with those in the Test Guide.

Textbook questions appear at the end of each section and quiz your knowledge of important concepts presented in that section.

TEST GUIDE

Test Guide written questions prepare you for the FAA written exam. Questions are grouped into the same chapters and sections as in the textbook and are cross-referenced to Learning Statement Code. Answers reference the books and sections where the material is covered.

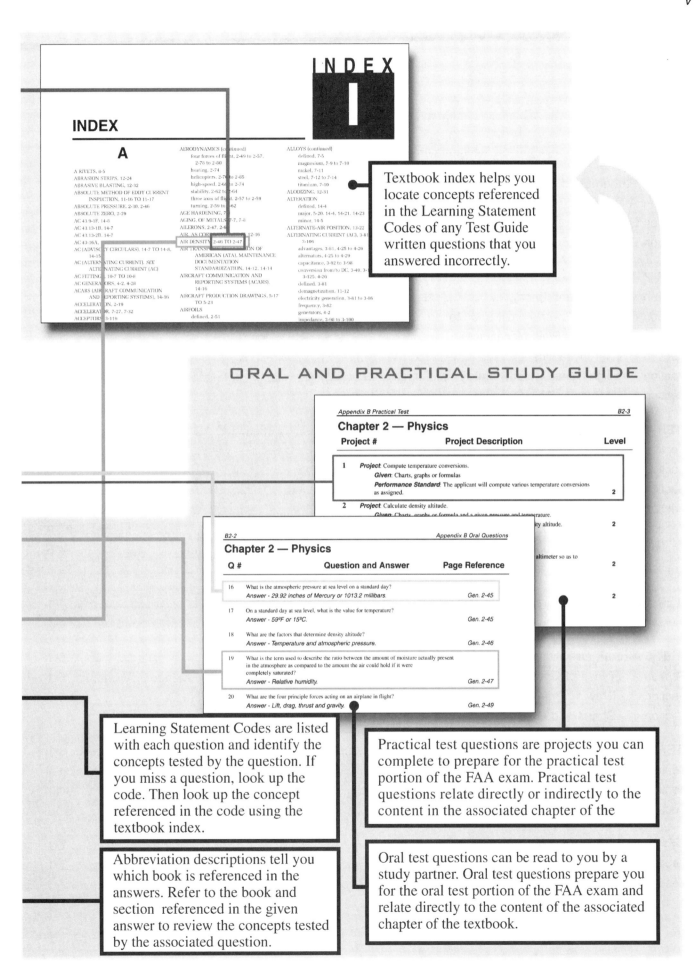

INDEX

A

A RIVETS, 8-5
ABRASION STRIPS, 12-24
ABRASIVE BLASTING, 12-32
ABSOLUTE METHOD OF EDDY CURRENT
  INSPECTION, 11-16 TO 11-17
ABSOLUTE PRESSURE, 2-10, 2-46
ABSOLUTE ZERO, 2-29
AC 43.9-1F, 14-8
AC 43.13-1B, 14-7
AC 43.13-2B, 14-7
AC 43-16A,
AC (ADVISORY CIRCULARS), 14-7 TO 14-8,
  14-15
AC (ALTERNATING CURRENT). SEE
  ALTERNATING CURRENT (AC)
AC FITTING, 10-7 TO 10-8
AC GENERATORS, 4-2, 4-28
ACARS (AIRCRAFT COMMUNICATION
  AND REPORTING SYSTEMS), 14-16
ACCELERATION, 2-19
ACCELERATOR, 7-27, 7-32
ACCEPTORS, 3-119

AERODYNAMICS (continued)
  four forces of flight, 2-49 to 2-57,
    2-78 to 2-80
  heating, 2-74
  helicopters, 2-76 to 2-85
  high-speed, 2-69 to 2-74
  stability, 2-62 to 2-64
  three axes of flight, 2-57 to 2-59
  turning, 2-59 to 2-62
AGE HARDENING, 7-
AGING, OF METALS, 7-7, 7-8
AILERONS, 2-47, 2-66
AIR, AS COR... ...12-16
AIR DENSITY, 2-46 TO 2-47
AIR TRANSPORT... ...ION OF
  AMERICAN (ATA), MAINTENANCE
  DOCUMENTATION
  STANDARDIZATION, 14-12, 14-14
AIRCRAFT COMMUNICATION AND
  REPORTING SYSTEMS (ACARS),
  14-16
AIRCRAFT PRODUCTION DRAWINGS, 5-17
  TO 5-23
AIRFOILS
  defined, 2-51

ALLOYS (continued)
  defined, 7-5
  magnesium, 7-9 to 7-10
  nickel, 7-11
  steel, 7-12 to 7-14
  titanium, 7-10
ALODIZING, 12-31
ALTERATION
  defined, 14-4
  major, 5-20, 14-4, 14-21, 14-23
  minor, 14-5
ALTERNATE-AIR POSITION, 13-22
ALTERNATING CURRENT (AC), 3-81
  3-106
  advantages, 3-81, 4-25 to 4-26
  alternators, 4-25 to 4-29
  capacitance, 3-92 to 3-98
  conversion from/to DC, 3-40, 3-4
    3-125, 4-26
  defined, 3-81
  demagnetization, 11-12
  electricity generation, 3-81 to 3-86
  frequency, 3-82
  generators, 4-2
  impedance, 3-98 to 3-100

> Textbook index helps you locate concepts referenced in the Learning Statement Codes of any Test Guide written questions that you answered incorrectly.

ORAL AND PRACTICAL STUDY GUIDE

Appendix B Practical Test   B2-3

Chapter 2 — Physics

Project #	Project Description	Level
1	**Project**: Compute temperature conversions. **Given**: Charts, graphs or formulas **Performance Standard**: The applicant will compute various temperature conversions as assigned.	2
2	**Project**: Calculate density altitude. **Given**: Charts, graphs or formula and a given pressure and temperature.	2
	...ity altitude.	2
	...altimeter so as to	2
		2

B2-2   Appendix B Oral Questions

Chapter 2 — Physics

Q #	Question and Answer	Page Reference
16	What is the atmospheric pressure at sea level on a standard day? Answer - 29.92 inches of Mercury or 1013.2 millibars.	Gen. 2-45
17	On a standard day at sea level, what is the value for temperature? Answer - 59°F or 15°C.	Gen. 2-45
18	What are the factors that determine density altitude? Answer - Temperature and atmospheric pressure.	Gen. 2-46
19	What is the term used to describe the ratio between the amount of moisture actually present in the atmosphere as compared to the amount the air could hold if it were completely saturated? Answer - Relative humidity.	Gen. 2-47
20	What are the four principle forces acting on an airplane in flight? Answer - Lift, drag, thrust and gravity.	Gen. 2-49

> Learning Statement Codes are listed with each question and identify the concepts tested by the question. If you miss a question, look up the code. Then look up the concept referenced in the code using the textbook index.

> Practical test questions are projects you can complete to prepare for the practical test portion of the FAA exam. Practical test questions relate directly or indirectly to the content in the associated chapter of the

> Abbreviation descriptions tell you which book is referenced in the answers. Refer to the book and section referenced in the given answer to review the concepts tested by the associated question.

> Oral test questions can be read to you by a study partner. Oral test questions prepare you for the oral test portion of the FAA exam and relate directly to the content of the associated chapter of the textbook.

TABLE OF CONTENTS

Preface

Thank you for purchasing this A&P Technician General Test Guide. This Test Guide will help you understand the answers to the test questions so you can take the FAA Computerized Knowledge, Oral, and Practical exams with confidence. It includes FAA Aviation Mechanic General Knowledge test questions, sample oral test questions, and samples of typical practical projects that an FAA Designated Examiner may assign during the Practical exam. For the Computerized Knowledge Exam portion of the Test Guide, the correct answers are included with explanations, along with study references. Explanations of why the other choices are wrong have been included where appropriate. Questions are organized by topic with explanations conveniently located next to each question. Figures identical to those on the FAA test also are included.

The material for the General Mechanic Oral and Practical exams is included in Appendix B of the Test Guide. Since the Oral and Practical exam questions are not public domain information, our questions may not reflect the exact questions that you will be asked during your test. However, we feel confident that if you can answer the sample oral questions and perform the practical projects that we present in this Test Guide, you should have no difficulty passing your FAA exams. Our sample questions and projects reflect the most current information that the FAA requires Designated Mechanic Examiners to use during testing. Please note that this Test Guide is intended to be a supplement to your instructor-led maintenance training, not a stand-alone learning tool.

UPDATES OF FAA QUESTIONS — You can obtain free updates for the FAA questions in this Test Guide by visiting Jeppesen's website. These updates are generally valid within one year of book publication. If you are using an older test guide, the web site may not update all the questions that have changed since the book was printed.

To find Test Prep Updates, go to *www.jeppesen.com/testprep*.

Introduction

The A&P Technician General Test Guide is designed to help you prepare for the FAA Aviation Mechanic General Knowledge computerized test. It covers FAA exam material that applies to general knowledge related to aircraft maintenance.

We recommend that you use this Test Guide in conjunction with the Jeppesen A&P Technician General Textbook. The Test Guide is organized along the same lines as the General Textbook, with 15 chapters and distinctive sections within most chapters. Questions are covered in the Test Guide in the same sequence as the material in the textbook. References to applicable chapters and pages in the various textbooks are included along with the answers.

Within the chapters, the FAA exam questions and answers appear side by side. The first line of the explanation for each question contains the correct answer and the page reference if the question is covered in the A&P Technician General Textbook. There is also a reference to an FAA or other authoritative source document, if appropriate.

Example: Answer B. JSGT 13C

Next is a brief explanation of the correct answer. An explanation of why the other answers are incorrect is sometimes included. In cases where no page reference or authoritative source document is given, consider the explanation as a supplement to the textbook.

Abbreviations used in the Test Guide are as follows:

- AC — Advisory Circular
- ASTM — American Society for Testing and Materials
- FA 150 — Airborne Digital Logic Principles
- FAH — FAA Airframe Handbook (AC 65-15A until it is superseded by FAA-H-8083-32)
- FAR — Federal Aviation Regulation
- FGH — FAA General Handbook (previously AC 65-9A; now FAA-H-8083-30)
- FPH — FAA Powerplant Handbook (AC 65-12A until it is superseded by FAA-H-8083-31)
- JSAB — Jeppesen Aircraft Batteries
- JSAC — Advanced Composites
- JSAD — The Aviation Dictionary
- JSAT — Jeppesen Airframe Textbook
- JSGT — Jeppesen General Textbook
- JSHM — Helicopter Maintenance
- JSHS — Aircraft Hydraulic Systems
- JSPT — Jeppesen Powerplant Textbook
- JSTS — Transport Category Aircraft Systems
- JSTT — Aircraft Tires and Tubes
- JSWB — Aircraft Weight and Balance
- MMM — Manufacturer's Maintenance Manual
- PHB — Pilot's Handbook of Aeronautical Knowledge (FAA-H-8083-25)
- TEP2 — Aircraft Gas Turbine Powerplants
- TSO — Technical Standard Order
- WBH — FAA Aircraft Weight and Balance Handbook (FAA-H-8083-1)

Since the FAA does not provide answers with their test questions, the answers in this Test Guide are based on official reference documents and, in our judgment, are the best choice of the available answers. Some questions which were valid when the FAA Computerized Test was originally released may no longer be appropriate due to changes in regulations or official operating procedures. However, with the computer test format, timely updating and validation of questions is anticipated. Therefore, when taking the FAA test, it is important to answer the questions according to the latest regulations or official operating procedures.

Appendix A includes Learning Statement Codes from the FAA test materials. Learning Statement Codes have replaced the subject matter knowledge codes previously used on FAA knowledge tests. Appendix B is a listing by chapter of sample questions and suggested answers that may be asked during the Oral and Practical Tests.

Figures in the Test Guide are the same as those used in the FAA Computerized Testing Supplement. These figures, which are referred to in many of the questions, are placed throughout the Test Guide as close as practical to the applicable questions.

While good study material is beneficial, it is important to realize that to become a safe, competent technician, you need more than just the academic knowledge required to pass a written test. A certified Airframe and Powerplant Mechanic's school will give you the practical shop skills that are indispensable to mechanics working in the field.

WHO CAN TAKE THE TEST

The Aviation Mechanic General Exam is often taken in conjunction with the Airframe or Powerplant exams. When you are ready to take these tests, you must present to the FAA, either a graduation certificate or certificate of completion from a certificated aviation maintenance technician school, or documentary evidence of practical work experience. For a single rating, you must show that you have at least 18 months of practical experience with the procedures, practices, and equipment generally used in constructing, maintaining, or altering airframes or powerplants. To test for both ratings, you must show at least 30 months of practical experience concurrently performing the duties appropriate to both the airframe and powerplant ratings. Documentary evidence of practical experience must be satisfactory to the administrator.

You must also provide evidence of a permanent mailing address, appropriate identification, and proof of your age. The identification must include a current photograph, your signature, and your residential address, if different from your mailing address. You may present this information in more than one form of identification, such as a driver's license, government identification card, passport, alien residency (green) card, or a military identification card.

Once the FAA is satisfied that you meet the eligibility requirements for an aircraft mechanic's certificate, you will be given two FAA Form 8610-2 forms to complete. Once filled out, an FAA inspector will review the forms for accuracy and completeness, and then sign them, authorizing you to take the required FAA tests. DO NOT LOSE THESE FORMS. You will be required to present them to FAA designated testing personnel to show evidence of eligibility to take the Airman Knowledge, Oral and Practical Exams.

HOW TO PREPARE FOR THE FAA TEST

It is important to realize that to become a safe, competent mechanic, you need more than just the academic knowledge required to pass a test. For a comprehensive training program, we recommend a structured maintenance school with qualified instructors. An organized course of instruction will help you complete the course in a timely manner, and you will be able to have your questions answered.

Regardless of whether you are in a structured ground training program, you will find that this Test Guide is an excellent training aid to help you prepare for the FAA tests. The guide contains all of the FAA questions as they are presented in the FAA computerized test format. By reviewing the questions and studying the Jeppesen Maintenance Training materials, you should be well equipped to take the test.

You will also benefit more from your study if you test yourself as you proceed through the Test Guide. Cover the answers as you read each question, and choose what you consider the best answer. You may want to mark the questions you miss for further study and review prior to taking the FAA exam.

The sooner you take the exam after you complete your study, the better. This way, the information will be fresh in your mind, and you will be more confident when you actually take the FAA test.

GENERAL INFORMATION—FAA COMPUTERIZED TEST

Detailed information on FAA computer testing is contained in FAA Order 8080.6, Conduct of Airman Knowledge Tests Via The Computer Medium. This FAA order provides guidance for Flight District Standards Offices (FSDOs) and personnel associated with organizations that are participating in, or are seeking to participate in, the FAA Computer-Assisted

Airman Knowledge Testing Program. You may also refer to FAA Order 8300.1, Airworthiness Inspector's Handbook, for guidance on computer testing by FAR Part 147 maintenance training schools that hold examining authority.

As a test applicant, you don't need all of the details contained in FAA Orders, but you may be interested in some of the general information about computer testing facilities. A Computer Testing Designee (CTD) is an organization authorized by the FAA to administer FAA airman knowledge tests via the computer medium. A Computer Testing Manager (CTM) is a person selected by the CTD to serve as manager of its national computer testing program. A Testing Center Supervisor (TCS) is a person selected by the CTM, with FAA approval, to administer FAA airman knowledge tests at approved testing centers. The TCS is responsible for the operation of the testing center.

CTDs are selected by the FAA's Flight Standards Service. Those selected may include companies, schools, universities, or other organizations that meet specific requirements. For example, they must clearly demonstrate competence in computer technology, centralized database management, national communications network operation and maintenance, national facilities management, software maintenance and support, and technical training and customer support. They must provide computer-assisted testing, test administration, and data transfer service on a national scale. This means they must maintain a minimum of 20 operational testing centers geographically dispersed throughout the United States. In addition, CTD's must offer operational hours that are convenient to the public. An acceptable plan for test security is also required.

WHAT TO EXPECT ON THE COMPUTERIZED TEST

Computer testing centers are required to have an acceptable method for the "on-line" registration of test applicants during normal business hours. They must provide a dual method for answering questions, such as keyboard, touch screen, or mouse. Features that must be provided also include an introductory lesson to familiarize you with computer testing procedures, the ability to return to a test question previously answered (for the purpose of review or answer changes), and a suitable display of multiple-choice and other question types on the computer screen in one frame. Other required features include a display of the time remaining for the completion of the test, a "HELP" function which permits you to review test questions and optional responses, and provisions for your test score on an Airman Computer Test Report.

On the computerized tests, the selection of questions is done for you, and you will answer the questions that appear on the screen. You will be given a specific amount to time to complete the test, which is based on past experience with others who have taken the exam. If you are prepared, you should have plenty of time to complete the test. After you begin the test, the screen will show you the time remaining for completion. When taking the test, keep the following points in mind:

1. Answer each question in accordance with the latest regulations and procedures. If the regulation or procedure has recently changed, and you answer according to the recent change, you will receive credit for the affected question. However, these questions will normally be deleted or updated on the FAA computerized tests.

2. Read each question carefully before looking at the possible answers. You should clearly understand the problem before attempting to solve it.

3. After formulating an answer, determine which of the alternatives most nearly corresponds with that answer. The answer chosen should completely resolve the problem.

4. From the answers given, it may appear that there is more than one possible answer; however, there is only one answer that is correct and complete. The other answers are either incomplete or are derived from popular misconceptions.

5. Make sure you select an answer for each question. Questions left unanswered will be counted as incorrect.

6. If a certain question is difficult for you, it is best to proceed to other questions. After you answer the less difficult questions, return to those which were unanswered. The computerized test format helps you identify unanswered questions, as well as those questions you wish to review.

7. When solving a calculator problem, select the answer nearest your solution. The problem has been checked with various types of calculators; therefore, if you have solved it correctly, your answer will be closer to the correct answer than the other choices.

8. Generally, the test results will be available almost immediately. Your score will be recorded on an Airman Computer Test Report form, which includes learning statement codes for incorrect answers. To determine the knowledge area in which a particular question was incorrectly answered, compare the learning statement codes on this report to Appendix A, in this book.

TEST MATERIALS, REFERENCE MATERIALS, AND AIDS

You are allowed to use an electronic calculator for this test. Simple programmable memories, which allow addition to, subtraction from, or retrieval of one number from the memory, are acceptable. Simple functions such as square root or percent keys are also acceptable.

In addition, you may use any reference materials provided with the test. You will find that these reference materials are the same as those in this book.

RETESTING

As stated in FAR section 65.19, an applicant who fails a test may not apply for retesting until 30 days after the date the test was failed. However, the applicant may apply for retesting before the 30 days have expired provided the applicant presents a signed statement from an airman holding the certificate and rating sought by the applicant. The statement must indicate that the airman has given the applicant additional instruction in each of the subjects failed and that the airman considers the applicant ready for retesting.

WHERE TO TAKE THE TEST

Testing is administered via computer at FAA-designated test centers. As indicated, these CTDs are located throughout the U.S. You can expect to pay a fee and the cost varies at different locations. The following are approved testing designees at the time of publication of this test guide. You may want to check with your local FSDO for changes.

Computer Assisted Testing Services (CATS)
1-800-947-4228
Outside U.S. (650) 259-8550

PSI/LaserGrade Computer Testing
1-800-211-2754
Outside U.S. (360) 896-9111

CHAPTER 1

MATHEMATICS

SECTION A - ARITHMETIC

Section A of Chapter 1 contains information on the fundamentals of arithmetic. Included are the number system, signed numbers, fractions, scientific notation, powers and roots, percentage, ratio, and proportion.

1-1   AMG053
What power of 10 is equal to 1,000,000?

A– 10 to the fourth power.
B– 10 to the fifth power.
C– 10 to the sixth power.

1-1. Answer C. JSGT 1A, FGH
When using scientific notation, you can quickly determine the power of ten by counting the number of zeros. In this problem, 1,000,000 has six zeros which is equal to 10 to the sixth power.

1-2   AMG053
Which of the following is equal to the square root of (-1776) ÷ (-2) - 632?

A– 128.
B– 256.
C– 16.

1-2. Answer C. JSGT 1A, FGH
The square root of a number is the root of that number multiplied by itself. In this case the number is a complex number where you must follow the order of operation, where the times (x) and divide (÷) operations precede the add (+) and subtraction (-) process. First, divide -1776 by -2. The result is 888. Now, subtract 632. The answer is 256. The square root of 256 is 16.

1-3   AMG053
Find the square root of 3,722.1835.

A– 61.00971
B– 61.00
C– 61.0097

1-3. Answer C. JSGT 1A, FGH
The square root of a number is the root of that number multiplied by itself. You can calculate the square root of 3,722.1835 by using a calculator with a square root function, or by multiplying each selection by itself to see which one equals 3,722.1835. The answer is 61.0097.

1-4   AMG053
8,019.0514 x 1/81 is equal to the square root of

A– 9,108.
B– 9,081.
C– 9,801.

1-4. Answer C. JSGT 1A, FGH
Begin solving this problem by converting 1/81 into a decimal. The decimal equivalent of 1/81 is .012 (1 ÷ 81 = .012). Next, multiply 8,019.0514 by .012, the decimal equivalent of 1/81. The product of these two numbers is 99.0006 (8,019.0514 x .012 = 99.0006). Now, square 99.0006 to find the answer 9,802.1 (99.0006^2 = 9,801.1). 9,801 is the closest.

1-5   AMG053
Find the cube of 64.

A– 4.
B– 192.
C– 262,144.

1-5. Answer C. JSGT 1A, FGH
The cube of a number is that number multiplied by itself three times. The answer is 262,144 or (64 x 64 x 64 = 262,144).

1-6   AMG053
Find the value of 10 raised to the negative sixth power.

A– 0.000010
B– 0.000001
C– 0.0001

1-6. Answer B. JSGT 1A, FGH
When working with powers of 10, view the equation as (1×10^x). A negative exponent indicates you must move the decimal to the left. In (1×10^{-6}), move the decimal of 1 to the left six places. Therefore, (1×10^{-6}) is equal to .000001.

1-7   AMG053
What is the square root of 4 raised to the fifth power?

A– 32.
B– 64.
C– 20.

1-7. Answer A. JSGT 1A, FGH
The square root of four is two. Two multiplied by itself five times equals 32.

$$(\sqrt{4})^5 = (2)^5 = 32$$

1-8   AMG053
The number 3.47 x 10 to the negative fourth power is equal to

A– .00347
B– 34,700.0
C– .000347

1-8. Answer C. JSGT 1A, FGH
When working with powers of 10, a negative exponent indicates you must move the decimal to the left. The number of places the decimal should be moved is equivalent to the exponent's value. Therefore, 3.47 x 10^{-4} equals .000347.

1-9   AMG053
Which alternative answer is equal to 16,300?

A– 1.63 x 10 to the fourth power.
B– 1.63 x 10 to the negative third power.
C– 163 x 10 to the negative second power.

1-9. Answer A. JSGT 1A, FGH
When working with powers of 10, a positive exponent indicates you must move the decimal to the right. The number of places the decimal should be moved is equivalent to the exponent's value. Therefore, 16,300 is equal to 1.63 x 10^4.

1-10   AMG053
Find the square root of 124.9924.

A– 111.8 x 10 to the third power.
B– .1118 x 10 to the negative second power.
C– 1,118 x 10 to the negative second power.

1-10. Answer C. JSGT 1A, FGH
Here you must find the square root expressed in scientific notation. The square root of 124.9924 = 11.18. When working with scientific notation, a negative exponent indicates you must move the decimal to the left; whereas, a positive exponent indicates you should move the decimal to the right. The number of places the decimal is moved is equivalent to the exponent's value. Therefore, 11.18 is equal to $1,118 \times 10^{-2}$.

1-11   AMG053
What is the square root of 16 raised to the fourth power?

A– 1,024.
B– 4,096.
C– 256.

1-11. Answer C. JSGT 1A, FGH
The square root of 16 is four. Multiply four by itself four times to get an answer of 256.

$$(\sqrt{16})^4 = (4)^4 = 256$$

1-12   AMG053
The result of 7 raised to the third power plus the square root of 39 is equal to

A– 349.24
B– .34924
C– 343.24

1-12. Answer A. JSGT 1A, FGH
7^3 is equal to 343 (7 x 7 x 7 = 343). The square root of 39 equals 6.24. The sum of these two values is 349.24.

$$7^3 + \sqrt{39} = 343 + 6.24 = 349.24$$

1-13   AMG053
Find the square root of 1,824.

A– 42.708 x 10 to the negative second power.
B– .42708
C– .42708 x 10 to the second power.

1-13. Answer C. JSGT 1A, FGH
In this problem you must find the square root expressed in scientific notation. The square root of 1,824 is 42.708. When working with powers of 10, a negative exponent indicates you must move the decimal to the left; whereas, a positive exponent indicates you should move the decimal to the right. The number of places the decimal is moved is equivalent to the exponent's value. Using scientific notation, the answer is $.42708 \times 10^2$.

1-14   AMG053
What power of 10 is equal to 1,000,000,000?

A– 10 to the sixth power.
B– 10 to the tenth power.
C– 10 to the ninth power.

1-14. Answer C. JSGT 1A, FGH
When using scientific notation, you can quickly determine the power of ten by counting the number of zeros. In this problem, 1,000,000,000 has nine zeros, which is equal to 10 to the ninth power.

1-15   AMG053
(Refer to figure 53 on page 1-4.)
Solve the equation.

A– .0297
B– .1680
C– .0419

1-15. Answer C. JSGT 1A, FGH
Begin by calculating the square roots in the numerator and squaring the denominator. Next, add the two values in the numerator and divide the sum by the denominator. The answer is .0419.

$$\frac{\sqrt{31}+\sqrt{43}}{(17)^2} = \frac{5.57+6.56}{289} = \frac{12.13}{289} = .0419$$

$$\frac{\sqrt[2]{31} \; + \; \sqrt[2]{43}}{(17)^2} \; =$$

Figure 53. Equation.

1-16   AMG053
Select the fraction which is equal to 0.0250.

A– 1/4
B– 1/40
C– 1/400

1-16. Answer B. JSGT 1A, FGH
The decimal value .025 also can be written as

25/1000

This fraction can be reduced to

25/1000 = 1/40

1-17   AMG053
1.21875 is equal to

A– 83/64.
B– 19/16.
C– 39/32.

1-17. Answer C. JSGT 1A, FGH
To begin, convert the decimal value to a fraction. The fractional equivalent of 1.21875 is

1 (21,875/100,000)

This fraction can be reduced to 7/32.

(21,875/100,000) ÷ (25/25) = (875/4,000) ÷ (25/25) = (35/160) ÷ (5/5) = (7/32)

Now convert 1-7/32 to an improper fraction by multiplying the whole number by the denominator and adding it to the numerator. The answer is 39/32.

1-18   AMG053

Express 7/8 as a percent.

A– 8.75 percent.
B– .875 percent.
C– 87.5 percent.

1-18. Answer C. JSGT 1A, FGH

When converting a fraction to a percentage, divide the numerator by the denominator and multiply the result by 100. The equivalent percentage value of 7/8 is 87.5 percent (7 ÷ 8 = .875 x 100 = 87.5).

1-19   AMG053

What is the speed of a spur gear with 42 teeth driven by a pinion gear with 14 teeth turning 420 RPM?

A– 588 RPM.
B– 160 RPM.
C– 140 RPM.

1-19. Answer C. JSGT 1A, FGH

To begin, determine the ratio of the two gears. The ratio is 42:14, or 3:1 when simplified. However, since the drive gear is smaller than the gear it's turning, the speed of the driven gear (spur gear) is less than the drive gear (pinion gear). To determine the speed of the spur gear divide the pinion gear RPM by 3. The speed of the spur gear is 140 RPM (420 ÷ 3 = 140).

1-20   AMG053

An engine develops 108 horsepower at 87 percent power. What horsepower would be developed at 65 percent power?

A– 80.
B– 70.
C– 64.

1-20. Answer A. JSGT 1A, FGH

You can solve this problem by calculating the amount of horsepower generated by 1 percent of power and then multiplying that number by 65. To determine the horsepower generated by 1 percent power, divide 108 HP by 87 percent. Approximately 1.24 HP is generated by each 1 percent of power. Therefore, 65 percent power generates 80.69 HP (1.24 x 65 = 80.69).

1-21   AMG053

A certain aircraft bolt has an overall length of 1-1/2 inches, with a shank length of 1-3/16 inches, and a threaded portion length of 5/8 inch. What is the grip length?

A– .5625 inch.
B– .8750 inch.
C– .3125 inch.

1-21. Answer A. JSGT 1A, FGH

A bolt's shank length goes from the bottom of the head to the end of the shank. On the other hand, grip length goes from the bottom of the head to the beginning of the threads. To determine the grip length of the bolt described in the question, you must convert the bolt's shank length to an improper fraction (1-3/16 = 19/16). Next, convert the threaded portion length to 16ths of an inch (5/8 = 10/16). Subtracting the thread length from the shank length provides the grip length of 9/16 (19/16 − 10/16 = 9/16) or .5625 inch.

1-22   AMG053

Select the fractional equivalent for a 0.0625 inch-thick sheet of aluminum.

A– 1/16.
B– 1/32.
C– 3/64.

1-22. Answer A. JSGT 1A, FGH

To convert a decimal to a common fraction, write the decimal as a fraction and reduce it to its lowest terms. For example, .0625 is equivalent to 625 ten-thousandths or

(625/10,000)

This reduces to 1/16.

(625/10,000) ÷ (625/625) = (1/16)

1-23   AMG053

Express 5/8 as a percent.

A– .625 percent.
B– 6.25 percent.
C– 62.5 percent.

1-23. Answer C. JSGT 1A, FGH

To convert a fraction to a percent, divide the numerator (5) by the denominator (8) and multiply the product by 100. The equivalent percent value of 5/8 is 62.5 percent (5 ÷ 8 = .625 x 100 = 62.5).

1-24   AMG053

What is the speed ratio of an input gear with 36 teeth meshed to a gear with 20 teeth?

A– 9:5
B– 1:0.56
C– 1:1.8

1-24. Answer C. JSGT 1A, FGH

The ratio of the input, or driving gear, to the driven gear is 36:20 or 9:5. The revolution, or speed, ratio is the inverse of this, or 1:1.8.

1-25   AMG053

A pinion gear with 14 teeth is driving a spur gear with 42 teeth at 140 RPM. Determine the speed of the pinion gear.

A– 588 RPM.
B– 420 RPM.
C– 240 RPM.

1-25. Answer B. JSGT 1A, FGH

To begin, determine the ratio of the two gears. The ratio is 14:42, or 1:3 when simplified. This means that for every one turn of the driven gear (spur gear), the drive gear (pinion gear) turns three times. Therefore, if the driven gear turns at 140 RPM, the drive gear will turn at 420 RPM (140 x 3 = 420).

1-26   AMG053

An engine of 98 horsepower maximum is running at 75 percent power. What is the horsepower being developed?

A– 87.00
B– 33.30
C– 73.50

1-26. Answer C. JSGT 1A, FGH

If an engine has a maximum horsepower of 98 HP and the engine is run at 75 percent power, then the amount of horsepower developed equals 75 percent times 98 HP. The amount of horsepower developed is 73.5 HP (98 x .75 = 73.5).

1-27   AMG053

The parts department's profit is 12 percent on a new magneto. How much does the magneto cost if the selling price is $145.60?

A– $128.12
B– $125.60
C– $130.00

1-27. Answer C. JSGT 1A, FGH

If the price includes a 12 percent profit, then $145.60 is equal to 112 percent of the cost. To determine the magneto's cost, divide $145.60 by 112 percent to find what 1 percent is worth. In this case, 1 percent of the price is $1.30 (145.60 ÷ 112 = 1.30). Now, multiply the 1 percent price by 100 percent to get the magneto's cost of $130.00 (1.30 x 100 = 130.00). $128.12 is incorrect because it represents the price if 12 percent of the selling price is deducted from the selling price.

1-28   AMG053

A blueprint shows a hole of 0.17187 to be drilled. Which fraction size drill bit is most nearly equal?

A– 11/64.
B– 9/32.
C– 11/32.

1-28. Answer A. JSGT 1A, FGH

To convert 0.17187 to a common fraction, rewrite it as a fraction and reduce it to its simplest terms:

(17,187/100,000) = (11/64)

Another way to solve this problem is to divide the numerator by the denominator for each of the three choices and find which is closest to 0.17187.

1-29   AMG053

If an engine is turning 1,965 RPM at 65 percent power, what is its maximum RPM?

A– 2,653.
B– 3,023.
C– 3,242.

1-29. Answer B. JSGT 1A, FGH

To determine the maximum RPM, you must divide the known RPM by the decimal equivalent of the percentage. Based on this, the engine turns at a maximum of 3,023 RPM (1,965 ÷ .65 = 3,023).

1-30   AMG053

Which decimal is most nearly equal to a bend radius of 31/64?

A– 0.2065
B– 0.4844
C– 0.3164

1-30. Answer B. JSGT 1A, FGH

To convert a fraction to a decimal, divide the numerator by the denominator. The decimal equivalent of 31/64 is .484375 (31 ÷ 64 = .484375). 0.4844 is the closest.

1-31   AMG053

Sixty-five engines are what percent of 80 engines?

A– 81 percent.
B– 65 percent.
C– 52 percent.

1-31. Answer A. JSGT 1A, FGH

This problem asks what percentage 65 is of 80. To calculate this, divide 65 by 80 and multiply the answer by 100. The answer is 81.25 percent (65 ÷ 80 = .8125 x 100 = 81.25). 81 percent is the closest.

1-32   AMG053

The radius of a piece of round stock is 7/32. Select the decimal which is most nearly equal to the diameter.

A– 0.2187
B– 0.4375
C– 0.3531

1-32. Answer B. JSGT 1A, FGH

To convert a fraction to a decimal, divide the numerator by the denominator. The decimal equivalent of 7/32 is .21875 (7 ÷ 32 = .21875). To determine the diameter, multiply the radius by two. The diameter is 0.4375 (.21875 x 2 = .4375).

1-33   AMG053

What is the ratio of 10 feet to 30 inches?

A– 4:1
B– 1:3
C– 3:1

1-33. Answer A. JSGT 1A, FGH

To get a ratio, both measurements must be in inches. Ten feet is equal to 120 inches. The ratio is 120:30 which reduces to 4:1.

1-34 AMG053
Maximum life for a certain part is 1100 hours. Recently, 15 of these parts were removed from different aircraft with an average life of 835.3 hours. What percent of the maximum part life has been achieved?

A–75.9 percent.
B–76.9 percent.
C–75.0 percent.

1-34. Answer A. JSGT 1A, FGH
To determine a percentage, divide the number for which percentage is desired by the maximum or total number and multiply by 100%.

$(835.3/1100) \times 100\% = 75.9\%$

1-35 AMG053
What is the ratio of a gasoline fuel load of 200 gallons to one of 1,680 pounds?

A–5:7
B–2:3
C–5:42

1-35. Answer A. JSGT 1A, FGH
In a ratio, both numbers must be in like terms. Because of this, you must convert gallons to pounds. One gallon of gasoline weighs 6 lbs., so 200 gallons weighs 1,200 lbs. The ratio now becomes 1,200:1,680. This simplifies to 5:7.

1-36 AMG053
(Refer to figure 59 on page 1-8.)
Solve the equation.

A–+31.25
B––5.20
C––31.25

1-36. Answer B. JSGT 1A, FGH
This problem involves the multiplication and division of signed numbers. Remember, division or multiplication of unlike signs always results in a negative number, whereas division or multiplication of like signs results in a positive number. The answer is –5.20.

$$\frac{-4\overline{)125}}{-6\overline{)-36}} = \frac{-31.25}{6} = -5.20$$

$$\frac{-4\ \overline{|\,125}}{-6\ \overline{|\,-36}} =$$

Figure 59. Equation.

1-37   AMG053

(Refer to figure 65 on page 1-9.)

Which of the figures is using scientific notation?

A–1.

B–2.

C–Both 1 and 2.

1-37. Answer A. JSGT 1A, FGH

When expressing a number in scientific notation, the base number is multiplied by ten raised to a given power (exponent). In conventional form the base number is expressed with the first significant digit as a single digit whole number, followed by the second and third significant digits rounded to the nearest 100th. The base number is then multiplied by the power of ten raised to a positive or negative integer.

$$1 \quad 3.47 \times 10^4 = 34{,}700.$$

$$2 \quad 2(4^{10}) = 2{,}097{,}152.$$

Figure 65. Scientific Notation.

SECTION B - ALGEBRA

This section introduces you to the basic operations of algebra. It covers solving for a variable, the correct order of operations, and solving complex equations.

1-38　AMG053
(Refer to figure 69 on page 1-10.)
Solve the equation.

A– 12.
B– 60.
C– 76.

1-38. Answer A. JSGT 1B, FGH
When solving this equation, begin by solving the square roots first. Once this is done, you can perform addition and subtraction.

$$\sqrt{100} + \sqrt{36} - \sqrt{16} = 10 + 6 - 4 = 12$$

$$\left(\sqrt{100} + \sqrt{36} - \sqrt{16} \right) =$$

Figure 69. Equation.

1-39　AMG053
(Refer to figure 52 on page 1-10.)
Solve the equation.

A– 115
B– 4.472
C– 5

1-39. Answer C. JSGT 1B, FGH
To solve this problem, begin by solving everything in parentheses. Remember, any number raised to the zero power is 1. Next, multiply where appropriate and then add. The answer is 5.

$$\sqrt{(-4)^0 + 6 + (\sqrt[4]{1296})(\sqrt{3})^2} = \sqrt{[1 + 6 + (6 \times 3)]}$$
$$= \sqrt{(1 + 6 + 18)}$$
$$= \sqrt{25}$$
$$= 5$$

$$\sqrt{(-4)^0 + 6 + (\sqrt[4]{1296})(\sqrt{3})^2} =$$

Figure 52. Equation.

1-40　AMG053
Solve the equation. $[(4 \times -3) + (-9 \times 2)] \div 2 =$

A– –30.
B– –15.
C– –5.

1-40. Answer B. JSGT 1B, FGH
Complex problems such as this require the operations to be done in a particular order. Begin by doing everything in parentheses. This simplifies the equation to $[-12 + -18] \div 2$. Now, solve what is in the brackets and divide the result by 2. The answer is -15.

$$[-12 + -18] \div 2 = -30 \div 2 = -15.$$

1-41   AMG053

Solve the equation. (64 x 3/8) ÷ 3/4 =

A– 18.

B– 24.

C– 32.

1-41. Answer C. JSGT 1B, FGH

To begin, convert the fractions in the equation to decimal numbers by dividing the numerator by the denominator. The decimal equivalent of 3/8 is .375 (3 ÷ 8 = .375) and 3/4 is .75 (3 ÷ 4 = .75). When solving any equation, you must do what is in parentheses first. Once this is done, you can divide by .75. The answer is 32. (64 x .375) ÷ .75 = 24 ÷ .75 = 32.

1-42   AMG053

Solve the equation. (32 x 3/8) ÷ 1/6 =

A– 12.

B– 2.

C– 72.

1-42. Answer C. JSGT 1B, FGH

To begin, convert the fractions in the equation to decimal numbers by dividing the numerator by the denominator. The decimal equivalent of 3/8 is .375 (3 ÷ 8 = .375) and to 1/6 is .167 (1 ÷ 6 = .167).When solving any equation, you must do what is in parentheses first. Once this is done, you can divide by .167. The answer is 71.86. 72 is the closest. (32 x .375) ÷ .167 = 12 ÷ .167 = 71.86.

1-43   AMG053

Solve the equation. 4 – 3 [–6 (2 + 3) + 4] =

A– 82.

B– -25.

C– -71.

1-43. Answer A. JSGT 1B, FGH

When solving any equation, you must do what is in parentheses first, and then brackets. This is followed by the operation of multiplication and then addition. The answer is 82.

4 - 3 [- 6 (2 + 3) + 4] = 4 - 3 [- 6 × 5 + 4]

= 4 - 3[-30 + 4]

= 4 - 3[-26]

= 4 - (-78)

= 82

1-44   AMG053

Solve the equation. -6 [-9 (-8+4) - 2(7+3)] =

A– –332.

B– 216.

C– –96.

1-44. Answer C. JSGT 1B, FGH

When solving any equation, you must do what is in parentheses first, then brackets. This is followed by the operation of multiplication and then addition. The answer is -96.

-6 [-9 (-8 + 4) - 2 (7 + 3)] = -6 [-9 (-4) - 2(10)]

= -6 [36 - 20]

= -6 [16]

= -96

1-45   AMG053
Solve the equation. $(-3 + 2)(-12 - 4) + (-4 + 6) \times 3 =$

A– 20.
B– 22.
C– 28.

1-45. Answer B. JSGT 1B, FGH
When solving any equation, you must do what is in parentheses first. This is followed by the operation of multiplication and then addition. The answer is 22.

$(-3 + 2) (-12 - 4) + (-4 + 6) \times 3 = (-1) (-16) + (2) \times 3$

$= 16 + 6$

$= 22$

1-46   AMG053
Solve the equation. $1/2 \, (-30 + 34) \, 5 =$

A– 10.
B– 95.
C– 160.

1-46. Answer A. JSGT 1B, FGH
When solving complex equations, begin by solving everything in parentheses first. Once this is done, you can perform multiplication and division followed by addition and subtraction.

$1/2 \, (-30 + 34) \, 5 = 1/2 \, (4) \, 5 = (2) \, 5 = 10$

1-47   AMG053
(Refer to figure 58 on page 1-12.)
Solve the equation.

A– 174.85
B– –81.49
C– 14.00

1-47. Answer C. JSGT 1B, FGH
When solving complex equations, begin by solving everything in parentheses first. Once this is done, you can perform multiplication, followed by addition. The answer 14.00 is closest.

$$\frac{(-35 + 25)(-7) + (\pi)(16^{-2})}{\sqrt{25}} = \frac{(-10)(-7) + (3.1416)(.0039)}{5}$$

$$= \frac{70 + .0123}{5}$$

$$= \frac{70.0123}{5}$$

$$= 14.002$$

$$\frac{(-35 + 25)(-7) + (\pi)(16^{-2})}{\sqrt{25}} =$$

Figure 58. Equation

1-48   AMG053
(Refer to figure 60 on page 1-13.)
Solve the equation.

A– 11.9
B– 11.7
C– 11.09

1-48. Answer A. JSGT 1B, FGH
When solving complex equations, begin by solving everything in parentheses first. Once this is done, you can perform multiplication and division, followed by addition. The answer is 11.9.

$$\frac{(-5+23)(-2)+(3^{-3})(\sqrt{64})}{-27 \div 9} = \frac{18(-2)+(.037)(8)}{-3}$$

$$= \frac{-36+.2963}{-3}$$

$$= \frac{-35.7037}{-3}$$

$$= 11.9$$

$$\frac{(-5 \;+\; 23)\;(-2)\;+\;(3^{-3})\;(\sqrt{64})}{-27 \;\div\; 9} \;=$$

Figure 60. Equation

1-49   AMG053
(Refer to figure 70 on page 1-13.)
Which alternative answer is equal to 5.59?

A– 1.
B– 2.
C– 3.

1-49. Answer A. JSGT 1B, FGH
When solving any equation, you must do what is in parenthesis first. This is followed by the operation of multiplication (simplifying exponents), division, and then addition. Here are the solutions to the three equations.

1. (5.57) + (6.56) ÷ 289 = (5.57) + .023 = 5.59
2. (5.57 + 6.56) ÷ 289 = 12.13 ÷ 289 = .04
3. (5.57) + (6.56) − 289 = 12.13 − 289 = −276.87

$$1.\ (\sqrt{31}) + (\sqrt{43}) \div 17^2$$

$$2.\ (\sqrt{31} + \sqrt{43}) \div 17^2$$

$$3.\ (\sqrt{31}) + (\sqrt{43}) - 17^2$$

Figure 70. Alternative Answer.

1-50   AMG053

An airplane flying a distance of 750 miles used 60 gallons of gasoline. How many gallons will it need to travel 2,500 miles?

A– 200.
B– 31,250.
C– 9,375.

1-50. Answer A. JSGT 1B, FGH

To solve this problem, you must first calculate how many miles the airplane can fly on one gallon of gas. To do this, divide the miles flown (750) by the number of gallons used (60). The airplane can fly 12.5 miles on one gallon of gas. To determine the amount of gas required to fly 2,500 miles, divide 2,500 by 12.5. A total of 200 gallons (2,500 ÷ 12.5 = 200) are required to fly 2,500 miles.

1-51   AMG053

An airplane flying a distance of 875 miles used 70 gallons of gasoline. How many gallons will it need to travel 3,000 miles?

A– 250.
B– 240.
C– 144.

1-51. Answer B. JSGT 1B, FGH

875 miles divided by 70 gallons equals 12.5 miles per gallon. 3,000 miles ÷ 12.5 miles per gallon = 240 gallons.

SECTION C - GEOMETRY AND TRIGONOMETRY

Section C of Chapter 1 applies the math techniques you learned in the previous two sections. It discusses the computation of area, trigonometric functions, the metric system and metric conversions, and the use of math hardware such as electronic calculators.

1-52   AMG044

What size sheet of metal is required to fabricate a cylinder 20 inches long and 8 inches in diameter? (Note: C = π x D)

A– 20" x 25-5/32".
B– 20" x 24-9/64".
C– 20" x 25-9/64".

1-52. Answer C. JSGT 1C, FGH

The height of the cylinder is 20 inches. Therefore, the height of the sheet of metal must be 20 inches. To determine the length required, you must calculate the circumference of the cylinder using the formula given. The circumference is 25.132 (C = π x D = 3.1416 x 8 = 25.132) which is slightly smaller than 25-9/64. Therefore, a 20 inch x 25-9/64 inch sheet of metal is required to fabricate the cylinder.

1-53   AMG044

A rectangular-shaped fuel tank measures 60 inches in length, 30 inches in width, and 12 inches in depth. How many cubic feet are within the tank?

A– 12.5
B– 15.0
C– 21.0

1-53. Answer A. JSGT 1C, FGH

To determine the volume of a rectangle, multiply the length (L) times the width (W) times the depth (D). However, the question asks for cubic feet and the dimensions are given in inches. Therefore, you must convert the inches into feet and then compute the volume. The answer is 12.5 cubic feet (5 feet x 2.5 feet x 1 foot = 12.5 cubic feet).

1-54   AMG044

Select the container size that will be equal in volume to 60 gallons of fuel. (7.5 gal = 1 cu. ft.)

A– 7.5 cubic feet.
B– 8.0 cubic feet.
C– 8.5 cubic feet.

1-54. Answer B. JSGT 1C, FGH

Using the given relationship of 7.5 gal = 1 cu. ft., you can determine the number of cubic feet required to hold 60 gallons by dividing 60 by 7.5. The answer is 8 cubic feet (60 ÷ 7.5 = 8).

1-55   AMG044

What is the piston displacement of a master cylinder with a 1.5-inch diameter bore and a piston stroke of 4 inches?

A– 9.4247 cubic inches.
B– 7.0686 cubic inches.
C– 6.1541 cubic inches.

1-55. Answer B. JSGT 1C, FGH

When asked to compute piston displacement, you must calculate the volume of the cylinder. To calculate the volume of a cylinder, use the formula:

$$V = \pi r^2 h$$

Where (V) is the volume, (r) is the radius of the cylinder, (or half the bore) and (h) is the height or stroke of the piston. The displacement is 7.0686 cubic inches

$(3.1416 \times .75^2 \times 4) = 7.0686.$

1-56   AMG044

How many gallons of fuel will be contained in a rectangular-shaped tank which measures 2 feet in width, 3 feet in length, and 1 foot 8 inches in depth? (7.5 gal = 1 cu. ft.)

A– 66.6.
B– 75.
C– 45.

1-56. Answer B. JSGT 1C, FGH

The first step in solving this problem is to calculate the volume of the tank. This is done by multiplying the length times the width times the height. The volume is 10 cubic feet (3 x 2 x 1.667 = 10). Using the given relationship of 7.5 gal. = 1 cu. ft., you can determine the number of gallons the tank will hold by multiplying the volume times 7.5 gallons. The tank holds 75 gallons (10 x 7.5 = 75).

1-57   AMG044

A rectangular-shaped fuel tank measures 27-1/2 inches in length, 3/4 foot in width, and 8-1/4 inches in depth. How many gallons will the tank contain? (231 cu. in. = 1 gal.)

A– 7.366
B– 8.83
C– 170.156

1-57. Answer B. JSGT 1C, FGH

The first step in solving this problem is to calculate the volume of the tank. This is done by converting all dimensions to inches and then multiplying the length times the width times the height. The volume is 2,041.875 cubic inches (27.5 x 9 x 8.25 = 2,041.875). Using the given relationship of 231 cubic inches = 1 gallon, you can determine the number of gallons the tank will hold by dividing the volume by 231 cubic inches. The tank holds 8.84 gallons (2,041.875 ÷ 231 = 8.84). 8.83 is the closest.

1-58   AMG044

A four-cylinder aircraft engine has a cylinder bore of 3.78 inches and is 8.5 inches deep. With the piston on bottom center, the top of the piston measures 4.0 inches from the bottom of the cylinder. What is the approximate piston displacement of this engine?

A– 200 cubic inches.
B– 360 cubic inches.
C– 235 cubic inches.

1-58. Answer A. JSGT 1C, FGH

When asked to compute displacement, you must calculate the volume of cylinder. To calculate the volume of a cylinder, use the formula:

$$V = \pi r^2 h$$

Where (v) is the volume, (r) is the radius of the cylinder, (or half the bore) and (h) is the height or stroke of the piston measured from the top of the piston to the top of the cylinder. The displacement of each cylinder is 50.5 cubic inches ($3.1416 \times 1.89^2 \times 4.5 = 50.5$). To determine the displacement of the entire engine, multiply the displacement of each cylinder by the number of cylinders. The engine displacement is 202 cubic inches (50.5 x 4 = 202). 200 cubic inches is the closest.

1-59   AMG044

A rectangular-shaped fuel tank measures 37-1/2 inches in length, 14 inches in width, and 8-1/4 inches in depth. How many cubic inches are within the tank?

A– 525.
B– 433.125.
C– 4,331.25.

1-59. Answer C. JSGT 1C, FGH

When calculating the volume of an object multiply the length times the width times the height. The volume is 4,331.25 cubic inches (37.5 x 14 x 8.25 = 4,331.25).

1-60   AMG044

A six-cylinder engine with a bore of 3.5 inches, a cylinder height of 7 inches and a stroke of 4.5 inches will have a total piston displacement of

A– 256.88 cubic inches.
B– 259.77 cubic inches.
C– 43.3 cubic inches.

1-60. Answer B. JSGT 1C, FGH

When asked to compute displacement, you must calculate the volume of the cylinder. To calculate the volume of a cylinder, use the formula:

$V = \pi r^2 h$

Where (V) is the volume, (r) is the radius of the cylinder, (or half the bore) and (h) is the height or stroke of the piston. The displacement of each cylinder is 43.295 cubic inches ($3.1416 \times 1.75^2 \times 4.5 = 43.295$). To determine the displacement of the entire engine, multiply the displacement of each cylinder by the number of cylinders. The engine displacement is 259.77 ($43.295 \times 6 = 259.77$).

1-61   AMG044

What is the surface area of a cube where a side (edge) measures 7.25 inches?

A– 381.078 cu. in.
B– 315.375 sq. in.
C– 52.5625 sq. in.

1-61. Answer B. JSGT 1C, FGH

The surface area of a cube is equal to the surface area of one side multiplied by six. Surface area = (7.25 in.^{2}) x 6 or 315.375 sq. in. Cubing 7.25 inches gives you the cube volume of 381.078 cu. in., but the question asks for surface area, not volume.

1-62   AMG044

(Refer to figure 54 on page 1-17.)
Compute the area of the trapezoid.

A– 52.5 square feet.
B– 60 square feet.
C– 76.5 square feet.

1-62. Answer A. JSGT 1C, FGH

To compute the area of a trapezoid, use the formula

$A = 1/2 \, (b_1 + b_2) \, h$

The answer is 52.5 square feet.

$A = 1/2 \, (9 + 12) \, 5 = 52.5$ square feet.

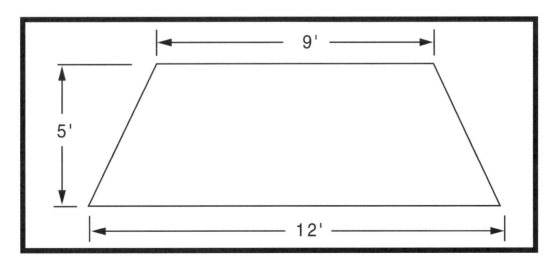

Figure 54. Trapezoid Area.

1-63   AMG044
(Refer to figure 55 on page 1-18.)
Find the area of the triangle shown.

A– 12 square inches.
B– 6 square inches.
C– 15 square inches.

1-63. Answer B. JSGT 1C, FGH
The area of a triangle is calculated using the formula:

A = 1/2 bh

The base (b) of the triangle is 4 inches, and the height (h) is 3 inches. The area of the triangle is 6 square inches (1/2 x 4 x 3 = 6).

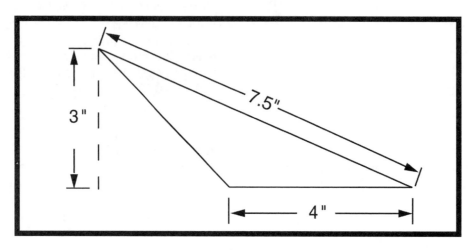

Figure 55. Triangle Area.

1-64   AMG044
(Refer to figure 56 on page 1-18.)
Compute the area of the trapezoid.

A– 24 square feet.
B– 48 square feet.
C– 10 square feet.

1-64. Answer C. JSGT 1C, FGH
To compute the area of a trapezoid use the formula

A = 1/2 (b_1+ b_2) h

The answer is 10 square feet.

A = 1/2 (4 + 6) 2 = 10 square feet.

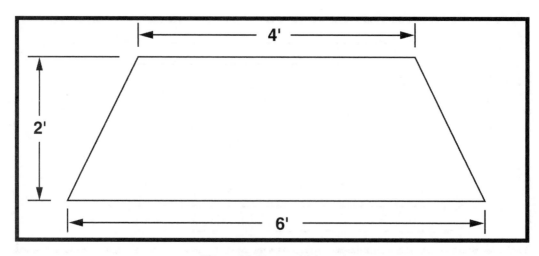

Figure 56. Trapezoid Area.

1-65   AMG044
(Refer to figure 57 on page 1-19.)
Determine the area of the triangle formed by points A, B, and C. A to B = 7.5 inches. A to D = 16.8 inches.

A– 42 square inches.
B– 63 square inches.
C– 126 square inches.

1-65. Answer B. JSGT 1C, FGH
The area of a triangle is calculated using the formula

A = 1/2 bh

The base (b) in this case is the distance from B to C, which is the same as the distance from A to D or 16.8 inches. The height (h) is the distance from A to B or 7.5 inches. Therefore, 1/2 x (16.8 x 7.5) = 63.

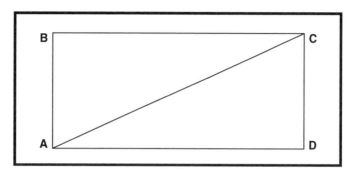

Figure 57. Triangle Area.

1-66   AMG044
(Refer to figure 71 on page 1-19.)
What is the volume of a sphere with a radius of 4.5 inches?

A– 47.71 cubic inches
B– 381.7 square inches
C– 381.7 cubic inches

1-66. Answer C. JSGT 1C, FGH
Solving the equation for the volume of a sphere requires you to know its diameter. In this problem, the radius is given, which is one-half of the diameter. Therefore, the diameter is 9 inches (2 x 4.5). Solving the equation then:

$1/6 \times \pi \times D^3 =$

$1/6 \times 3.14 \times 9^3 =$

$1/6 \times 3.14 \times 729 =$

.167 x 2289.06 = 382.27

The area of an object is measured in square units (inches) while volume is measured in cubic units (inches). Using a calculator without rounding provides an answer closer to 381.7 cubic inches.

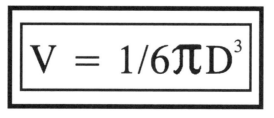

Figure 71. Volume of a Sphere.

PHYSICS

SECTION A - MATTER AND ENERGY

The first secton of Chapter 2 introduces some basic physical concepts, including the chemical nature of matter, the physical nature of matter, and energy.

2-1   AMG027
The boiling point of a given liquid varies

A– directly with pressure.
B– inversely with pressure.
C– directly with density.

2-1. Answer A. JSGT 2A, FGH
If two values are directly related, increasing one value will increase the other value. The boiling point of a liquid goes up as the pressure goes up, so they are said to be directly related.

SECTION B - WORK, POWER, FORCE, AND MOTION

Section B of Chapter 2 contains information on power, force, stress, strain, and motion.

2-2   AMG099

An engine that weighs 350 pounds is removed from an aircraft by means of a mobile hoist. The engine is raised 3 feet above its attachment mount, and the entire assembly is then moved forward 12 feet. A constant force of 70 pounds is required to move the loaded hoist. What is the total work input required to move the hoist?

A– 840 foot-pounds.
B– 1,890 foot-pounds.
C– 1,050 foot-pounds.

2-2. Answer A. JSGT 2B, FGH

Work is determined by the formula W = F x D, where (F) is the force applied and (D) represents the distance moved. The question asks for the work required to move the hoist only; therefore, the work required is 840 foot-pounds (70 pounds x 12 feet = 840 foot-pounds). 1,050 foot-pounds represents the work required to lift the engine and 1,890 footpounds is the amount of work required to lift the engine and move the hoist.

2-3   AMG099

How much work input is required to lower (not drop) a 120-pound weight from the top of a 3-foot table to the floor?

A– 120 pounds of force.
B– 360 foot-pounds.
C– 40 foot-pounds.

2-3. Answer B. JSGT 2B, FGH

Work is calculated through the formula W = F x D, where (F) represents the applied force or weight and (D) represents the distance the object is moved. In this example, 360 foot-pounds of work are required (120 x 3 = 360).

2-4   AMG099

In physics, which of the following factors are necessary to determine power?
1. Force exerted.
2. Distance moved.
3. Time required.

A– 1 and 2.
B– 2 and 3.
C– 1, 2, and 3.

2-4. Answer C. JSGT 2B, FGH

To determine power (P), you must know the force (F) that is exerted, the distance (D) the force moves the object, and the time (t) required to do the work. This can be seen in the formula

P = (F x D) / t

2-5   AMG027

Which of the following is Newton's First Law of Motion, generally termed the Law of Inertia?

A– To every action there is an equal and opposite reaction.
B– Force is proportional to the product of mass and acceleration.
C– Every body persists in its state of rest, or of motion in a straight line, unless acted upon by some outside force.

2-5. Answer C. JSGT 2B

Newton's First Law of Motion explains the effect of inertia on a body. It states that a body at rest tends to remain at rest, and a body in motion tends to remain in motion (straight line and constant velocity), unless acted on by some outside force.

2-6   AMG099

What force must be applied to roll a 120-pound barrel up an inclined plane 9 feet long to a height of 3 feet (disregard friction)?

$$L \div I = R \div E$$

L = Length of ramp, measured along the slope
I = Height of ramp
R = Weight of object to be raised or lowered
E = Force required to raise or lower object

A– 40 pounds.
B– 120 pounds.
C– 360 pounds.

2-6. Answer A. JSGT 2B, FGH

To determine the force, or effort, required to move the barrel up the ramp, use the formula given ($L \div I = R \div E$).

$$9 \div 3 = 120 \div E$$

$$3 = 120/E$$

$$3E = 120$$

$$E = 40$$

2-7   AMG099

(Refer to figure 61 on page 2-4.)
The amount of force applied to rope A to lift the weight is

A– 12 pounds.
B– 15 pounds.
C– 20 pounds.

2-7. Answer B. JSGT 2B, FGH

The mechanical advantage of a pulley system is equal to the number of ropes supporting the resistance minus the rope you are pulling on. In this example, the mechanical advantage is four. This means that for every one pound of effort exerted on the rope, four pounds are lifted. In this problem, 60 pounds requires a force of 15 pounds ($60 \div 4 = 15$).

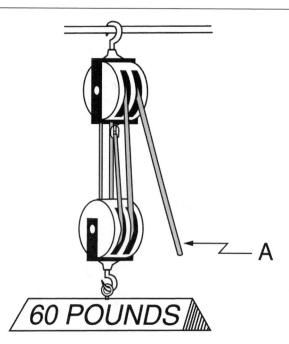

Figure 61. Physics.

SECTION C - GAS AND FLUID MECHANICS

Section C discusses basic gas and fluid mechanics. Included in this section is information on temperature, pressure, the gas laws, fluid mechanics, and sound.

2-8   AMG027
Which statement concerning Bernoulli's principle is true?

A– The pressure of a fluid increases at points where the velocity of the fluid increases.
B– The pressure of a fluid decreases at points where the velocity of the fluid increases.
C– It applies only to gases.

2-8. Answer B. JSGT 2C, FGH
Bernoulli's Principle states that when a fluid is in motion, the outward pressure exerted decreases as the fluid velocity increases.

2-9   AMG055
What force is exerted on the piston in a hydraulic cylinder if the area of the piston is 1.2 square inches and the fluid pressure is 850 PSI?

A– 1,020 pounds.
B– 960 pounds.
C– 850 pounds.

2-9. Answer A. JSGT 2C, FGH
Pascal's Law states that any force applied to a confined fluid is transmitted equally and undiminished in all directions. The amount of force (F) applied can be determined by multiplying the fluid pressure (P) times the area (A) in which the fluid is contained. The force exerted on the piston is 1,020lbs. (850 psi x 1.2 sq. in. = 1,020 lbs.).

2-10   AMG055
The force that can be produced by an actuating cylinder whose piston has a cross-sectional area of 3 square inches operating in a 1,000 PSI hydraulic system is most nearly

A– 3,000 pounds.
B– 334 pounds.
C– 1,000 pounds.

2-10. Answer A. JSGT 2C, FGH
According to Pascal's Law, Force = Pressure x Area. Substituting the values given, the force produced is 3,000 pounds (1,000 PSI x 3 sq. in. = 3,000 pounds).

2-11   AMG027
Which of the following is NOT considered a method of heat transfer?

A– Convection.
B– Conduction.
C– Diffusion.

2-11. Answer C. JSGT 2C, FGH
Heat is transferred by three methods: conduction, convection, and radiation.

2-12   AMG027

Under which conditions will the rate of flow of a liquid through a metering orifice (or jet) be the greatest (all other factors being equal)?

A– Unmetered pressure — 18 PSI, metered pressure — 17.5 PSI, atmospheric pressure — 14.5 PSI.
B– Unmetered pressure — 23 PSI, metered pressure — 12 PSI, atmospheric pressure — 14.3 PSI.
C– Unmetered pressure — 17 PSI, metered pressure — 5 PSI, atmospheric pressure — 14.7 PSI.

2-12. Answer C. JSGT 2C, FGH

Bernoulli's principle states that the pressure of a fluid decreases at points where the velocity of the fluid increases. Therefore, the flow rate (velocity) in this problem is greatest when the difference between the metered and unmetered pressure is greatest.

2-13   AMG027

If the volume of a confined gas is doubled (without the addition of more gas), the pressure will (assume the temperature remains constant)

A– increase in direct proportion to the volume increase.
B– remain the same.
C– be reduced to one-half its original value.

2-13. Answer C. JSGT 2C, FGH

Boyle's law states that the volume of an enclosed dry gas varies inversely with its pressure, provided the temperature remains constant. Therefore, when the volume of a gas is doubled, the pressure is cut in half.

2-14   AMG027

If the temperature of a confined liquid is held constant and its pressure is tripled, the volume will

A– triple.
B– be reduced to one-third its original volume.
C– remain the same.

2-14. Answer C. JSGT 2C, FGH

For all practical purposes, liquids are considered incompressible. In other words, an increase in fluid pressure is accompanied by a negligible reduction in volume.

2-15   AMG055

If the fluid pressure is 800 PSI in a 1/2-inch line supplying an actuating cylinder with a piston area of 10 square inches, the force exerted on the piston will be

A– 4,000 pounds.
B– 8,000 pounds.
C– 800 pounds.

2-15. Answer B. JSGT 2C, FGH

The size of the supply line has no affect on the answer to this problem. Simply apply Pascal's Law (Force = Pressure x Area). The force exerted on the piston is 8,000 pounds (800 PSI x 10 sq. in. = 8,000 pounds).

2-16   AMG027

Which statement concerning heat and/or temperature is true?

A– There is an inverse relationship between temperature and heat.
B– Temperature is a measure of the kinetic energy of the molecules of any substance.
C– Temperature is a measure of the potential energy of the molecules of any substance.

2-16. Answer B. JSGT 2C, FGH

Heat is a form of energy that causes molecular agitation within a material. The amount of agitation is measured by temperature. The temperature at which molecular motion stops is known as Absolute Zero.

2-17   AMG027

If both the volume and the absolute temperature of a confined gas are doubled, the pressure will

A–not change.
B–be halved.
C–become four times as great.

2-18   AMG055

If a double-acting actuating cylinder in a 3,000 PSI system has a piston with a surface area of three square inches on the extension side, and a rod with a cross-section area of one square inch attached to the piston on the other side, approximately how much force will the actuator be able to produce when retracting?

A–9,000 pounds.
B–6,000 pounds.
C–3,000 pounds.

2-17. Answer A. JSGT 2C, FGH

The relationship between volume, temperature, and pressure of a confined gas is described by the General Gas Law. If both the volume and the absolute temperature are doubled, their effects cancel out and the pressure remains constant.

2-18. Answer B. JSGT 2C, FGH

To determine the force a hydraulic cylinder produces, multiply the piston area by the applied force. In this example, the piston area is three square inches on the extension side. However, the rod on the retraction side reduces the piston area by one square inch, to two square inches. Multiply the applied force of 3,000 pounds per square inch by two square inches to obtain the resulting force of 6,000 pounds.

SECTION D - AERODYNAMICS

Maintenance technicians must understand the atmospheric forces that act on aircraft. Chapter 2, Section D discusses the physics of flight and aerodynamics, as well as the forces of lift and drag. It introduces the axes of an airplane, stability, and aircraft flight controls and trim systems, including those of large aircraft.

2-19   AMG008
Which condition is the actual amount of water vapor in a mixture of air and water?

A– Relative humidity.
B– Dew point.
C– Absolute humidity.

2-19. Answer C. JSGT 2D, FGH
The actual amount of water vapor in a mixture of air and water is known as absolute humidity. Relative humidity is the ratio of the amount of water vapor present in the atmosphere to the amount that would be present if the air were saturated. Dew point is the temperature to which the air must be cooled to become saturated.

2-20   AMG008
Which will weigh the least?

A– 98 parts of dry air and 2 parts of water vapor.
B– 35 parts of dry air and 65 parts of water vapor.
C– 50 parts of dry air and 50 parts of water vapor.

2-20. Answer B. JSGT 2D, FGH
Humid air at a given temperature and pressure is lighter than dry air at the same temperature and pressure. Therefore, the choice with the greatest proportion of water vapor weighs the least.

2-21   AMG007
If all, or a significant part of a stall strip is missing on an airplane wing, a likely result will be

A– decreased lift in the area of installation at high angles of attack.
B– asymmetrical lateral control at low angles of attack.
C– asymmetrical lateral control at or near stall angles of attack.

2-21. Answer C. JSGT 2D, AC 61-21A
A stall strip is a small wedge attached to a wing's leading edge that causes the inboard portion of the wing to stall before the outboard portion. This allows the ailerons to maintain effectiveness up to the point of full stall. If part of a stall strip is missing, asymmetrical aileron control will result at or near stall angles of attack.

2-22   AMG008
Which is the ratio of the water vapor actually present in the atmosphere to the amount that would be present if the air were saturated at the prevailing temperature and pressure?

A– Absolute humidity.
B– Relative humidity.
C– Dew point.

2-22. Answer B. JSGT 2D, FGH
Relative humidity is the ratio of the amount of water vapor actually present in the atmosphere to the amount that would be present if the air were saturated at the prevailing temperature and pressure. Absolute humidity is the actual amount of water vapor in a mixture of air and water, and dewpoint is the temperature to which the air must be cooled to become saturated.

2-23   AMG008

Which atmospheric conditions will cause the true landing speed of an aircraft to be the greatest?

A—Low temperature with low humidity.
B—High temperature with low humidity.
C—High temperature with high humidity.

2-23. Answer C. JSGT 2D, FGH

True airspeed (TAS) represents the true speed of an airplane through the air. As air temperature and humidity increase, the density of the air decreases. As air density decreases, true airspeed increases. Therefore, high temperature with high humidity will cause an aircraft's landing speed to be greatest.

2-24   AMG008

What is absolute humidity?

A—The temperature to which humid air must be cooled at constant pressure to become saturated.
B—The actual amount of the water vapor in a mixture of air and water.
C—The ratio of the water vapor actually present in the atmosphere to the amount that would be present if the air were saturated at the prevailing temperature and pressure.

2-24. Answer B. JSGT 2D, FGH

Absolute humidity is the actual amount of water vapor present in a mixture of air and water. It is usually measured in grams per cubic meter or pounds per cubic foot. Dew point is the temperature to which humid air must be cooled at a constant pressure to become saturated, whereas the ratio of the water vapor actually present in the atmosphere to the amount that would be present if the air were saturated at the prevailing temperature and pressure is relative humidity.

2-25   AMG008

The temperature to which humid air must be cooled at constant pressure to become saturated is called

A—dew point.
B—absolute humidity.
C—relative humidity.

2-25. Answer A. JSGT 2D, FGH

Dew point is the temperature to which humid air must be cooled at a constant pressure to become saturated.

2-26   AMG007

The purpose of aircraft wing dihedral is to

A—increase lateral stability.
B—increase longitudinal stability.
C—increase lift coefficient of the wing.

2-26. Answer A. JSGT 2D, AC 61-21A

Lateral stability, or roll stability, is increased through the use of dihedral. In other words, the wings on either side of the airplane join the fuselage to form a slight V called dihedral.

2-27   AMG007

Aspect ratio of a wing is defined as the ratio of the

A—wingspan to the wing root.
B—square of the chord to the wingspan.
C—wingspan to the mean chord.

2-27. Answer C. JSGT 2D, AC 61-21A

A wing's aspect ratio is the ratio of the wing span to the average, or mean, chord.

2-28   AMG007

A wing with a very high aspect ratio (in comparison with a low aspect ratio wing) will have

A– increased drag at high angles of attack.
B– a low stall speed.
C– poor control qualities at low airspeed.

2-28. Answer B. JSGT 2D, AC 61-21A
A wing with a high aspect ratio has low wing loading and, therefore, stalls at a lower speed.

2-29   AMG007

An increase in the speed at which an airfoil passes through the air increases lift because

A– the increased speed of the airflow creates a greater pressure differential between the upper and lower surfaces.
B– the increased speed of the airflow creates a lesser pressure differential between the upper and lower surfaces.
C– the increased velocity of the relative wind increases the angle of attack.

2-29. Answer A. JSGT 2D, FGH
The faster an airfoil moves through the air, the greater the pressure differential between the upper and lower surfaces. The greater the pressure differential, the greater the lift.

2-30   AMG007

The purpose of stall strips on airplane wings is to

A– increase lift in the areas of installation.
B– prevent stall in the areas of installation.
C– ensure that the wing root areas stall first.

2-30. Answer C. JSGT 2D, FGH
Stall strips are often installed on the leading edge in the wing root area to help induce a separation of airflow, thus producing a stall. This aids in retaining lift over the outboard ends of the wings so that aileron control is still available during the initial onset of an aerodynamic stall.

SECTION E - HIGH-SPEED AERODYNAMICS

Section E describes factors affecting supersonic flight. Information on the compressibility of air, the speed of sound, supersonic flow patterns, and airfoils suitable to high-speed flight are discussed in detail. Critical mach number, supersonic engine inlets, and the problem of aerodynamic heating are described.

2-31   AMG007

The speed of sound in the atmosphere is most affected by variations in which of the following?

1. Sound frequency (cps).
2. Ambient temperature.
3. Barometric pressure.

A– 1.
B– 2.
C– 3.

2-31. Answer B. JSGT 2E, FGH

The speed of sound in the atmosphere varies with temperature. As the temperature decreases the speed of sound also decreases, and as temperature increases the speed of sound increases.

SECTION F - HELICOPTER AERODYNAMICS

The last section of Chapter 2 discusses rotary-wing aerodynamics. Some of the topics brought out in this section include translational lift, dissymmetry of lift, and gyroscopic precession. There are no FAA Test questions on this material. However, as a maintenance technician, you must be familiar with basic helicopter flight principles.

BASIC ELECTRICITY

SECTION A - THEORY AND PRINCIPLES

The first section of Chapter 3 introduces the basic theory and principles of electricity. The section begins by discussing how electricity was discovered and continues by explaining electron theory, static electricity, magnetism, electromagnetism, and sources of electricity. Additional information contained in this section includes the relationships explained by Ohm's law as well as information on basic circuit elements and circuit considerations.

3-1   AMG031

How much power must a 24-volt generator furnish to a system which contains the following loads? (Note: 1 horsepower = 746 watts)

UNIT	RATING
One motor (75 percent efficient)	1/5 hp
Three position lights	20 watts each
One heating element	5 amp
One anticollision light	3 amp

A– 402 watts.
B– 385 watts.
C– 450 watts.

3-1. Answer C. JSGT 3A, FGH

To solve this problem, you must first calculate the power (P = EI) used by each unit.

One Motor (746 watts x 1/5 HP) ÷ 75%	199 watts
Position Lights (3 lights x 20 watts)	60 watts
Heating Element (24 volts x 5 amps)	120 watts
Anticollision Light (24 volts x 3 amps)	72 watts
The total required power output is	451 watts

450 watts is the closest.

3-2   AMG031

A 12-volt electric motor has 1,000 watts input and 1 horsepower output. Maintaining the same efficiency, how much input power will a 24-volt, 1-horsepower electric motor require? (Note: 1 horsepower = 746 watts)

A– 1,000 watts.
B– 2,000 watts.
C– 500 watts.

3-2. Answer A. JSGT 3A, FGH

As long as the same efficiency is maintained, a 1 HP motor requires 1,000 watts regardless of the system voltage. The advantage of using a higher system voltage is that less current is required and a smaller feed line can be used.

3-3   AMG031

A 1-horsepower, 24-volt DC electric motor that is 80 percent efficient requires 932.5 watts. How much power will a 1-horsepower, 12-volt DC electric motor that is 75 percent efficient require? (Note: 1 horsepower = 746 watts)

A–932.5 watts.
B–1,305.5 watts.
C–994.6 watts.

3-3. Answer C. JSGT 3A, FGH

If a motor operates at 100 percent efficiency it consumes 746 watts of energy for each horsepower developed. However, because there are always friction and heat loss, a motor is never 100 percent efficient and more than 746 watts is needed to produce 1 horsepower. To determine the number of watts required to produce 1 horsepower, divide the number of watts in 1 horsepower by the efficiency of the motor. A 1-horsepower motor that is 75 percent efficient requires 994.6 watts (746 watts ÷ .75 = 994.6 watts).

3-4   AMG031

The potential difference between two conductors which are insulated from each other is measured in

A–volts.
B–amperes.
C–coulombs.

3-4. Answer A. JSGT 3A, FGH

Potential difference is one way of expressing voltage. Other terms used include Potential, Electromotive Force (EMF), Voltage Drop, and IR Drop.

3-5   AMG031

(Refer to figure 4 on page 3-2.)
How much power is being furnished to the circuit?

A–575 watts.
B–2,875 watts.
C–2,645 watts.

3-5. Answer C. JSGT 3A, FGH

Because the circuit shown is purely resistive, you can calculate power by using the formula P = I x E. However, first you must determine the system voltage. Ohm's law states that volts (E) equals amperes (I) times resistance (R) or E = I x R. The circuit voltage is 115 volts (23 amps x 5 ohms = 115 volts). Now, use the power formula to calculate the amount of power being furnished. The answer is 2,645 watts (23 amps x 115 volts = 2,645 watts).

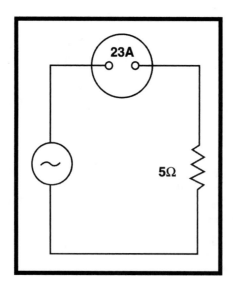

Figure 4. Circuit Diagram.

3-6   AMG015

The correct way to connect a test voltmeter in a circuit is

A– in series with a unit.
B– between source voltage and the load.
C– in parallel with a unit.

3-6. Answer C. JSGT 3A, FGH

Voltmeters are always connected in parallel with the unit being checked and proper polarity must be observed to prevent damage to the meter. It is handy to remember, measure voltage-across (parallel), measure current-through (series).

3-7   AMG015

Which term means .001 ampere?

A– Microampere.
B– Kiloampere.
C– Milliampere.

3-7. Answer C. JSGT 3A, FGH

Each of the terms listed here are common metric prefixes. You should be familiar with the values of all 3 prefixes listed in this question. Microampere = 0.000001 ampere, Kiloampere = 1,000 amps, and Milliampere = .001 ampere.

3-8   AMG015

.002KV equals

A– 20 volts.
B– 2.0 volts.
C– .2 volt.

3-8. Answer B. JSGT 3A, FGH

The metric prefix Kilo means 1,000. Therefore, .002KV is equal to 2 volts (.002 KV x 1,000 = 2.0 volts).

3-9   AMG015

(Refer to figure 9 on page 3-3.)
How many instruments (voltmeters and ammeters) are installed correctly?

A– Three.
B– One.
C– Two.

3-9. Answer C. JSGT 3A, FGH

Basic rules to follow are that ammeters are connected in series, voltmeters are connected in parallel, and proper polarity must be observed. In this circuit, the voltmeter in parallel with the light and the ammeter in series with the light and the battery are connected properly. The polarity on the second voltmeter is incorrect and the second ammeter is in parallel with the battery.

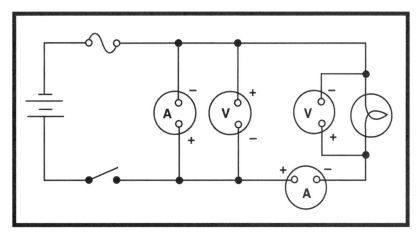

Figure 9. Circuit Diagram.

3-10   AMG031
What unit is used to express electrical power?

A– Volt.
B– Watt.
C– Ampere.

3-10. Answer B. JSGT 3A, FGH
The watt is used to express electrical power. The volt is a measure of electromotive force and the ampere is a measure of current flow.

3-11   AMG031
Which of these will cause the resistance of a conductor to decrease?

A– Decrease the length or the cross-sectional area.
B– Decrease the length or increase the cross-sectional area.
C– Increase the length or decrease the cross-sectional area.

3-11. Answer B. JSGT 3A, FGH
There are four factors which affect the resistance of a conductor. They are (1) the type of material used; (2) the length of the conductor; (3) the size of the cross sectional area; and (4) temperature. If you wish to decrease the resistance of a conductor, you can (1) select a different material, one that has a lower resistivity; (2) decrease the length of the conductor, the shorter the conductor the less the resistance; (3) increase the cross-sectional area of the conductor, a larger cross section results in a lower resistance; or (4) lower the temperature.

3-12   AMG042
Through which material will magnetic lines of force pass the most readily?

A– Copper.
B– Iron.
C– Aluminum.

3-12. Answer B. JSGT 3A, FGH
The measure of the ease with which lines of magnetic flux pass through a material is measured in terms of permeability. The permeability scale is based on a perfect vacuum with air used as a reference and is given the permeability of one. Flux can travel through iron much easier than air or other materials because it has a permeability of approximately 7,000.

3-13   AMG015
The voltage drop in a conductor of known resistance is dependent on

A– the voltage of the circuit.
B– only the resistance of the conductor and does not change with a change in either voltage or amperage.
C– the amperage of the circuit.

3-13. Answer C. JSGT 3A, FGH
Ohm's law states that two variables affect voltage. They are current and resistance. This can be seen in the formula $E = I \times R$. Since the resistance in an ordinary conductor is constant, the voltage drop in a conductor is dependant on the current flowing through the conductor.

3-14   AMG031
A thermal switch or thermal protector, as used in an electric motor, is designed to

A– close the integral fan circuit to allow cooling of the motor.
B– open the circuit in order to allow cooling of the motor.
C– reroute the circuit to ground.

3-14. Answer B. FGH
A thermal switch or thermal protector as used in an electric motor is designed to open the motor circuit when the operating temperature reaches a preset value. Upon cooling, these switches close the circuit to restore power to the motor.

3-15   AMG031

(Refer to figure 17 on page 3-5.)

Which of the components is a potentiometer?

A– 5.

B– 3.

C– 11.

3-15. Answer B. JSGT 3A, FGH

The component illustrated at 3 is a potentiometer. The component at 5 is a variable capacitor, and the component at 11 is an inductor or coil.

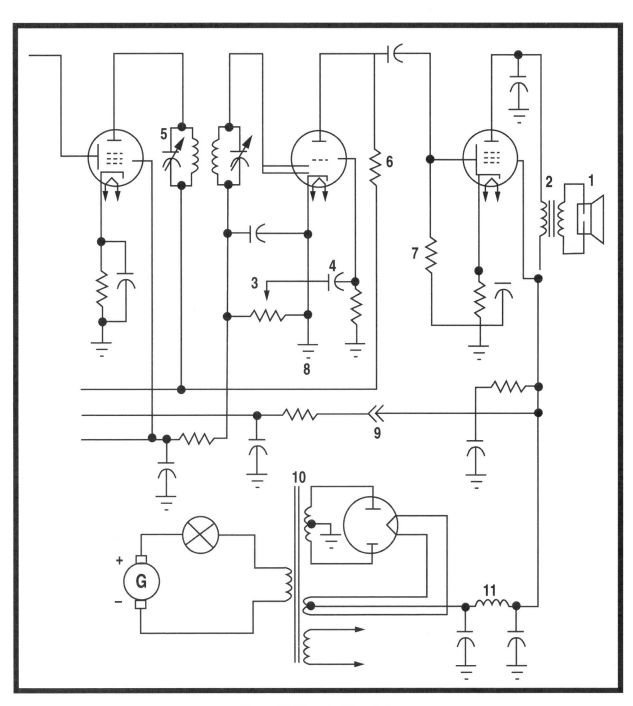

Figure 17. Electrical Symbols.

3-16   AMG031

(Refer to figure 17 on page 3-5.)
The electrical symbol represented at number 5 is a variable

A– inductor.
B– resistor.
C– capacitor.

3-16. Answer C. JSGT 3A, FGH

The component illustrated at 5 is a variable capacitor. This symbol is created by drawing an arrow through the symbol for a capacitor to indicate that its capacitance is variable. An inductor is illustrated at 11 and a resistor is illustrated at 6 and 7.

3-17   AMG031

(Refer to figure 21 on page 3-6.)
Which symbol represents a variable resistor?

A– 2.
B– 1.
C– 3.

3-17. Answer A. JSGT 3A, FGH

Selection 2 illustrates a resistor with an arrow to indicate it is variable. Selection 1 could be either a rheostat or potentiometer and selection 3 is a tapped resistor.

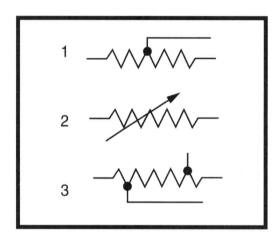

Figure 21. Electrical Symbols.

3-18   AMG053

How much current does a 30-volt, 1/2 horsepower motor that is 85-percent efficient draw from the bus? (Note: 1 horsepower = 746 watts)

A– 14.6 amperes.
B– 12.4 amperes.
C– 14.1 amperes.

3-18. Answer A. JSGT 3A, FGH

To solve this problem, you must use the formula $I = P \div E$, where (I) equals amps or current, (P) equals power or watts, and (E) equals volts. From the information given you can calculate that a 100 percent efficient 1/2 HP motor uses 373 watts of power ($746 \div 2 = 373$). However, the motor in this question is only 85 percent efficient. To determine the actual number of watts used to produce 1/2 HP, you must divide 373 watts by 85 percent. The actual power used is 438.8 watts ($373 \div 0.85 = 438.8$). Therefore, the current required is 14.6 amps. (438.8 watts $\div 30$ volts $= 14.6$ amps)

3-19   AMG031

What is the purpose of the ground symbol used in electrical circuit diagrams?

A– To show that there is common bus for connection of the source of electrical energy to the load.

B– To show the source of electrical energy for the load.

C– To show that there is a return path for the current between the source of electrical energy and the load.

3-19. Answer C. FGH

A ground symbol is commonly used in electrical circuit diagrams to indicate that the return path for electricity is carried through the chassis or frame of the aircraft. The symbol indicates that the electrical potential at the ground points is equal.

SECTION B - DIRECT CURRENT

Section B of Chapter 3 discusses the fundamentals of direct current (DC) including basic terminology and the structure of direct current. The section continues by discussing series DC circuits, parallel DC circuits, and how DC is converted to AC.

3-20   AMG015

Which requires the most electrical power during operation? (Note: 1 horsepower = 746 watts)

A– A 12-volt motor requiring 8 amperes.
B– Four 30-watt lamps in a 12-volt parallel circuit.
C– Two lights requiring 3 amperes each in a 24-volt parallel system.

3-20. Answer C. JSGT 3B, FGH

Power is defined in terms of watts (P), and is the product of volts (E) and amps (I). Each light in choice (C) requires 72 watts of power (3 amps x 24 volts = 72 watts). Since there are 2 lights, a total of 44 watts is required (72 watts x 2 lights = 144 watts). A 12-volt motor requiring 8 amperes requires 96 watts of power (12 volts x 8 amps = 96 watts), and Four 30-watt lamps in a 12-volt parallel circuit requires 120 watts (4 lamps x 30 watts = 120 watts). Therefore, two lights requiring 3 amperes each in a 24-volt parallel system is the correct answer since it requires the most electrical power.

3-21   AMG031

How many amperes will a 28-volt generator be required to supply to a circuit containing five lamps in parallel, three of which have a resistance of 6 ohms each and two of which have a resistance of 5 ohms each?

A– 1.11 amperes.
B– 1 ampere.
C– 25.23 amperes.

3-21. Answer C. JSGT 3B, FGH

This problem requires application of the formula for determining total resistance in a parallel circuit:

$$1 / [(1/R_1) + (1/R_2) + (1/R_3)]$$

The total resistance is 1.11 ohms. Once you know the voltage and resistance in a circuit, you can determine the amperes required by applying Ohm's law (I = E ÷ R). The answer is 25.23 amperes (28 volts ÷ 1.11 ohms = 25.23 amps).

3-22   AMG031

A 24-volt source is required to furnish 48 watts to a parallel circuit consisting of four resistors of equal value. What is the voltage drop across each resistor?

A– 12 volts.
B– 3 volts.
C– 24 volts.

3-22. Answer C. JSGT 3B, FGH

Kirchhoff's law states that in a parallel circuit, voltage remains constant and amperes vary across each resistance. Therefore, the voltage drop measured at each resistance in a 24-volt circuit must equal the applied voltage of 24 volts.

3-23   AMG031

A cabin entry light of 10 watts and a dome light of 20 watts are connected in parallel to a 30-volt source. If the voltage across the 10-watt light is measured, it will be

A– equal to the voltage across the 20-watt light.
B– half the voltage across the 20-watt light.
C– one-third of the input voltage.

3-23. Answer A. JSGT 3B, FGH

In a parallel circuit, the voltage remains constant across each path while amperes vary. Therefore, the voltage across the 10-watt light is equal to the voltage across the 20-watt light.

3-24   AMG031

A 14-ohm resistor is to be installed in a series circuit carrying .05 ampere. How much power will the resistor be required to dissipate?

A– At least .70 milliwatt.
B– At least 35 milliwatts.
C– Less than .035 watt.

3-24. Answer B. JSGT 3B, FGH

Given resistance (R) and current (I), you can calculate the circuit voltage (E) using the formula E = IR. The circuit voltage equals .7 volts (.05 amps x 14 ohms = .7 volts). Once voltage is known, you can calculate power (P) with the formula P = IE. The power the resistor must dissipate is .035 watts or 35 milliwatts (.05 amps x .7 volts = .035 watts).

3-25   AMG031

(Refer to figure 10 on page 3-9.)
What is the measured voltage of the series-parallel circuit between terminals A and B?

A– 1.5 volts.
B– 3.0 volts.
C– 4.5 volts.

3-25. Answer B. JSGT 3B, FGH

Probably the easiest way to see how these batteries are connected is to redraw the circuit (be careful to observe proper polarity). The measured voltage is 3 volts.

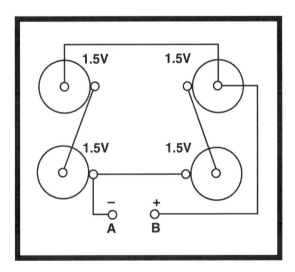

Figure 10. Battery Circuit.

3-26   AMG031

(Refer to figure 6 on page 3-10.)

If resistor R_5 is disconnected at the junction of R_4 and R_3 as shown, what will the ohmmeter read?

A– 2.76 ohms.
B– 3 ohms.
C– 12 ohms.

3-26. Answer B. JSGT 3B, FGH

With resistor R_5 disconnected, the ohmmeter reads the resistance of the remaining four resistors. R_3 and R_4 are in series and, therefore, can be combined, resulting in a total of 12 ohms. This 12 ohm total is in parallel with the remaining two resistors. The formula for parallel resistances is now used to calculate the total resistance of 3 ohms.

$$1/ [(1/12) + (1/6) + (1/12)] = 3 \text{ ohms}$$

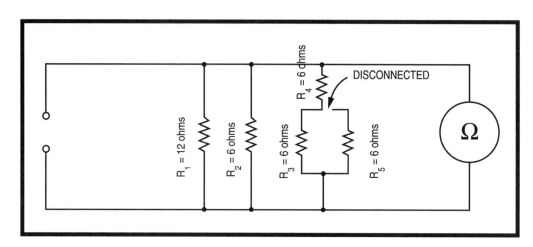

Figure 6. Circuit Diagram.

3-27   AMG031

(Refer to figure 7 on page 3-11.)

If resistor R_3 is disconnected at terminal D, what will the ohmmeter read?

A– Infinite resistance.
B– 10 ohms.
C– 20 ohms.

3-27. Answer A. JSGT 3B, FGH

By disconnecting resistor R_3 at terminal D, the flow is broken to the rest of the circuit, and the break in the resistor itself is identified by an infinite resistance reading on the ohmmeter. If resistor R_3 was not disconnected at terminal D, the ohmmeter would indicate the resistance of R_1 and R_2, which is 20 ohms.

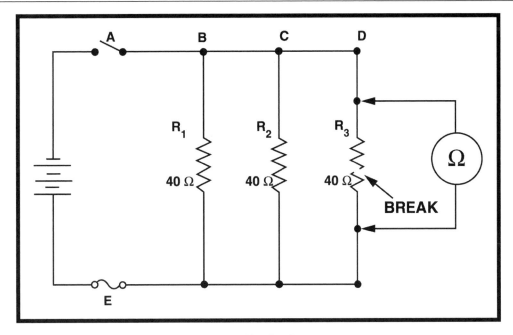

Figure 7. Circuit Diagram.

3-28   AMG031

(Refer to figure 8 on page 3-12.)

With an ohmmeter connected into the circuit as shown, what will the ohmmeter read?

A– 20 ohms.

B– Infinite resistance.

C– 10 ohms.

3-28. Answer C. JSGT 3B, FGH

Because of the break in resistor R_3, resistors R_1 and R_2 are the only resistances measured by the ohmmeter. These two resistors are connected in parallel and, therefore, their combined resistance can be calculated with the formula:

$1/ [(1/R_1) + (1/R_2)]$

The total resistance of R_1 and R_2 is 10 ohms = 10 ohms

$1/ [(1/20) + (1/20)] = 10$ ohms

and represents the value displayed on the meter.

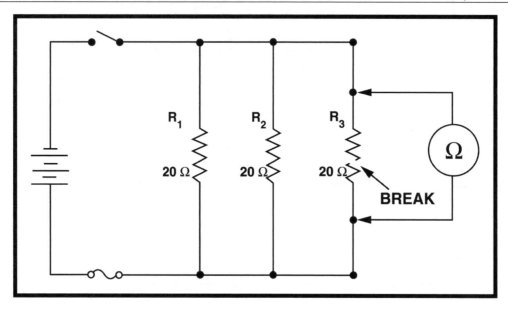

Figure 8. Circuit Diagram.

3-29   AMG031
(Refer to figure 64 on page 3-12.)
A 24-volt source is required to furnish 48 watts to a parallel circuit consisting of two resistors of equal value. What is the value of each resistor?

A– 24 ohms.
B– 12 ohms.
C– 6 ohms.

3-29. Answer A. JSGT 3B, FGH
Using the formula given, you can calculate the total resistance of 12 ohms (24 volts^2 ÷ 48 watts = 12 ohms). The formula for determining the individual resistance of two like resistors connected in parallel is r = R_t x 2, where (R) represents the resistance of each resistor and (R_t) represents the total resistance. The value of each resistor is 24 ohms (12 ohms x 2 = 24 ohms).

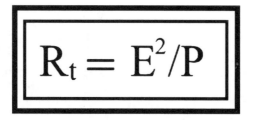

$$R_t = E^2/P$$

Figure 64. Resistance Total.

3-30   AMG031
Which requires the most electrical power? (Note: 1 horsepower = 746 watts)

A– Four 30-watt lamps arranged in a 12-volt parallel circuit.
B– A 1/5-horsepower, 24-volt motor which is 75 percent efficient.
C– A 24-volt anticollision light circuit consisting of two light assemblies which require 3 amperes each during operation.

3-30. Answer B. JSGT 3B, FGH
To answer this question, you must calculate the power requirements (wattage) of each unit listed.

Lamps...4 x 30 watts = 120W

24V motor...(746 watts x 1/5 HP) ÷ 75% = 198.93W

Anticollision 24 volts x 3 amps x 2 assemblies = 144W

A 1/5-horsepower, 24-volt motor that is 75 percent efficient requires the most electrical power.

3-31 AMG031

What is the operating resistance of a 30-watt light bulb designed for a 28-volt system?

A– 1.07 ohms.
B– 26 ohms.
C– 0.93 ohm.

3-31. Answer B. JSGT 3B, FGH

To determine resistance, Ohm's law states that resistance (R) equals volts (E) divided by amperes (I) or R = E ÷ I. Therefore, to solve this problem, amperes must be determined. Using the given information, you can calculate amps with the formula I = P ÷ E. The number of amperes in this circuit is 1.07 amps (30 watts ÷ 28 volts = 1.07 amps). With the number of amps known you can calculate the resistance. The operating resistance is 26.17 ohms (28 volts ÷ 1.07 = 26.17 ohms). 26 ohms is the closest.

3-32 AMG031

Which statement is correct when made in reference to a parallel circuit?

A– The current is equal in all portions of the circuit.
B– The total current is equal to the sum of the currents through the individual branches of the circuit.
C– The current in amperes can be found by dividing the EMF in volts by the sum of the resistors in ohms.

3-32. Answer B. JSGT 3B, FGH

In a parallel circuit, the voltage remains constant across each unit and the current flow varies with each unit's resistance. However, Kirchhoff's law states that the current flowing to a point must equal the current flowing away from the point. Therefore, the total current flow in a parallel circuit is equal to the sum of the currents through each branch of the circuit.

3-33 AMG031

If three resistors of 3 ohms, 5 ohms, and 22 ohms are connected in series in a 28-volt circuit, how much current will flow through the 3-ohm resistor?

A– 9.3 amperes.
B– 1.05 amperes.
C– 0.93 ampere.

3-33. Answer C. JSGT 3B, FGH

Kirchhoff's law states that in a series circuit, current remains constant and voltage varies across each resistor. To determine the current, use the formula I = E ÷ R. The total resistance in a series circuit is calculated by adding all the resistances. The total resistance in this circuit is 30 ohms (3 + 5 + 22 = 30 ohms). The total current within the circuit is .93 amps (28 volts ÷ 30 ohms = .93 amps). Since current remains constant, the 3 ohm resistor has .93 amps flowing through it.

3-34 AMG031

A circuit has an applied voltage of 30 volts and a load consisting of a 10-ohm resistor in series with a 20-ohm resistor. What is the voltage drop across the 10-ohm resistor?

A– 10 volts.
B– 20 volts.
C– 30 volts.

3-34. Answer A. JSGT 3B, FGH

In a series circuit, the current is the same in all parts of the circuit, but the voltage drop varies with the resistance of each unit. However, before the voltage drop can be determined in this problem, you must calculate the total resistance and current. Total resistance equals 30 ohms (10 + 20 = 30). Now, use the formula I = E ÷ R to calculate the current flowing through the circuit. There is 1 amp flowing through the circuit (30 volts ÷ 30 ohms = 1 amp). To determine the voltage drop across the 10 ohm resistor use the formula $E_1 = I \times R_1$. The voltage drop across the 10 ohm resistor is 10 volts (1 amp x 10 ohms = 10 volts).

3-35   AMG031

Which is correct in reference to electrical resistance?

A– Two electrical devices will have the same combined resistance if they are connected in series as they will have if connected in parallel.

B– If one of three bulbs in a parallel lighting circuit is removed, the total resistance of the circuit will become greater.

C– An electrical device that has a high resistance will use more power than one with a low resistance with the same applied voltage.

3-35. Answer B. JSGT 3B, FGH

In a parallel circuit, the greater the number of resistors, the less the total resistance. If you remove a resistor from a parallel circuit, the total resistance in the circuit goes up. This is the same as plugging too many appliances into a single outlet in your house causing the circuit breaker to pop. The total resistance goes down, the current flow goes up, and the breaker overloads.

3-36   AMG031

A 48-volt source is required to furnish 192 watts to a parallel circuit consisting of three resistors of equal value. What is the value of each resistor?

A– 36 ohms.
B– 4 ohms.
C– 12 ohms.

3-36. Answer A. JSGT 3B, FGH

To solve this problem, you must use three Ohm's law formulas. First, determine the total current in the circuit using the formula $I = P \div E$. The current is 4 amps (192 watts $\div$ 48 volts = 4 amps). Now, calculate the circuit's total resistance using the formula $R = E \div I$. Total resistance is 12 ohms (48 volts $\div$ 4 amps = 12 ohms). To determine the resistance of each resistor use the formula $r = R_T \times n$ where r = the resistance of each resistor, R_T = total resistance, and n = the number of resistors in the circuit. The value of each resistor is 36 ohms (12 ohms x 3 = 36 ohms).

3-37   AMG031

Which is correct concerning a parallel circuit?

A– Total resistance will be smaller than the smallest resistor.

B– Total resistance will decrease when one of the resistances is removed.

C– Total voltage drop is the same as the total resistance.

3-37. Answer A. JSGT 3B, FGH

According to Kirchhoff's law, the total resistance in a parallel circuit is always less than the smallest resistor. This can also be derived from the formula

$$R_T = 1/ [(1/R_1) + (1/R_2) + (1/R_3)]$$

3-38   AMG031

(Refer to figure 11 on page 3-15.)
Find the total current flowing in the wire between points C and D.

A– 6.0 amperes.
B– 2.4 amperes.
C– 3.0 amperes.

3-38. Answer C. JSGT 3B, FGH

Current flow in a parallel circuit varies with the resistance value of each branch. To determine the amount of current flowing from point C to point D you must first calculate the circuit's total resistance. This is done with the formula

1/ [(1/8) + (1/10) + (1/40)]

The total resistance is 4 ohms. Now determine the total current flowing through the circuit using the formula $I = E \div R$. The total current is 6 amps (24 volts ÷ 4 ohms = 6 amps). Since this is a parallel circuit, once the current reaches point C a portion of it proceeds to R_1 and the rest to point D. To calculate the amount of current that flows between point C and D, you must calculate the amount of current flowing to R_1. To do this, use the formula $I_{R1} = E \div R_1$. The current drop across R_1 is 3 amps (24 volts ÷ 8 ohms = 3 amps). This leaves 3 amps to flow between points C and D (6 amps − 3 amps = 3 amps).

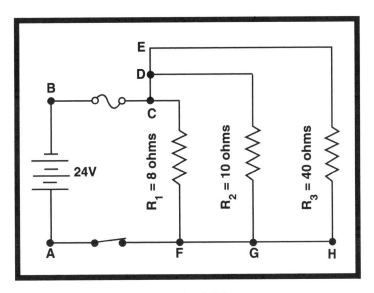

Figure 11. Circuit Diagram.

3-39   AMG031

(Refer to figure 11 on page 3-15.)
Find the voltage across the 8-ohm resistor.

A– 8 volts.
B– 20.4 volts.
C– 24 volts.

3-39. Answer C. JSGT 3B, FGH

In a parallel circuit, the voltage remains constant across each resistor. This means the voltage across the 8-ohm resistor is equal to the source voltage of 24 volts.

3-40   AMG031
(Refer to figure 12 on page 3-16.)
Find the total resistance of the circuit.

A– 16 ohms.
B– 2.6 ohms.
C– 21.2 ohms.

3-40. Answer C. JSGT 3B, FGH
When solving complex circuit problems for total resistance, begin by solving the parallel branches first. The formulas given can be used if you begin by solving for R_a and then continue by solving for R_b, R_c, and R_t, respectively. Solving for R_a combines resistors R_4 and R_5. The combined resistance of R_4 and R_5 is 4 ohms. Since R_2 and $R_{4,5}$ are in series, add these resistances. This is demonstrated in the formula $R_b = R_a + R_2$. The combined resistance of R_2, and $R_{4,5}$ is 16 ohms (4 ohms + 12 ohms = 16 ohms). Now, using the formula to solve for R_c, combine the resistances of R_3 and $R_{2,4,5}$, which are in parallel. The combined resistance is 3.2 ohms. The final step is to add the remaining two resistances (R_1 and $R_{2,3,4,5}$), which are in series. The total resistance in the circuit is 21.2 ohms (18 ohms + 3.2 ohms = 21.2 ohms).

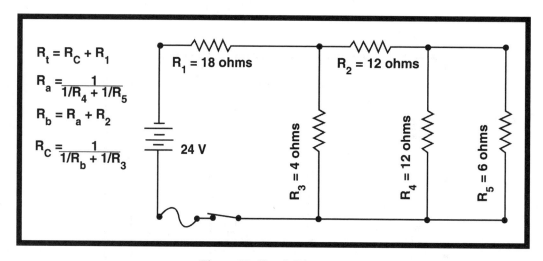

Figure 12. Circuit Diagram.

3-41   AMG015
(Refer to figure 13 on page 3-17.)
Determine the total current flow in the circuit.

A– 0.2 ampere.
B– 1.4 amperes.
C– 0.8 ampere.

3-41. Answer B. JSGT 3B, FGH
The total current flow in a parallel circuit is equal to the sum of the current flowing through each branch of the circuit. You can calculate the current in each branch using the formula $I = E \div R$. Resistor 1 has .4 amps of current (12V ÷ 30 ohms = .4 amps). Resistor 2 has .2 amps of current (12V ÷ 60 ohms = .2 amps). And, resistor 3 has .8 amps of current (12V ÷ 15 ohms = .8 amps). This results in a total current flow of 1.4 amps (.4 + .2 + .8 = 1.4).

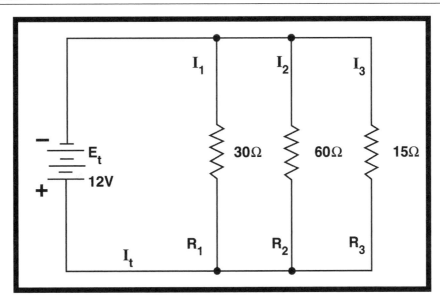

Figure 13. Circuit Diagram.

3-42   AMG031

(Refer to figure 14 on page 3-17.)

The total resistance of the circuit is

A– 25 ohms.

B– 35 ohms.

C– 17 ohms.

3-42. Answer C. JSGT 3B, FGH

When presented with a series-parallel circuit and asked to calculate the total resistance, begin at the point farthest from the power source and work back to the power. Here, you can begin by finding the total resistance of R_2, R_3, and R_4, which are in parallel. Their combined resistance is 2 ohms.

$$1/ [(1/4) + (1/6) + (1/12)] = 2 \text{ ohms}$$

Now, all resistances are in series. To determine the total resistance of a series circuit add all the resistances. The circuit's total resistance is 17 ohms (5 ohms + 2 ohms + 10 ohms = 17 ohms).

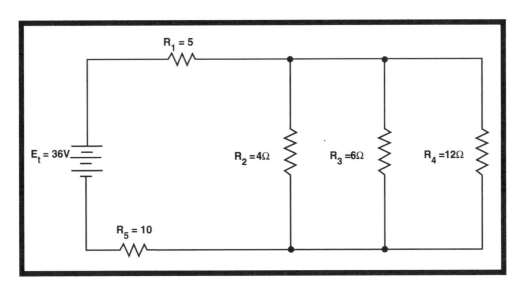

Figure 14. Circuit Diagram.

SECTION C - BATTERIES

Section C looks at the primary and secondary cell batteries found in aviation. The main emphasis in this section falls on the characteristics and principles associated with lead-acid and nickel-cadmium batteries. This includes operational characteristics as well as how to service each type of battery.

3-43   AMG031

A lead-acid battery with 12 cells connected in series (no-load voltage = 2.1 volts per cell) furnishes 10 amperes to a load of 2-ohms resistance. The internal resistance of the battery in this instance is

A– 0.52 ohm.
B– 2.52 ohms.
C– 5.0 ohms.

3-43. Answer A. JSGT 3C, FGH

To calculate internal resistance, subtract the closed circuit voltage from the no-load voltage and divide by closed circuit current. The no-load voltage is 25.2 volts (12 cells x 2.1 volts = 25.2 volts), the closed circuit voltage is 20 volts (10 amps x 2 ohms = 20 volts), and the closed circuit current is 10 amps. The battery's internal resistance is .52 ohms. (25.2 volts – 20 volts) ÷ 10 amps = .52 ohms

3-44   AMG031

If electrolyte from a lead-acid battery is spilled in the battery compartment, which procedure should be followed?

A– Apply boric acid solution to the affected area followed by a water rinse.
B– Rinse the affected area thoroughly with clean water.
C– Apply sodium bicarbonate solution to the affected area followed by a water rinse.

3-44. Answer C. JSGT 3C, AC 43.13-1B

Sodium bicarbonate (baking soda) is used to neutralize the electrolyte from a lead-acid battery. If electrolyte is spilled, you should immediately apply sodium bicarbonate and rinse the contaminated area with water.

3-45   AMG031

Which statement regarding the hydrometer reading of a lead-acid storage battery electrolyte is true?

A– The hydrometer reading does not require a temperature correction if the electrolyte temperature is 80°F.
B– A specific gravity correction should be subtracted from the hydrometer reading if the electrolyte temperature is above 20°F.
C– The hydrometer reading will give a true indication of the capacity of the battery regardless of the electrolyte temperature.

3-45. Answer A. JSGT 3C, FGH

A hydrometer accurately measures the specific gravity of battery electrolyte when it is at or near 80°F. For temperatures above 90°F or below 70°F, it is necessary to apply a correction factor. Some hydrometers are equipped with a scale inside the tube. With other hydrometers it is necessary to refer to a chart provided by the manufacturer.

3-46   AMG031
A fully charged lead-acid battery will not freeze until extremely low temperatures are reached because

A– the acid is in the plates, thereby increasing the specific gravity of the solution.
B– most of the acid is in the solution.
C– increased internal resistance generates sufficient heat to prevent freezing.

3-46. Answer B. JSGT 3C, FGH
When a lead-acid battery is fully charged, the electrolyte contains a high concentration of sulfuric acid. This high concentration of acid raises the specific gravity of the electrolyte and lowers the freezing point. A fully charged lead-acid battery has a freezing point of –80° to –90°F.

3-47   AMG031
What determines the amount of current which will flow through a battery while it is being charged by a constant voltage source?

A– The total plate area of the battery.
B– The state-of-charge of the battery.
C– The ampere-hour capacity of the battery.

3-47. Answer B. JSGT 3C, FGH
When a battery is discharged, its low voltage allows a large amount of current to flow into the battery. As the battery charges and the voltage rises, the current flow decreases.

3-48   AMG031
Which of the following statements is/are generally true regarding the charging of several aircraft batteries together?
1. Batteries of different voltages (but similar capacities) can be connected in series with each other across the charger, and charged using the constant current method.
2. Batteries of different ampere-hour capacity and same voltage can be connected in parallel with each other across the charger, and charged using the constant voltage method.
3. Batteries of the same voltage and same ampere-hour capacity must be connected in series with each other across the charger, and charged using the constant current method.

A– 3.
B– 2 and 3.
C– 1 and 2.

3-48. Answer C. JSGT 3C, FGH
Choices 1 and 2 are correct. One of the nice features of constant-current chargers is that they can be used to charge batteries of different voltage at the same time. To do this, the batteries must be connected in series so that the current supply is the same to each battery (current is the same in all parts of a series circuit). The constant-current charge requires more time to charge a battery fully, as well as additional monitoring to avoid overcharging. You can also charge multiple batteries using a constant-voltage charger. When doing this, the batteries may have different ampere-hour ratings but they must have the same voltage and be connected in parallel.

3-49   AMG031
The method used to rapidly charge a nickel-cadmium battery utilizes

A– constant current and constant voltage.
B– constant current and varying voltage.
C– constant voltage and varying current.

3-49. Answer C. JSGT 3C, FGH
Whenever a battery is charged rapidly, it is a constant-voltage type charge. When using a constant-voltage charge on a nickel-cadmium battery the voltage remains constant and the current decreases as the battery charges.

3-50   AMG031

The purpose of providing a space underneath the plates in a lead acid battery's cell container is to

A– ensure that the electrolyte quantity ratio to the number of plates and plate area is adequate.
B– prevent sediment buildup from contacting the plates and causing a short circuit.
C– allow for convection flow of the electrolyte in order to provide for cooling of the plates.

3-50. Answer B. JSAB Page 2

The positive and negative plates are kept apart by porous separators and held off the bottom of the container to prevent sediment from building up and shorting out the plates.

3-51   AMG031

Which condition is an indication of improperly torqued cell link connections of a nickel-cadmium battery?

A– Light spewing at the cell caps.
B– Toxic and corrosive deposit of potassium carbonate crystals.
C– Heat or burn marks on the hardware.

3-51. Answer C. JSGT 3C, FGH

If the cell link connections are not properly torqued, arcing and overheating may occur. You can identify this condition by the presence of heat or blue marks on the hardware.

3-52   AMG031

The presence of small amounts of potassium carbonate deposits on the top of nickel-cadmium battery cells that have been in service for a time is an indication of

A– normal operation.
B– excessive gassing.
C– excessive plate sulfation.

3-52. Answer A. JSGT 3C, FGH

Most nickel-cadmium batteries develop an accumulation of white, potassium carbonate powder on top of the cells during normal operation. If there is an excessive amount, check the voltage regulator and the level of electrolyte in the cells.

3-53   AMG031

What is the likely result of servicing and charging nickel-cadmium and lead acid batteries together in the same service area?

A– Lowered amp-hour capacities for both types of batteries.
B– Reduced battery service life for both types of batteries.
C– Contamination of both types of batteries.

3-53. Answer C. JSGT 3C, FGH

A separate storage and maintenance area should be provided for nickel-cadmium and lead acid batteries. The electrolyte used in lead-acid batteries is chemically opposite of that used in nickel-cadmium batteries. Any electrolyte transfer from one type to the other will result in contamination.

3-54   AMG031

The electrolyte of a nickel-cadmium battery is highest when the battery is

A– in a fully charged condition.
B– in a discharged condition.
C– under a no-load condition.

3-54. Answer A. JSGT 3C, FGH

During the discharge of a nickel-cadmium battery, the plates absorb a quantity of electrolyte. During recharge, the plates release the electrolyte and the level of the electrolyte rises. When fully charged, the electrolyte level of a nickel-cadmium battery is at its highest.

3-55 AMG031

The end-of-charge voltage of a 19-cell nickel-cadmium battery, measured while still on charge,

A– must be 1.2 to 1.3 volts per cell.

B– must be 1.4 volts per cell.

C– depends upon its temperature and the method used for charging.

3-56 AMG031

Nickel-cadmium batteries which are stored for a long period of time will show a low liquid level because

A– of the decrease in the specific gravity of the electrolyte.

B– electrolyte evaporates through the vents.

C– electrolyte becomes absorbed into the plates.

3-57 AMG031

How can the state-of-charge of a nickel-cadmium battery be determined?

A– By measuring the specific gravity of the electrolyte.

B– By a measured discharge.

C– By the level of the electrolyte.

3-58 AMG031

What may result if water is added to a nickel-cadmium battery when it is not fully charged?

A– Excessive electrolyte dilution.

B– Excessive spewing is likely to occur during the charging cycle.

C– No adverse effects since water may be added anytime.

3-55. Answer C. JSGT 3C, FGH

The end of charge voltage, measured while the cell is on charge, depends upon its temperature and the method used for charging it.

3-56. Answer C. JSGT 3C, FGH

When a nickel-cadmium battery is stored for a long period of time, it may lose some or all of its charge. When this happens, the electrolyte is absorbed into the plates and the electrolyte level in the cell drops.

3-57. Answer B. JSGT 3C, FGH

Since the electrolyte of a nickel-cadmium battery does not react chemically with the cell plates, the specific gravity of the electrolyte does not change appreciably. For this reason, you cannot use a hydrometer to determine the state of charge in a nickel-cadmium battery. The only way to determine the condition of a nickel-cadmium battery is to fully charge it, then discharge it at a specified rate and measure its amp-hour capacity.

3-58. Answer B. JSGT 3C, FGH

When discharged, the plates of a nickel-cadmium battery absorb a quantity of the electrolyte. On recharge, the plates release the electrolyte and the level of electrolyte rises. When fully charged, the electrolyte is at its highest level. Therefore, water should be added only when the battery is fully charged. If water is added to a nickel-cadmium battery that is not fully charged, excessive spewing will occur during the charging cycle.

3-59   AMG031

In nickel-cadmium batteries, a rise in cell temperature

A–causes an increase in internal resistance.
B–causes a decrease in internal resistance.
C–increases cell voltage.

3-59. Answer B. JSGT 3C, FGH

The nickel-cadmium battery has a very low internal resistance. However, if a nickel-cadmium battery is subjected to high temperatures, the cellophane-like material that separates the plates begins to breakdown. The breakdown of this material decreases the battery's internal resistance further. Therefore, as cell temperature in a nickel-cadmium battery increases, internal resistance decreases.

3-60   AMG031

When a charging current is applied to a nickel-cadmium battery, the cells emit gas

A–toward the end of the charging cycle.
B–throughout the charging cycle.
C–especially if the electrolyte level is high.

3-60. Answer A. JSGT 3C, FGH

A nickel-cadmium cell emits gas during the end of the charging cycle. The gas is caused by decomposition of the water in the electrolyte into hydrogen at the negative plates and oxygen at the positive plates. Caution should be observed as this gas is explosive. Proper ventilation must be provided while charging batteries.

3-61   AMG031

Which of the following best describes the contributing factors to thermal runaway in a nickel-cadmium battery installed in an aircraft?

A–High internal resistance intensified by high cell temperatures and a high current discharge/charge rate in a constant potential charging system.
B–Low internal resistance intensified by high cell temperatures and a high voltage discharge/charge rate in a constant current charging system.
C–Low internal resistance intensified by high cell temperatures and a high current discharge/charge rate in a constant potential charging system.

3-61. Answer C. JSGT 3C, FGH

The nickel-cadmium battery has a very low internal resistance. However, if a nickel-cadmium battery is subjected to high temperatures, the cellophane-like material that separates the plates begins to break down, decreasing the internal resistance further. Therefore, as cell temperature in a nickel-cadmium battery increases, internal resistance decreases allowing more current to flow with a constant potential charging system. This increased current flow causes the temperature to rise, further lowering the internal resistance which allows current flow to increase even more. This condition is called thermal runaway.

3-62   AMG031

Nickel-cadmium battery cases and drain surfaces which have been affected by electrolyte should be neutralized with a solution of

A–boric acid.
B–sodium bicarbonate.
C–potassium hydroxide.

3-62. Answer A. JSGT 3C, AC 43.13-1B

Nickel-cadmium battery electrolyte is a strong base and, therefore, it must be neutralized by using an acid. A boric acid solution is the standard for this purpose. Sodium bicarbonate is used to neutralize the electrolyte from lead acid batteries.

SECTION D - ALTERNATING CURRENT

Section D builds on the electrical theory discussed in prior sections to introduce the principles of alternating current (AC). Once you are familiar with the basic terminology and theory associated with alternating current, the section continues by discussing purely resistive AC circuits, as well as the principles of inductance and capacitance. The section closes by looking at three-phase alternating current and how AC is converted to DC.

3-63   AMG031

The working voltage of a capacitor in an AC circuit should be

A– equal to the highest applied voltage.
B– at least 20 percent greater than the highest applied voltage.
C– at least 50 percent greater than the highest applied voltage.

3-63. Answer C. JSGT 3D, FGH

The working voltage of the capacitor is the maximum voltage that can be steadily applied without danger of arc-over, and depends on the type and thickness of the dielectric. When installing a capacitor in a circuit, the working voltage should be at least 50 percent greater than the highest applied voltage.

3-64   AMG031

The term that describes the combined resistive forces in an AC circuit is

A– resistance.
B– reactance.
C– impedance.

3-64. Answer C. JSGT 3D, FGH

The flow of current in an AC circuit is opposed by three things: resistance, inductive reactance, and capacitive reactance. The combined effect of these three elements is known as impedance, and is represented by the letter Z. Impedance is obtained by finding the vector sum of the three oppositions.

3-65   AMG031

The basis for transformer operation in the use of alternating current is mutual

A– inductance.
B– capacitance.
C– reactance.

3-65. Answer A. JSGT 3D, FGH

A basic transformer consists of two coils of wire. When alternating current flows through one coil, the changing lines of flux radiate out and cut across the second coil. Anytime lines of flux cut across another conductor, they induce a voltage in that conductor even though there is no electrical connection between the two. This is known as mutual inductance and is the basis for transformer operation.

3-66   AMG031

The opposition offered by a coil to the flow of alternating current is called (disregard resistance)

A– impedance.
B– reluctance.
C– inductive reactance.

3-66. Answer C. JSGT 3D, FGH

When alternating current flows through a coil of wire, a voltage is induced in the wire in the opposite direction of the applied voltage. This counter-EMF opposes the flow of current through the coil and is called inductive reactance.

3-67   AMG031

An increase in which of the following factors will cause an increase in the inductive reactance of a circuit?

A– Inductance and frequency.
B– Resistance and voltage.
C– Resistance and capacitive reactance.

3-67. Answer A. JSGT 3D, FGH

Inductive reactance is calculated with the formula:

$$X_L = 2 \pi f L$$

If all other circuit values remain constant, the greater the inductance (L), the greater the inductive reactance. Furthermore, as the frequency (f) increases, inductive reactance also increases. Therefore, inductive reactance is directly proportional to the circuit inductance and frequency and an increase in either results in an increase in inductive reactance.

3-68   AMG031

In an AC circuit, the effective voltage is

A– equal to the maximum instantaneous voltage.
B– greater than the maximum instantaneous voltage.
C– less than the maximum instantaneous voltage.

3-68. Answer C. JSGT 3D, FGH

The effective voltage of alternating current is the same as the voltage of a direct current which produces the same heating effect. The effective voltage is always less than the maximum instantaneous voltage of the AC. Effective voltage in an AC circuit is also known as root mean squared, or RMS voltage and is calculated by multiplying .707 times the maximum instantaneous voltage.

3-69   AMG031

The amount of electricity a capacitor can store is directly proportional to the

A– distance between the plates and inversely proportional to the plate area.
B– plate area and is not affected by the distance between the plates.
C– plate area and inversely proportional to the distance between the plates.

3-69. Answer C. JSGT 3D, FGH

The capacity of a capacitor is affected by three variables: the area of the plates, the distance between the plates, and the dielectric constant of the material between the plates. The capacity is directly proportional to the plate area and inversely proportional to the distance between the plates. In other words, if the plate area increases the capacity increases, and if the distance between the plates increases total capacity decreases.

3-70   AMG031

Unless otherwise specified, any values given for current or voltage in an AC circuit are assumed to be

A– instantaneous values.
B– effective values.
C– maximum values.

3-70. Answer B. JSGT 3D, FGH

In the study of alternating current, all values given for current and voltage are assumed to be effective values unless otherwise specified and, in practice, only the effective values of voltage and current are used. AC voltmeters and ammeters measure the effective value.

3-71   AMG031

When different rated capacitors are connected in parallel in a circuit, the total capacitance is (Note: $C_T = C_1 + C_2 + C_3...$)

A– less than the capacitance of the lowest rated capacitor.

B– equal to the capacitance of the highest rated capacitor.

C– equal to the sum of all the capacitances.

3-71. Answer C. JSGT 3D, FGH

As seen in the formula given, when capacitors are connected in parallel, the total capacitance is equal to the sum of all the capacitances. Connecting capacitors in parallel gives the same effect as adding the areas of their plates.

3-72   AMG015

When inductors are connected in series in a circuit, the total inductance is (where the magnetic fields of each inductor do not affect the others) (Note: $L_T = L_1 + L_2 + L_3...$)

A– less than the inductance of the lowest rated inductor.

B– equal to the inductance of the highest rated inductor.

C– equal to the sum of the individual inductances.

3-72. Answer C. JSGT 3D, FGH

As seen in the formula given, when inductors are connected in series, the total inductance is equal to the sum of all the inductances.

3-73   AMG031

What is the total capacitance of a certain circuit containing three capacitors with capacitances of .25 microfarad, .03 microfarad, and .12 microfarad, respectively? (Note: $C_T = C_1 + C_2 + C_3...$)

A– .4 µF.

B– .04 pF.

C– .04 µF.

3-73. Answer A. JSGT 3D, FGH

As seen in the formula given, capacitances in parallel are additive. The total capacitance equals .4µF (.25 + .03 + 0.12 = .4).

3-74   AMG031

(Refer to figure 1 on page 3-26.)

When different rated capacitors are connected in series in a circuit, the total capacitance is

A– less than the capacitance of the lowest rated capacitor.

B– greater than the capacitance of the highest rated capacitor.

C– equal to the sum of all the capacitances.

3-74. Answer A. JSGT 3D, FGH

When capacitors are connected in series, the total capacitance of the circuit is less than that of any single capacitor. This can be seen in the formula used to calculate total capacitance in a series circuit.

$$C_T = \frac{1}{1/C_1 + 1/C_2 + 1/C_3 \ldots}$$

Figure 1. Equation.

3-75   AMG031
(Refer to figure 2 on page 3-26.)
What is the total capacitance of a circuit containing three capacitors in series with capacitances of .02 microfarad, .05 microfarad, and .10 microfarad, respectively?

A–.170 μF.
B–0.125 pF.
C–.0125 μF.

3-75. Answer C. JSGT 3D, FGH
To calculate total capacitance in a series circuit, use the formula in figure 2. The total capacitance is .0125 μF.

Remember, total capacitance in a series circuit is less than any single capacitor.

$$C_T = \frac{1}{1/C_1 + 1/C_2 + 1/C_3}$$

Figure 2. Equation.

3-76   AMG031
(Refer to figure 3 on page 3-27.)
When more than two inductors of different inductances are connected in parallel in a circuit, the total inductance is

A– less than the inductance of the lowest rated inductor.
B– equal to the inductance of the highest rated inductor.
C– equal to the sum of the individual inductances.

3-76. Answer A. JSGT 3D, FGH
Total inductance in a parallel circuit is calculated using the formula in figure 3. As you can see, total inductance in a parallel circuit equals the reciprocal sum of the reciprocal of the inductances. This means that total inductance in a parallel circuit is always less than the inductance of the lowest rated inductor.

$$L_T = \frac{1}{1/L_1 + 1/L_2 + 1/L_3 \ldots}$$

Figure 3. Equation.

3-77   AMG031

When calculating power in a reactive or inductive AC circuit, the true power is

A– more than the apparent power.
B– less than the apparent power in a reactive circuit and more than the apparent power in an inductive circuit.
C– less than the apparent power.

3-77. Answer C. JSGT 3D, FGH

True power equals voltage times the portion of current that is in phase with the voltage. Apparent power, on the other hand, equals voltage times total current in and out of phase with the voltage. When capacitance or inductance is added to a circuit, the current and voltage are not exactly in phase. Therefore, true power in a reactive or inductive AC circuit is always less than the apparent power.

3-78   AMG031

(Refer to figure 5 on page 3-27.)

What is the impedance of an ac-series circuit consisting of an inductor with a reactance of 10 ohms, a capacitor with a reactance of 4 ohms, and a resistor with a resistance of 8 ohms?

A– 22 ohms.
B– 5.29 ohms.
C– 10 ohms.

3-78. Answer C. JSGT 3D, FGH

This is an application of the formula given for computing impedance. Since reactance values are already in ohms, plug the values given into the formula and perform the required calculations. The answer is 10 ohms.

$$\sqrt{8^2 + (10-4)^2} = 10 \ ohms$$

$$Z = \sqrt{R^2 + (X_L - X_C)^2}$$

Z = Impedance
R = Resistance
X_L = Inductance Reactance
Z_C = Capacitive Reactance

Figure 5. Formula.

3-79   AMG031

Transfer of electrical energy from one conductor to another without the aid of electrical connections

A– is called induction.
B– is called capacitance.
C– can cause excessive arcing and heat, and as a result is practical for use only with low voltages/amperages.

3-79. Answer A. JSGT 3D, FGH

Anytime a wire passes through a magnetic field, electrical energy is induced into the wire. Therefore, if you were to arrange two conductors (not connected electrically) such that the magnetic field surrounding one cuts through the other conductor, a current would be induced in the second conductor. This process is called induction and is the principle by which transformers operate.

3-80   AMG031

What happens to the current in a voltage step-up transformer with a ratio of 1 to 4?

A– The current is stepped down by a 1 to 4 ratio.
B– The current is stepped up by a 1 to 4 ratio.
C– The current does not change.

3-80. Answer A. JSGT 3D, FGH

A transformer cannot generate power. Therefore, if a transformer steps up the voltage, it must step down the current by the same ratio. This is evident in the formula for power ($P = I \times E$). If voltage increases current must decrease, and if voltage decreases current must increase.

SECTION E - ELECTRONIC CONTROL DEVICES

Section E of Chapter 3 introduces semiconductor theory. It begins by looking at the principles of vacuum tubes and then applies those principles to modern semiconductor devices such as diodes, transistors, and logic gates.

3-81   AMG031

Capacitors are sometimes used in DC circuits to

A– counteract inductive reactance at specific locations.
B– smooth out slight pulsations in current/voltage.
C– assist in stepping voltage and current up and/or down.

3-81. Answer B. JSGT 3E, FGH

During fluctuations in voltage, a capacitor will absorb potential during variations above nominal voltage, and discharge potential during variations below nominal voltage. This smooths out pulsations in the nominal voltage.

3-82   AMG031

Diodes are used in electrical power circuits primarily as

A– cutout switches.
B– rectifiers.
C– relays.

3-82. Answer B. JSGT 3E, FGH

The most important characteristic of a diode is that it permits current to flow in one direction only. The effect is like an electron check valve that permits flow in one direction but blocks any attempt to flow in the opposite direction. This characteristic permits diodes to be used to rectify AC to DC.

3-83   AMG031

In a P-N-P transistor application, the solid state device is turned on when the

A– base is negative with respect to the emitter.
B– base is positive with respect to the emitter.
C– emitter is negative with respect to the base.

3-83. Answer A. JSGT 3E, FGH

To turn on a transistor, a small amount of current must flow into the base and the emitter-base must be forward-biased. A P-N-P transistor is forwardbiased when the base is negative with respect to the emitter.

3-84   AMG031

In an N-P-N transistor application, the solid state device is turned on when the

A– emitter is positive with respect to the base.
B– base is negative with respect to the emitter.
C– base is positive with respect to the emitter.

3-84. Answer C. JSGT 3E, FGH

To turn on a transistor, a small amount of current must flow into the base and the emitter-base must be forward-biased. An N-P-N transistor is forwardbiased when the base is positive with respect to the emitter.

3-85   AMG031

Typical application for zener diodes is as

A– full-wave rectifiers.
B– half-wave rectifiers.
C– voltage regulators.

3-85. Answer C. JSGT 3E, FGH

Zener diodes, sometimes called "breakdown diodes" are primarily used for voltage regulation. They are designed so that they will break down and allow current flow in the reverse-biased direction when the circuit potential is equal to or in excess of the desired Zener voltage rating.

3-86   AMG031

Forward biasing of a solid state device will cause the device to

A– conduct via zener breakdown.
B– conduct.
C– turn off.

3-86. Answer B. JSGT 3E, FGH

If a voltage source is attached to a semi-conductor diode with a positive terminal connected to the P material, and a negative terminal to the N material, it is said to be forward-biased and will conduct.

3-87   AMG015

(Refer to figure 23 on page 3-30.)
If an open occurs at R_1, the light

A– cannot be turned on.
B– will not be affected.
C– cannot be turned off.

3-87. Answer C. JSGT 3E, FGH

This is a dimming circuit and shows a potentiometer with a resistor R_1 that prevents the light from being completely turned off. The light can be operated from full dim to full bright. An open at R_1 reduces the voltage drop across R_2 and increases the brightness of the bulb at all settings. The most appropriate answer is that the light cannot be turned off.

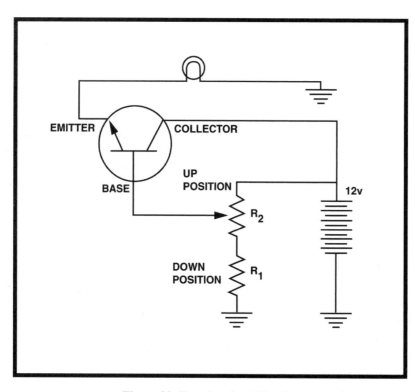

Figure 23. Transistorized Circuit.

3-88 AMG031

(Refer to figure 22 on page 3-31.)
Which illustration is correct concerning bias application and current (positive charge) flow?

A–1.
B–2.
C–3.

3-88. Answer A. JSGT 3E, FGH

In order for current to flow in a transistor, the emitter-base junction must be forward-biased. Forward biasing requires the base of an NPN transistor to be positive with respect to the emitter, which is true in Illustration 1. Positive charge flow defines the current flow as being from positive to negative, which is also depicted in Illustration 1. Illustration 2 is incorrect because the emitter-base junction is reverse biased and no current can flow. Illustration 3 is incorrect because the emitter and collector on this PNP transistor are connected backwards and no current can flow.

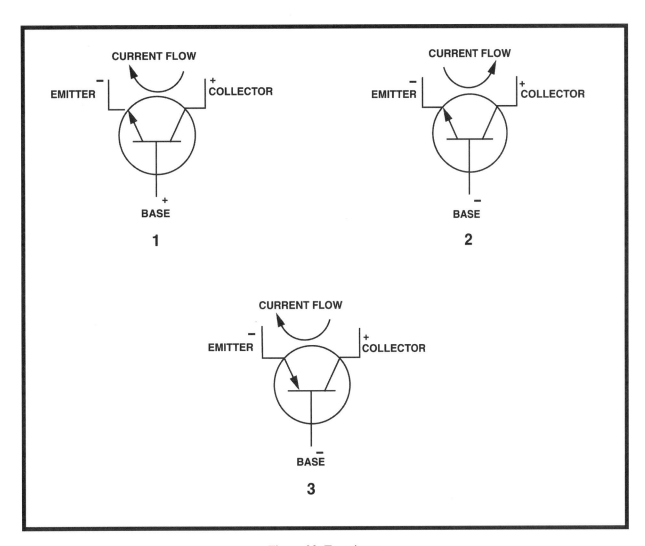

Figure 22. Transistors.

3-89   AMG031
(Refer to figure 23 on page 3-30.)
If R₂ sticks in the up position, the light will

A– be on full bright.
B– be very dim.
C– not illuminate.

3-89. Answer A. JSGT 3E, FGH
If R_2 sticks in the up position, maximum current flows to the base of the NPN transistor. This results in maximum bias of the base-emitter. With maximum bias in the base-emitter and reverse bias in the base-collector, maximum current flows to the light and it illuminates fully.

3-90   AMG031
(Refer to figure 24 on page 3-32.)
Which statement concerning the depicted logic gate is true?

A– Any input being 1 will produce a 0 output.
B– Any input being 1 will produce a 1 output.
C– All inputs must be 1 to produce a 1 output.

3-90. Answer B. JSGT 3E, FA-150-1
Figure 24 represents a logic OR gate. In an OR gate, any input of 1 (on) results in an output of 1 (on). For example, if input number 1, OR input number 2, OR input number 3 are 1 (on), the output will be 1 (on).

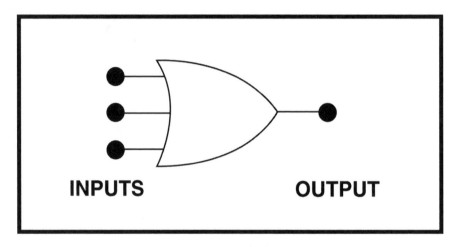

Figure 24. Logic Gate.

3-91   AMG031
(Refer to figure 25 on page 3-33.)
In a functional and operating circuit, the depicted logic gate's output will be 0

A– only when all inputs are 0.
B– when all inputs are 1.
C– when one or more inputs are 0.

3-91. Answer C. JSGT 3E, FA-150-1
Figure 25 represents a logic AND gate. In an AND gate, every input must be 1 (on) in order for the output to be 1 (on). For example, input number 1, AND input number 2, AND input number 3 must be 1 (on) for the output to be 1 (on). However, if one or more inputs are 0 (off) the output will be 0 (off). Only when all inputs are 0 is incorrect because having all inputs at 0 is not the only condition that results in a 0 output.

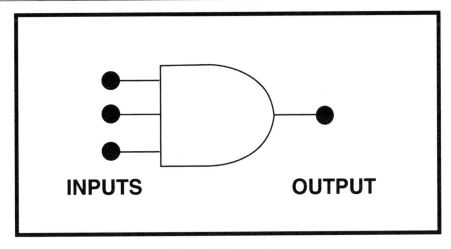

Figure 25. Logic Gate.

3-92   AMG031
(Refer to figure 26 on page 3-33.)
Which of the logic gate output conditions is correct
with respect to the given inputs?

A– 1.
B– 2.
C– 3.

3-92. Answer B. JSGT 3E, FA-150-1
The illustrations in figure 26 represent exclusive OR
gates. This type of logic gate is designed to produce a
1 (on) output whenever the two inputs are dissimilar.
Selection 2 is the only illustration that has an output of
1 (on) with two dissimilar inputs.

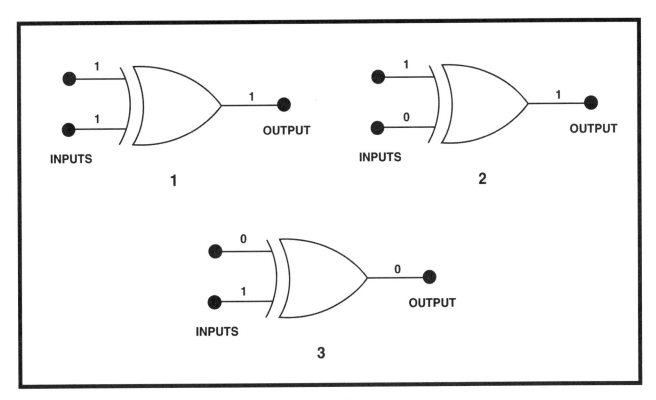

Figure 26. Logic Gates.

3-93   AMG031

Capacitors are sometimes used in DC circuits to

A– counteract inductive reactance at specific locations.

B– smooth out slight pulsations in current/voltage.

C– assist in stepping voltage and current up and/or down.

3-93. Answer B. JSGT 3E, FGH

Capacitors are often used to help smooth out slight variations in current/voltage to aid in reducing electromagnetic interference caused by pulsating DC electricity. Answer A is incorrect because inductive reactance is not a factor in a purely DC circuit. Answer C is incorrect since a transformer is primarily used to step up or step down voltage and current, although a capacitor can be used to store large amounts of voltage.

3-94   AMG031

Which of the following are commonly used as rectifiers in electrical circuits?

1. Anodes.
2. Cathodes.
3. Diodes.

A– 3, 1.

B– 3, 2.

C– 3.

3-94. Answer C. JSGT 3E, FGH

Diodes and vacuum tubes are commonly used to rectify AC electricity into DC electricity.

SECTION F - ELECTRICAL MEASURING INSTRUMENTS

This section introduces the various types of electrical measuring devices the A&P technician could encounter. While this section presents valuable information on ohmmeters, ammeters, milliammeters, and microammeters, there are no FAA Test questions on this section.

SECTION G - CIRCUIT ANALYSIS

Section G of Chapter 3 draws on the information presented in the previous sections to introduce the principles of troubleshooting. In addition to basic system and component troubleshooting, Section G discusses some common aircraft electrical circuits and explains their basic operating principles.

3-95   AMG015

When referring to an electrical circuit diagram, what point is considered to be at zero voltage?

A–The circuit breaker.
B–The fuse.
C–The ground reference.

3-95. Answer C. FGH

The common reference point in a circuit is called the ground. This is the reference point from which most circuit voltages are measured, and is normally considered to be at zero potential.

3-96   AMG015

(Refer to figure 15 on page 3-37.)
With the landing gear retracted, the red indicator light will not come on if an open occurs in wire

A–number 19.
B–number 7.
C–number 17.

3-96. Answer A. JSGT 3G, FGH

With the up limit switch in the gear up position, power is supplied to the red light from the bus through the 5 amp breaker, wire #19 and then wire #8. The red indicator light will not come on if a break occurs in either wire #19 or #8. Wire #7 and #17 supply current to the press-to-test circuit for the red and green lights, respectively.

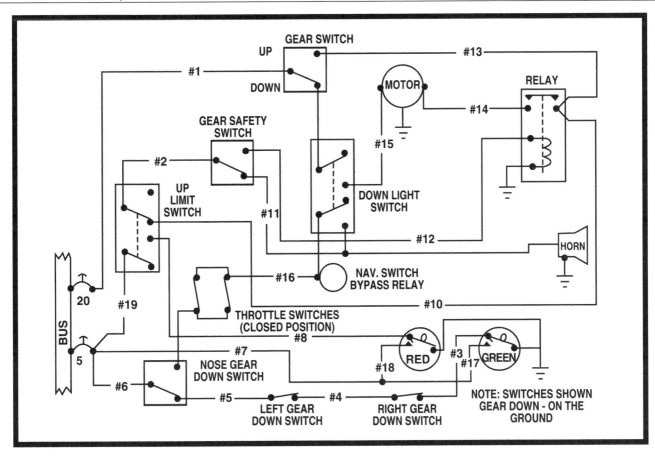

Figure 15. Landing Gear Circuit.

3-97   AMG015
(Refer to figure 15 on page 3-37.)
The No. 7 wire is used to

A– complete the PUSH-TO-TEST circuit.
B– open the UP indicator light circuit when the landing gear is retracted.
C– close the UP indicator light circuit when the landing gear is retracted.

3-97. Answer A. JSGT 3G, FGH
Wire #7 supplies power to the #18 and #17 wires of the press-to-test function on both the red and green indicator lights. This system allows the flight crew to make certain that the bulb is not burned out.

3-98   AMG015
(Refer to figure 15 on page 3-37.)
When the landing gear is down, the green light will not come on if an open occurs in wire

A– number 7.
B– number 6.
C– number 17.

3-98. Answer B. JSGT 3G, FGH
When the landing gear is in the down position, power is supplied to the green light from the bus through the 5 amp breaker, then wire #6 through the nose gear down switch, then wire numbers #5, #4, and #3. A break in any of these would prevent the light from illuminating. Wire #7 and #17 supply current to the press-to-test circuit.

3-99   AMG015

(Refer to figure 16 on page 3-38.)

What will be the effect if the PCO relay fails to operate when the left-hand tank is selected?

A– The fuel pressure crossfeed valve will not open.
B– The fuel tank crossfeed valve open light will illuminate.
C– The fuel pressure crossfeed valve open light will not illuminate.

3-99. Answer C. JSGT 3G, FGH

If the PCO relay does not operate, switch 13 will not be able to close. Switch 13 and switch 15 must both be closed to supply power to the fuel pressure crossfeed valve open light in the cockpit. With switch 13 open, the light will not illuminate.

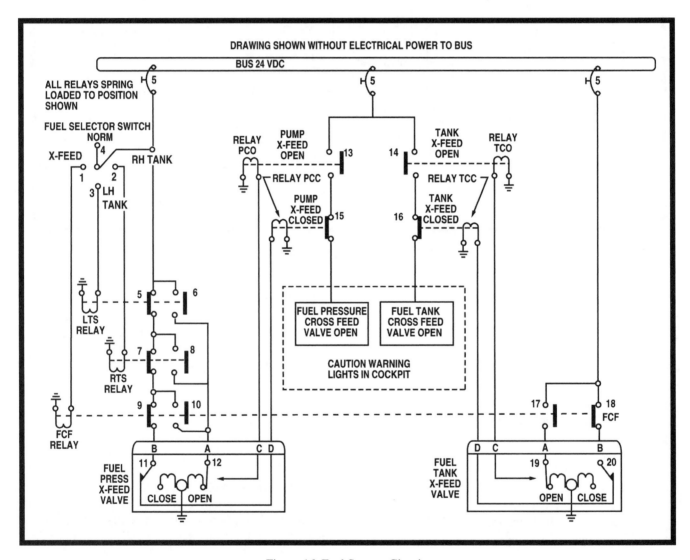

Figure 16. Fuel System Circuit.

3-100 AMG015

(Refer to figure 16 on page 3-38.)

The TCO relay will operate if 24-volts DC is applied to the bus and the fuel tank selector is in the

A– right-hand tank position.
B– crossfeed position.
C– left-hand tank position.

3-100. Answer B. JSGT 3G, FGH

When the fuel selector switch is in the crossfeed position, power is supplied to the FCF relay, which in turn powers switch number 17. Through this switch the crossfeed valve is energized, closing switch 19 and allowing relay TCO to be energized.

3-101 AMG015

(Refer to figure 16 on page 3-38.)

With power to the bus and the fuel selector switched to the right-hand tank, how many relays in the system are operating?

A– Three.
B– Two.
C– Four.

3-101. Answer A. JSGT 3G, FGH

When the system has power to the bus, and the fuel selector is switched to the right-hand tank, power is fed from the bus to the RTS relay. This relay opens switch 7 and closes switch 8. Opening switch 7 removes power from cross-feed valve switch 11 which in turn removes power from relay PCC causing switch 15 to open. When switch 8 closes, power flows to switch 12 in the cross-feed valve and feeds power to relay PCO which closes switch 13. A total of three relays have been operated.

3-102 AMG015

(Refer to figure 16 on page 3-38.)

When electrical power is applied to the bus, which relays are energized?

A– PCC and TCC.
B– TCC and TCO.
C– PCO and PCC.

3-102. Answer A. JSGT 3G, FGH

A note at the top left of the schematic tells you that all relays are spring loaded to the position shown. When power is supplied to the bus it has a path through switches 5, 7, 9, and 11 to the PCC relay. Power also has a path through switches 18 and 20 to relay TCC.

3-103 AMG015

(Refer to figure 16 on page 3-38.)

Energize the circuit with the fuel tank selector switch selected to the left-hand position. Using the schematic, identify the switches that will change position.

A– 5, 9, 10, 11, 12, 13, and 15.
B– 3, 5, 6, 7, 11, and 13.
C– 5, 6, 11, 12, 13, 15, and 16.

3-103. Answer C. JSGT 3G, FGH

With the bus energized and the fuel selector in the left-hand position, relay LTS receives power which changes the position of switches 5 and 6. Opening switch 5 causes switch 11 to open and remove power from relay PCC, allowing switch 15 to close. (Note: switch 15 is shown closed because it is spring loaded to that position when the circuit is not energized.) Closing switch 6 energizes switch 12 which allows power to flow to relay PCO and close switch 13. On the other side of the circuit, when power is supplied to the bus, relay TCC energizes and opens switch 16.

3-104   AMG015

(Refer to figure 18 on page 3-40.)

When the landing gears are up and the throttles are retarded, the warning horn will not sound if an open occurs in wire

A– No. 4.

B– No. 2.

C– No. 9.

3-104. Answer A. JSGT 3G, FGH

The warning horn receives power from the bus through wire #7. For the horn to sound, the circuit must be completed from the horn to ground through wire #6, the throttle switch (which is closed when the throttles are retarded), wire #4, the left gear switch (drawn in the down position), and finally wire #14 to ground. If wire #4 were to break, the circuit could not be completed.

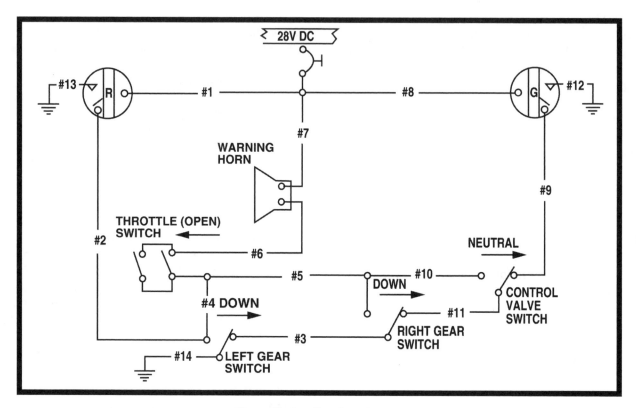

Figure 18. Landing Gear Circuit.

3-105   AMG015

(Refer to figure 18 on page 3-40.)

The control valve switch must be placed in the neutral position when the landing gears are down to

A– permit the test circuit to operate.

B– prevent the warning horn from sounding when the throttles are closed.

C– remove the ground from the green light.

3-105. Answer B. JSGT 3G, FGH

When the gear is down, you do not want the warning horn to sound when you retard the throttles. If the control valve switch were not in the neutral position, the warning horn would have a path to ground through wires #6, #5, #10, #11, #3, and #14.

3-106   AMG015

(Refer to figure 19 on page 3-41.)

Under which condition will a ground be provided for the warning horn through both gear switches when the throttles are closed?

A–Right gear up and left gear down.
B–Both gears up and the control valve out of neutral.
C–Left gear up and right gear down.

3-106. Answer C. JSGT 3G, FGH

The only way the warning horn can be grounded through both gear switches is if the left gear is up and the right gear is down. Trace the circuit from the 28V source through wire #10 to the horn, then wire #11 to the throttle switches, which are closed in this problem. After current passes through the throttle switches, it continues through wire #12 to the left gear switch which must be in the up position to provide a path through wire #5 to the right gear switch which must be down to complete the circuit.

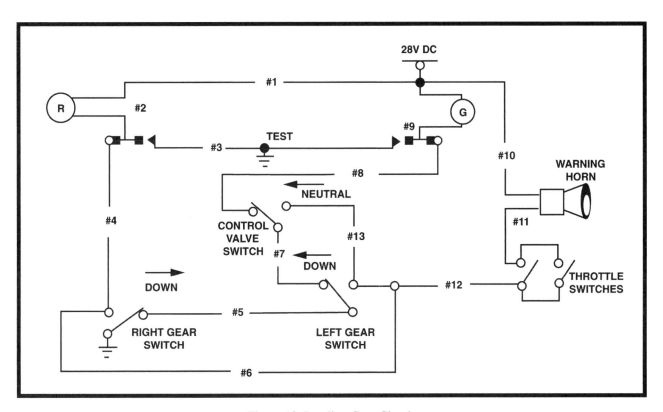

Figure 19. Landing Gear Circuit.

3-107   AMG015

(Refer to figure 19 on page 3-41.)

When the throttles are retarded with only the right gear down, the warning horn will not sound if an open occurs in wire

A–No. 5.
B–No. 13.
C–No. 6.

3-107. Answer A. JSGT 3G, FGH

With the conditions described, trace the circuit from the 28V source through wire #10 to the horn, then wire #11 to the throttle switches, which are closed in this problem. After current passes through the throttle switches, it passes through wire #12 to the left gear switch which must be in the up position to provide a path through wire #5 to the right gear switch which must be down to complete the circuit. If a break in wire #5 occurs, the warning horn will not sound.

3-108   AMG015

(Refer to figure 19 on page 3-41.)

When the landing gears are up and the throttles are retarded, the warning horn will not sound if an open occurs in wire

A– No. 6.
B– No. 5.
C– No. 7.

3-108. Answer A. JSGT 3G, FGH

Under the conditions described, trace the circuit from the source through wire #10 to the warning horn, then wire #11 to the throttle switches, which would be closed. After current passes through the throttle switches, it continues through wire #12, wire #6, and the grounded right gear switch, which is in the up position. If wire #6 were open, the warning horn would not sound.

3-109   AMG015

(Refer to figure 20 on page 3-42.)

Troubleshooting an open circuit with a voltmeter as shown in this circuit will

A– permit current to flow and illuminate the lamp.
B– create a low resistance path and the current flow will be greater than normal.
C– permit the battery voltage to appear on the voltmeter.

3-109. Answer C. JSGT 3G, FGH

When the voltmeter is connected across the open resistor, the voltmeter closes the circuit by paralleling (shunting) the burned-out resistor. This allows current to flow from the negative terminal of the battery, through the switch, through the voltmeter and lamp, and back to the positive terminal of the battery. Since the resistance of the voltmeter is so high only a small amount of current flows in the circuit. The current is too low to light the lamp, but the voltmeter will read the battery voltage.

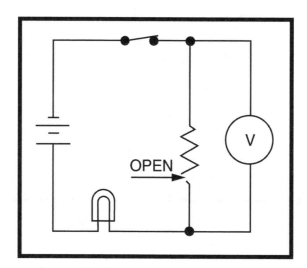

Figure 20. Circuit Diagram.

ELECTRICAL GENERATORS AND MOTORS

Chapter 4 in your textbook discusses several aspects of electrical generators and motors. By studying this chapter, you will become familiar with the various components associated with DC generators, alternators, and motors. In addition, information describing how to test and service these components is presented. While the material presented is valuable to the A&P technician, there are no FAA questions covered in this chapter.

ELECTRICAL GENERATORS AND MOTORS

This chapter does not contain any questions.

AIRCRAFT DRAWINGS

SECTION A - TYPES OF DRAWINGS

Section A of Chapter 5 begins by examining the three different types of working drawings: the detail drawing, assembly drawing, and installation drawing. The text continues by presenting the common methods of illustrating objects and looks at examples of each.

5-1   AMG013

(1) A detail drawing is a description of a single part.
(2) An assembly drawing is a description of an object made up of two or more parts. Regarding the above statements,

A– only No. 1 is true.
B– neither No. 1 nor No. 2 is true.
C– both No. 1 and No. 2 are true.

5-1. Answer C. JSGT 5A, FGH

Both statements 1 and 2 are correct. Detail drawings depict a single part, and usually give information about its size, shape, material, and method of manufacture. Assembly drawings, on the other hand, depict an object made up of two or more parts.

5-2   AMG014

Which statement is true regarding an orthographic projection?

A– There are always at least two views.
B– It could have as many as eight views.
C– One-view, two-view, and three-view drawings are the most common.

5-2. Answer C. JSGT 5A, FGH

When using orthographic projection, as many as six views can be depicted; however, one-, two-, or three-view drawings are most common.

5-3   AMG014

(1) Schematic diagrams indicate the location of individual components in the aircraft. (2) Schematic diagrams indicate the location of components with respect to each other within the system. Regarding the above statements,

A– only No. 1 is true.
B– both No. 1 and No. 2 are true.
C– only No. 2 is true.

5-3. Answer C. JSGT 5A, FGH

Only statement number 2 is correct. Schematic diagrams are used to explain a principle of operation, rather than show the parts as they actually appear. They do not indicate the location of individual components in the aircraft, but do indicate the location of components with respect to each other within the system.

5-4   AMG014

(Refer to figure 28 on page 5-2.)

Identify the bottom view of the object shown.

A– 1.

B– 2.

C– 3.

5-4. Answer B. JSGT 5A, FGH

When you rotate the front view 90 degrees to obtain a bottom view, the entire bottom surface is visible and is therefore depicted by four solid outlines. The channel in the center of the part is not visible so its sides would be projected by the use of hidden (dashed) lines, as depicted in selection 2. Views 1 and 3 each have solid lines depicting parts of the channel that would not be visible from the bottom view.

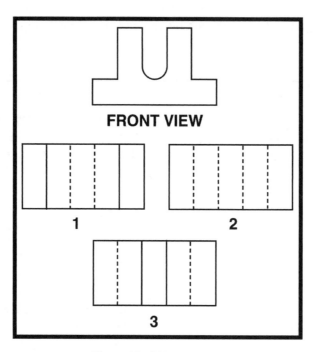

Figure 28. Object Views.

5-5   AMG014

(Refer to figure 29 on page 5-3.)

Identify the left side view of the object shown.

A– 1.

B– 2.

C– 3.

5-5. Answer C. JSGT 5A, FGH

This is an application of orthographic projection. The left side view is obtained by rotating the object 90 degrees, so the left side of the object faces you. Since the entire left side is visible, it is depicted by four solid (visible) lines. The step, on the other hand, is not visible and is depicted by a dashed (hidden) line.

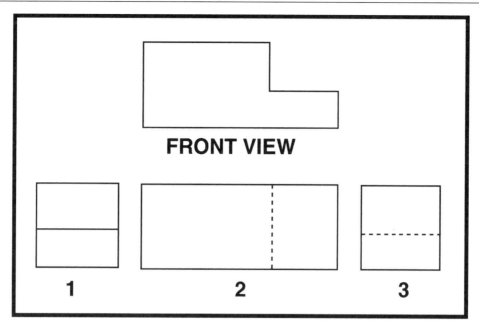

Figure 29. Object Views.

5-6   AMG014
(Refer to figure 30 on page 5-3.)
Identify the bottom view of the object.

A– 1.
B– 2.
C– 3.

5-6. Answer A. JSGT 5A, FGH
You must apply the rules of orthographic projection to obtain a bottom view. Once the object is rotated 90 degrees to obtain the bottom view, the four sides that make up the bottom would be visible and, therefore, be depicted with visible (solid) lines. The two steps would not be visible and are represented by hidden (dashed) lines, running vertically at the same distance from the ends that they appear in the front view.

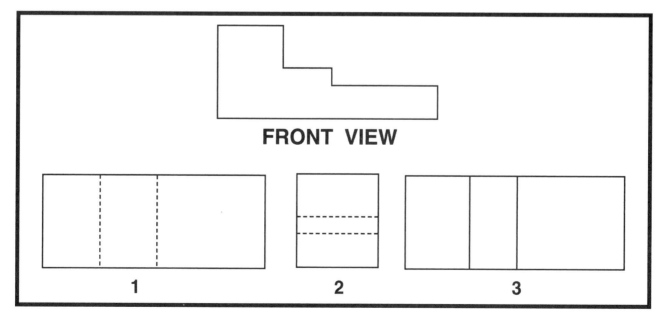

Figure 30. Object Views.

5-7   AMG001
For sketching purposes, almost all objects are composed of one or some combination of six basic shapes; these include the

A– angle, arc, line, plane, square, and circle.
B– triangle, circle, cube, cylinder, cone, and sphere.
C– triangle, plane, circle, line, square, and sphere.

5-7. Answer B. JSGT 5B, FGH
Almost all objects are comprised of some or a combination of six basic shapes. These include the triangle, circle, cube, cylinder, cone and sphere. The following are not shapes: angle, arc, line, and plane.

5-8   AMG013
What is the class of working drawing that is the description/depiction of a single part?

A– Installation drawing.
B– Assembly drawing.
C– Detail drawing.

5-8. Answer C. JSGT 5A, FGH
A detail drawing is classified as a working drawing and supplies all the information required to construct a part, including all dimensions, materials, and type of finish. Answer A is incorrect because an installation drawing shows where multiple parts and components are installed in or on an aircraft. Answer B is incorrect because an assembly drawing shows how two or more parts are brought together to create a subassembly.

5-9   AMG014
One purpose for schematic diagrams is to show the

A– functional location of components within a system.
B– physical location of components within a system.
C– size and shape of components within a system.

5-9. Answer A. JSGT 5A, FGH
Schematic diagrams illustrate the functional location of components with respect to each other within the system and are used mainly in troubleshooting.

5-10   AMG014
A hydraulic system schematic drawing would indicate the

A– specific location of the individual components within the aircraft.
B– direction of fluid flow through the system.
C– type and quantity of the hydraulic fluid.

5-10. Answer B. JSGT 5A, FGH
A schematic diagram is used to explain a principle of operation, rather than to show the parts as they actually appear, or as they function. In the case of hydraulic, fuel, or oil systems, a schematic drawing would show the direction of fluid flow.

5-11   AMG014
(1) A measurement should not be scaled from an aircraft print because the paper shrinks or stretches when the print is made. (2) When a detail drawing is made, it is carefully and accurately drawn to scale, and is dimensioned. Regarding the above statements,

A– only No. 2 is true.
B– both No. 1 and No. 2 are true.
C– neither No. 1 nor No. 2 is true.

5-11. Answer B. JSGT 5A, FGH
These are both true statements. While aircraft drawings are carefully and accurately drawn to scale, various copying processes, moisture, and age may cause the image on a drawing to differ significantly from the size to which it was originally drawn. For this reason, you should not scale off an aircraft drawing.

5-12   AMG014

The drawings often used in illustrated parts manuals are

A– exploded view drawings.
B– block drawings.
C– detail drawings.

5-12. Answer A. JSGT 5A, FGH

Illustrated parts lists often use exploded-view drawings to show every part that is in an assembly. All of the parts are shown in their relative positions, but are expanded outward, so that each part can be identified.

5-13   AMG014

A drawing in which the subassemblies or parts are shown as brought together on the aircraft is called

A– an assembly drawing.
B– an installation drawing.
C– a detail drawing.

5-13. Answer B. JSGT 5A, FGH

An installation drawing shows where subassemblies or parts are installed on an aircraft. An assembly drawing shows sufficient information to allow for the assembly of components, whereas a detail drawing shows sufficient detail to manufacture parts or components. Neither shows where parts are installed or brought together on the aircraft.

5-14   AMG014

What type of diagram is used to explain a principle of operation, rather than show the parts as they actually appear?

A– A pictorial diagram.
B– A schematic diagram.
C– A block diagram.

5-14. Answer B. JSGT 5A, FGH

A schematic diagram is used to explain a principle of operation, rather than the parts as they actually appear or function.

5-15   AMG014

In what type of electrical diagram are images of components used instead of conventional electrical symbols?

A– A pictorial diagram.
B– A schematic diagram.
C– A block diagram.

5-15. Answer A. JSGT 5A, FGH

Pilot's handbooks and some training manuals occasionally use pictorial diagrams of electrical and hydraulic systems. In a pictorial diagram, pictures of components are used instead of the conventional symbols found in schematic diagrams.

SECTION B - DRAWING PRACTICES

This section describes and presents accepted industry drawing practices. Included is a discussion on the various types of lines used in aircraft drawings as well as the symbology used to represent different materials. Another important topic within this section deals with the steps and procedures used to construct a sketch.

5-16   AMG014

What type of line is normally used in a mechanical drawing or blueprint to represent an edge or object not visible to the viewer?

A– Medium-weight dashed line.
B– Medium solid line.
C– Alternate short and long light dashes.

5-16. Answer A. JSGT 5B, FGH

The line described in this question is called a hidden line and is represented by a medium-weight dashed line.

5-17   AMG014

Which of the following terms is/are used to indicate specific measured distances from the datum and/or other points identified by the manufacturer to points in or on the aircraft? 1. Zone numbers. 2. Reference numbers. 3. Station numbers.

A– 1 and 3.
B– 3.
C– 2.

5-17. Answer B. JSGT 5B, FGH

Station numbers refer to a location in or on an aircraft measured in inches fore or aft of the nose or other zero station as determined by the manufacturer. Zone number is incorrect because they are primarily used on drawings to help locate information on the drawing. Reference number is incorrect because these are often used within a title block to refer to the numbers of other prints.

5-18   AMG013

(Refer to figure 27 on page 5-7.)
In the isometric view of a typical aileron balance weight, identify the view indicated by the arrow.

A– 1.
B– 3.
C– 2.

5-18. Answer B. JSGT 5B, FGH

The rear cavity is open from the direction of the arrow, which is why the lines are solid. The four screw holes are hidden from view and are represented by the dashed lines. The rounded nose of the weight has no edges or corners, so it is not depicted in the rear view.

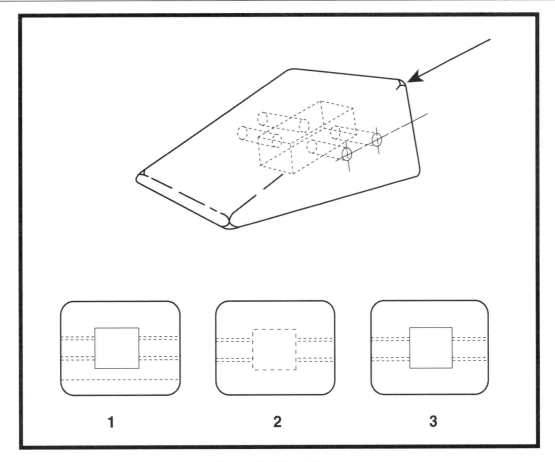

Figure 27. Object Views.

5-19   AMG014

Which statement is applicable when using a sketch for making a part?

A– The sketch may be used only if supplemented with three-view orthographic projection drawings.
B– The sketch must show all information to manufacture the part.
C– The sketch need not show all necessary construction details.

5-19. Answer B. JSGT 5B, FGH
A sketch may be used to manufacture a replacement part, when necessary. The sketch must provide all of the necessary information to fabricate the part.

5-20   AMG001

What should be the first step of the procedure in sketching an aircraft wing skin repair?

A– Draw heavy guidelines.
B– Lay out the repair.
C– Block in the views.

5-20. Answer C. JSGT 5B, FGH
There are four basic steps in making a sketch. First, determine what views are necessary to portray the object and block in the views using light construction lines. Second, complete the details and darken the object outline. Third, sketch extension and dimension lines and add detail. Finally, complete the drawing by adding notes, dimensions, a title, and a date.

5-21   AMG001
(1) According to FAR Part 91, repairs to an aircraft skin should have a detailed dimensional sketch included in the permanent records.
(2) On occasion, a mechanic may need to make a simple sketch of a proposed repair to an aircraft, a new design, or a modification.
Regarding the above statements,

A– only No. 1 is true.
B– only No. 2 is true.
C– both No. 1 and No. 2 are true.

5-21. Answer B. JSGT 5B, FGH
Only statement number 2 is correct. In executing FAA Form 337, the mechanic may need to make a sketch to describe a repair or alteration. The amount of detail necessary is only that which is required to adequately describe the work accomplished. Statement (1) is false. FAR Part 91 only requires a description or reference to acceptable data when work is performed. There is no requirement for a detailed dimension sketch to be included in an aircraft's permanent records.

5-22   AMG014
What material symbol is frequently used in drawings to represent all metals?

A– Steel.
B– Cast iron.
C– Aluminum.

5-22. Answer B. JSGT 5B, FGH
At times, a material may not be indicated symbolically when its exact specification must be shown elsewhere on the drawing. In this case, the diagonal section lines representing cast iron are often used as a generic section line, and the material specification is listed in the bill of materials or a note.

5-23   AMG001
A simple way to find the center of a circle on a sketch or drawing, or a circular piece of material is to

A– draw two non-parallel chord lines across the circle and then a corresponding perpendicular bisector line across each chord line.
B– draw two parallel chord lines across the circle and then a corresponding perpendicular bisector line across each chord line.
C– draw a single chord line across the circle and then a corresponding perpendicular bisector line across the chord line.

5-23. Answer A. JSGT 5B, FGH
The center of a circle is found by drawing two nonparallel chord lines across the circle. By drawing perpendicular lines from the center of both chord lines (bisector lines), the center of the circle is located where the two bisector lines intersect.

5-24   AMG001
(Refer to figure 31 on page 5-9.)
What are the proper procedural steps for sketching repairs and alterations?

A– 3, 1, 4, and 2.
B– 4, 2, 3, and 1.
C– 1, 3, 4, and 2.

5-24. Answer A. JSGT 5B, FGH
There are four basic steps in making a sketch. First, determine what views are necessary to portray the object and block in the views using light construction lines. Second, complete the details, and darken the object outline. Third, sketch extension and dimension lines, and add detail. Finally, complete the drawing by adding notes, dimensions, a title, and a date.

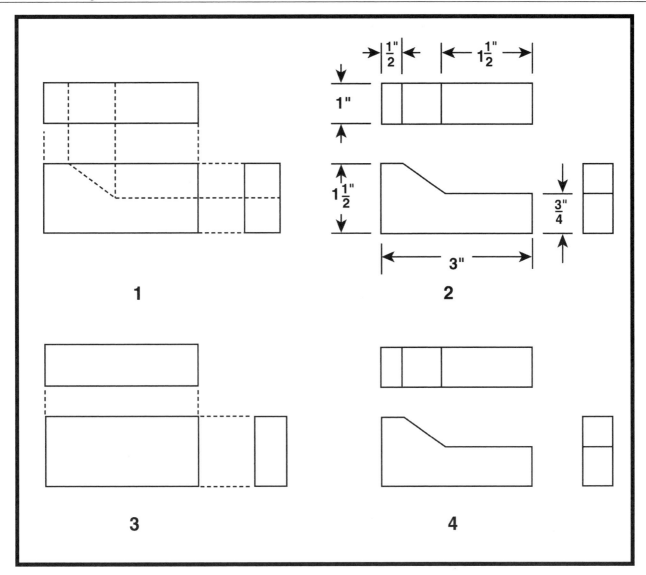

Figure 31. Sketches.

5-25   AMG001
(Refer to figure 32 on page 5-10.)
What is the next step required for a working sketch of the illustration?

A– Darken the object outlines.
B– Sketch extension and dimension lines.
C– Add notes, dimensions, title, and date.

5-25. Answer B. JSGT 5B, FGH
When making a sketch, after the details have been added and the object lines darkened, the next step is to sketch the extension and dimension lines.

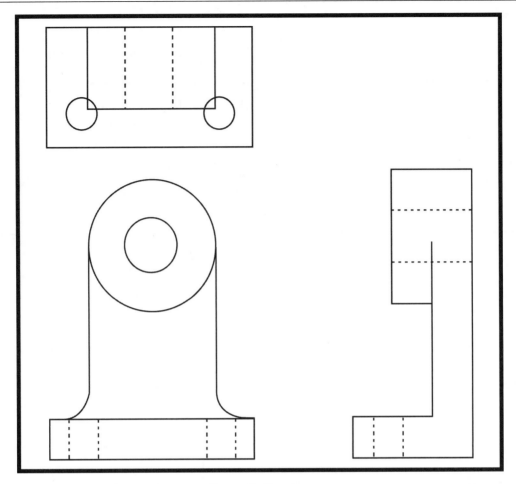

Figure 32. Sketches.

5-26   AMG014
(Refer to figure 33 on page 5-11.)
Which material section-line symbol indicates cast iron?

A– 1.
B– 2.
C– 3.

5-26. Answer C. JSGT 5B, FGH
Cast iron is indicated by thin parallel lines drawn on a 45° angle to the bottom of the drawing. This type of sectioning line is used for other materials when the exact specification for the material used appears elsewhere on the drawing.

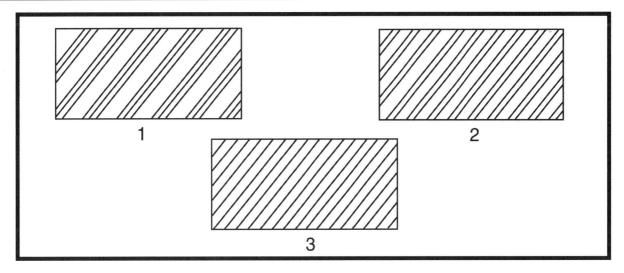

Figure 33. Material Symbols.

5-27   AMG014
The measurements showing the ideal or "perfect" sizes of parts on drawings are called

A–tolerances.
B–allowances.
C–dimensions.

5-27. Answer C. JSGT 5B, FGH
A drawing, to be meaningful, not only must show the shape of the part, but it must accurately give all needed dimensions. This is accomplished with dimensioning.

5-28   AMG014
Zone numbers on aircraft blueprints are used to

A–locate parts, sections, and views on large drawings.
B–indicate different sections of the aircraft.
C–locate parts in the aircraft.

5-28. Answer A. JSGT 5B, FGH
Zone numbers on drawings are similar to the numbers and letters printed on the borders of a map. They are used to help locate a particular point, or part on large drawings.

5-29   AMG014
When reading a blueprint, a dimension is given as 4.387 inches +.005 -.002. Which statement is true?

A–The maximum acceptable size is 4.390 inches.
B–The minimum acceptable size is 4.385 inches.
C–The minimum acceptable size is 4.382 inches.

5-29. Answer B. JSGT 5B, FGH
Given the dimension 4.387 (+ .005 − .002), you can add .005 to get a maximum size of 4.392, and subtract .002 to get a minimum size of 4.385.

5-30   AMG014
What is the allowable manufacturing tolerance for a bushing where the outside dimensions shown on the blueprint are: 1.0625 +.0025 −.0003?

A–.0028
B–1.0650
C–1.0647

5-30. Answer A. JSGT 5B, FGH
Tolerance is the difference between the extreme permissible dimensions. Here, the upper limit is + .0025 and the lower limit is − .0003. The difference is .0028 [.0025 − (− .0003) = .0028].

5-31   AMG014

In the reading of aircraft blueprints, the term "tolerance," used in association with aircraft parts or components,

A– is the tightest permissible fit for proper construction and operation of mating parts.

B– is the difference between extreme permissible dimensions that a part may have and still be acceptable.

C– represents the limit of galvanic compatibility between different adjoining material types in aircraft parts.

5-31. Answer B. JSGT 5B, FGH

Tolerance is the difference between extreme permissible dimensions, or the range of error that will be accepted or tolerated in a serviceable part. On the other hand, allowance is the difference between upper and lower dimensions, and represents the tightest permissible fit.

5-32   AMG014

(Refer to figure 34 on page 5-13.)

What is the dimension of the chamfer?

A– 1/16 x 37°

B– 0.3125 + .005 - 0

C– 0.0625 x 45°

5-32. Answer C. JSGT 5B, FGH

A chamfer is the corner of an object that has been tapered (usually at 45°) to relieve stress, ease assembly, or prevent damage to the part. The chamfer and its dimensions shown in figure 34 are depicted on the far left of the top drawing. Both the length and angle of a chamfer are typically given in a detailed drawing. In this question, you must convert the fraction given to a decimal. In this case, 1/16 inch is equivalent to 0.0625. Therefore, the dimension of the chamfer is 0.0625 x 45°.

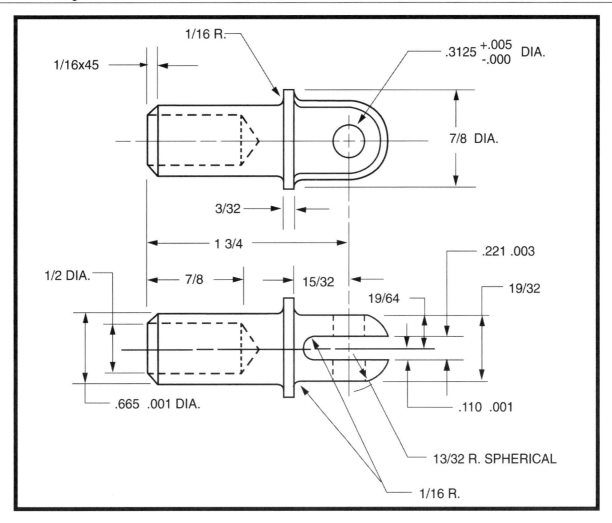

Figure 34. Aircraft Drawing.

5-33   AMG014
(Refer to figure 34 on page 5-13.)
What is the maximum diameter of the hole for the clevis pin?

A– 0.3175
B– 0.3130
C– 0.31255

5-33. Answer A. JSGT 5B, FGH
While neither hole on the drawing is labeled as a clevis pin, you should know that a clevis pin goes in a through hole. This eliminates the possibility that the question refers to the blind hole machined into the left half of the drawing. The top view depicts a through hole on the right side of the drawing with a dimension of .3125 (+.005, −.000). The maximum dimension of the hole is .3175 (.3125 + .005 = .3175).

5-34   AMG014
(Refer to figure 34 on page 5-13.)
What would be the minimum diameter of 4130 round stock required for the construction of the clevis that would produce a machined surface?

A– 55/64 inch.
B– 1 inch.
C– 7/8 inch.

5-34. Answer B. JSGT 5B, FGH
The largest diameter shown on the drawing is 7/8 inch. Since a machined surface is required, the stock material must have a diameter larger than 7/8 inch. The only diameter listed that is greater than 7/8 inch is 1 inch.

5-35   AMG014
(Refer to figure 34 on page 5-13.)
Using the information, what size drill would be
required to drill the clevis bolt hole?

A– 5/16 inch.
B– 21/64 inch.
C– 1/2 inch.

5-35. Answer A. JSGT 5B, FGH
The clevis bolt hole diameter is located on the right
side of the top drawing. The hole diameter is .3125,
which is the decimal equivalent of 5/16.

5-36   AMG014
(Refer to figure 35 on page 5-14.)
Identify the extension line.

A– 3.
B– 1.
C– 4.

5-36. Answer A. JSGT 5B, FGH
Extension lines are light lines extending from the point
where the measurement is made to a convenient
clear area where the dimension may be written
without cluttering the drawing. Selection 3 identifies an
extension line.

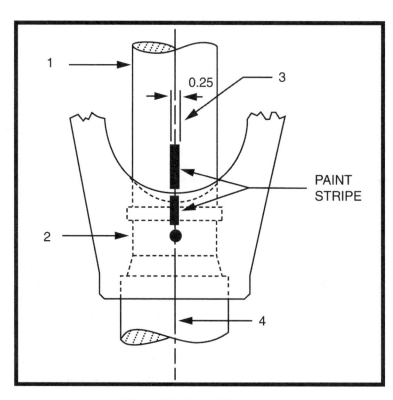

Figure 35. Aircraft Drawing.

5-37   AMG014
(Refer to figure 36 on page 5-15.)
The diameter of the holes in the finished object is

A– 3/4 inch.
B– 31/64 inch.
C– 1/2 inch.

5-37. Answer C. JSGT 5B, FGH
Each hole is referenced to Note 1. Note 1 specifies that
the holes should be initially drilled slightly undersize
with a 31/64 inch drill, and finished with a 1/2 inch
ream.

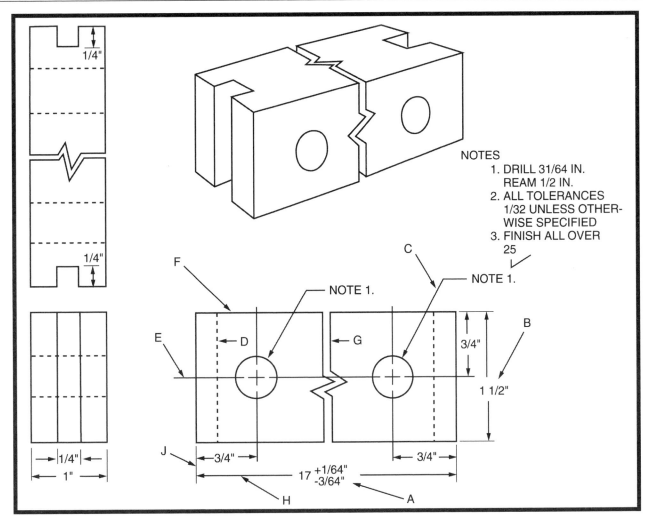

Figure 36. Aircraft Drawing.

5-38   AMG014

(Refer to figure 37 on page 5-16.)

The vertical distance between the top of the plate and the bottom of the lowest 15/64-inch hole is

A– 2.250
B– 2.242
C– 2.367

5-38. Answer C. JSGT 5B, FGH

To determine the distance, you must add the incremental distances depicted. The distances which need to be added are as follows: From the top of the plate to the center of the first hole (3/8"); from the center of the first hole to the center of the second hole (7/8"); from the center of the second hole to the center of the third hole (7/8"); from the center of the third hole to the center of the fourth hole (1/8"); and, finally, the distance from the center of the fourth hole to the bottom of the fourth hole (15/128"). Total these distances and convert to the decimal equivalent for a total measurement of 2.367".

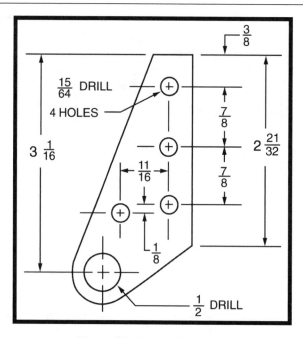

Figure 37. Aircraft Drawing.

5-39   AMG014
(Refer to figure 62 on page 5-17.)
The -100 in the title block (Area 1) is applicable to which doubler part number(s)?

A--101.
B--102.
C-Both.

5-39. Answer A. JSGT 5B, FAR 43, Appendix A
Find the -100 which is set vertically in the title block. The second block above it indicates that one -101 doubler is required for a -100 installation. Note that the -200 requires one -102 doubler. -101 is correct.

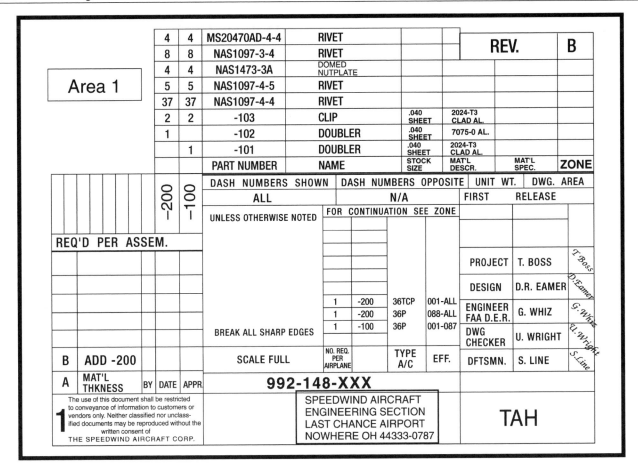

Figure 62. Part 1 of 3: Maintenance Data.

5-40   AMG013
(Refer to figure 62 on page 5-17, figure 62A on page 5-18 and figure 62B on page 5-19.)
Which doubler(s) require(s) heat treatment before installation?

A--101.
B--102.
C- Both.

5-40. Answer B. JSGT 5B, FGH
Areas 2 and 3 in figure 5-12 supply information on the preparation of these parts. Note that step 3 in area 3 of figure 5-13 instructs you to heat treat the -102 part to a hardness of -T6. Area 2 gives no heat treat instructions for a -101 part. -102 is correct.

Area 2

GENERAL NOTES – 100

1. All bends +/– .5°
2. All holes +/– .003.
3. Apply Alodine 1000.
4. Prime with MIL-P-23377 or equivalent.
5. Trim S-1 C just aft of the clip at STA. 355.750 and forward of the front face of the STA. 370.25 frame and remove from the airplane.
6. Position the -101 doubler as shown. Install wet with NAS1097AD-4-4 and -4-5 rivets and a faying surface seal of PR 1422. Pick up the rivet row that was in S-1 C and the aft rivets in STA 370.25. Tie doubler into front frame with clips as shown using MS20470AD-4-4 rivets through the clips and the frame.
7. Install 4 NAS1473-3A nutplates with NAS1097-3-4 rivets through the skin and doubler to retain the antenna.
8. Strip paint and primer from under the antenna footprint.
9. Treat skin with Alodine 1000.
10. Install antenna and apply weather seal fillet around antenna base.

Area 3

GENERAL NOTES – 200   Note: P. S. = Process Specification
                                                    IAW = in accordance with

1. All bends IAW P. S. 1000.
2. All holes IAW P. S. 1015.
3. Heat treat -102 to -T6 IAW P. S. 5602.
4. Alodine IAW P. S. 10000.
5. Prime IAW P. S. 10125.
6. Trim S-1 C just aft of the clip at STA. 355.750 and forward of the front face of the STA. 370.25 frame and remove from the airplane.
7. Position the -102 doubler as shown. Install wet with NAS1097AD-4-4 and -4-5 rivets, and a faying surface seal IAW P. S. of 41255. Pick up the rivet row that was in S-1 C and the aft rivets in STA 370.25. Add two edge rows as shown. Tie doubler into front frame with clips as shown using MS20470AD-4-4 rivets through the clips and the frame.
8. Install 4 NAS1473-3A nutplates with NAS1097-3-4 rivets through the skin and doubler to retain the antenna.
9. Strip paint and primer from under the antenna footprint.
10. Treat skin IAW P. S. 10000.
11. Install antenna and apply weather seal fillet around antenna base.

Figure 62A. Part 2 of 3: Maintenance Data.

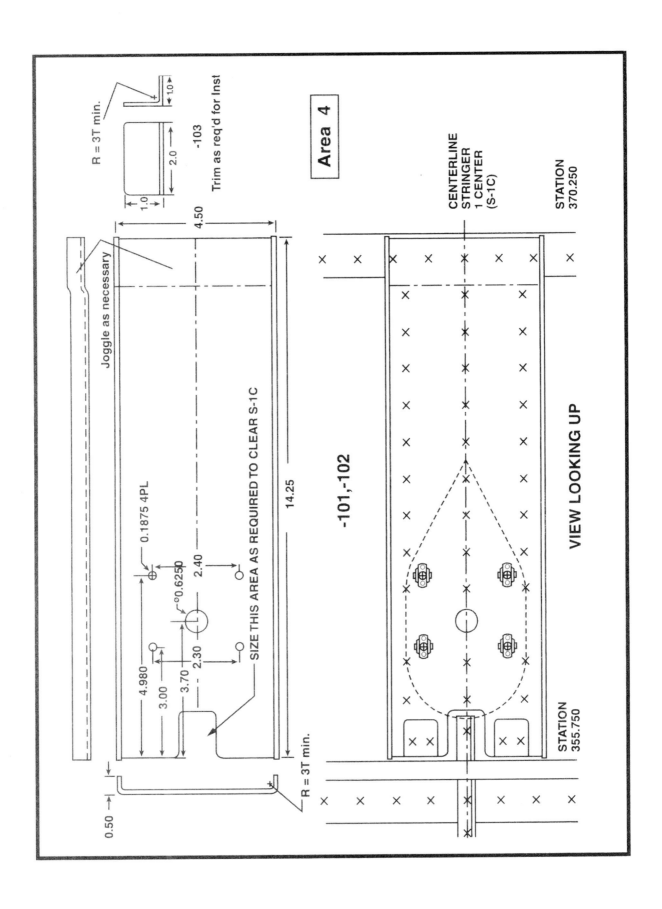

Figure 62B. Part 3 of 3: Maintenance Data.

5-41   AMG013

(Refer to figure 62 on page 5-17, figure 62A on page 5-18 and figure 62B on page 5-19.) Using only the information given (when bend allowance, set back, etc., have been calculated) which doubler is it possible to construct and install?

A--101.
B--102.
C-Both.

5-41. Answer A. JSGT 5B, FGH

The key to answering this question is in area three of figure 5-13 — General Notes -200. The -102 calls for process specifications not given in this data. Therefore, it is only possible to construct and install the -101.

5-42   AMG013

(Refer to figure 62 on page 5-17, figure 62A on page 5-18 and figure 62B on page 5-19.) How many parts will need to be fabricated by the mechanic in the construction and installation of one doubler?

A-2.
B-3.
C-4.

5-42. Answer B. JSGT 5B, FGH

Figure 5-12 shows that for either the -100 or -200 series installation the mechanic must fabricate one doubler of either the -101 or -102 series, and two - 103 series clips. The items in figure 5-12 are all prefabricated.

SECTION C - CHARTS AND GRAPHS

Section C looks at information that is presented in graphical and chart form. Since charts and graphs are common in the maintenance industry, you must be proficient in their use. This section looks at several charts, including performance, electrical, and cable tension charts.

5-43   AMG016

(Refer to figure 38 on page 5-21.)

An aircraft reciprocating engine has a 1,830 cubic-inch displacement and develops 1,250 brake-horsepower at 2,500 RPM. What is the brake mean effective pressure?

A– 217.
B– 205.
C– 225.

5-43. Answer A. JSGT 5C, FGH

To find this answer, begin by locating 1,250 HP on the top of the chart. From this value, drop down vertically until you reach the line representing 1,830 cubic inches of displacement. From this intersection, extend a line horizontally to the right until you intercept the line representing 2,500 RPM. Now, drop down vertically to read the brake mean effective pressure on the bottom line of the chart. The brake mean effective pressure is 217.

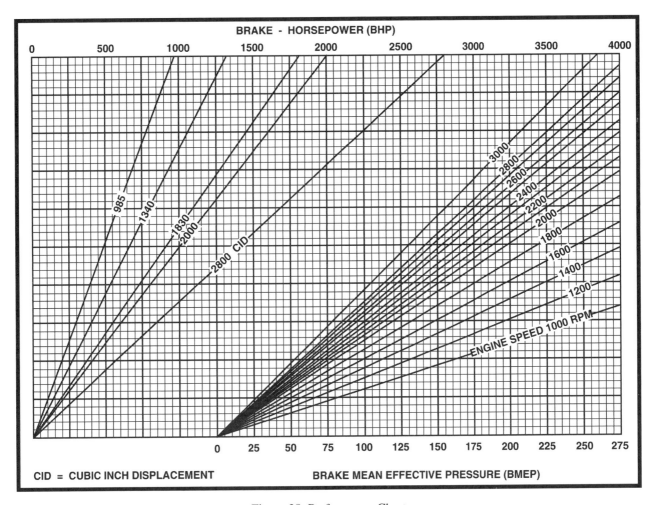

Figure 38. Performance Chart.

5-44 AMG016

(Refer to figure 38 on page 5-21.)
An aircraft reciprocating engine has a 2,800 cubic-inch displacement, develops 2,000 brake-horsepower, and indicates 270 brake mean effective pressure. What is the engine speed (RPM)?

A–2,200.
B–2,100.
C–2,300.

5-44. Answer B. JSGT 5C, FGH

Begin this problem by locating 2,000 HP at the top of the chart. Drop down vertically until you intersect the line representing the 2,800 cu. in. displacement. From this point extend a line horizontally to the right. Now, locate the 270 brake mean effective pressure along the bottom of the chart. From this point extend a line up vertically until it intersects the horizontal line drawn earlier. The intersection of these two lines represents the engine speed (RPM). The answer is 2,100 RPM.

5-45 AMG016

(Refer to figure 38 on page 5-21.)
An aircraft reciprocating engine has a 2,800 cubic-inch displacement and develops 2,000 brake-horsepower at 2,200 RPM. What is the brake mean effective pressure?

A–257.5
B–242.5
C–275.0

5-45. Answer A. JSGT 5C, FGH

At the top of the chart, locate 2,000 HP. From this value drop down vertically until you intersect the line representing the 2,800 cubic-inch displacement. From this point, extend a line horizontally to the right until you intercept the line representing 2,200 RPM. Now drop down vertically to read the brake mean effective pressure on the bottom line of the chart. The brake mean effective pressure is 257.5.

5-46 AMG015

(Refer to figure 39 on page 5-23.)
Determine the cable size of a 40-foot length of single cable in free air, with a continuous rating, running from a bus to the equipment in a 28-volt system with a 15-ampere load and a 1-volt drop.

A–No. 10.
B–No. 11.
C–No. 18.

5-46. Answer A. JSGT 5C, AC 43.13-1B

Locate the column on the left side of the chart that represents a circuit voltage of 28 with a 1 volt drop. Find the horizontal line representing 40 feet and follow it to the right until it intersects the diagonal line indicating 15 amps. Since this point is above curve 2, installation as a single cable in free-air is permitted. Now, drop a vertical line to the bottom of the chart. This line falls between wire sizes #10 and #12. Whenever the chart indicates a wire size between two sizes, you must select the larger wire. In this case you would use #10 wire.

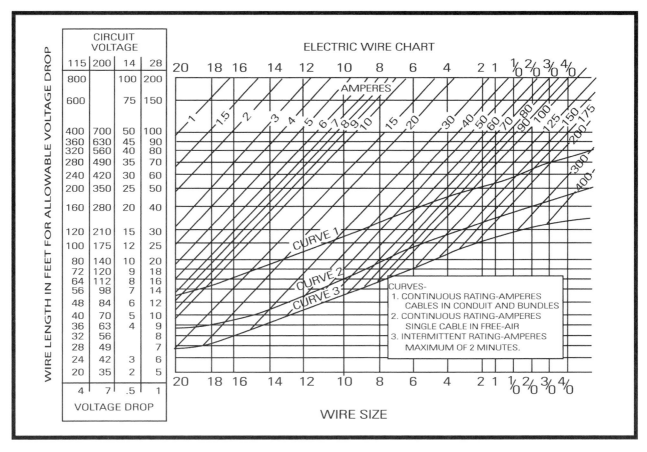

Figure 39. Electric Wire Chart.

5-47   AMG015

(Refer to figure 39 on page 5-23.)

Determine the maximum length of a No. 16 cable to be installed from a bus to the equipment in a 28-volt system with a 25-ampere intermittent load and a 1-volt drop.

A– 8 feet.
B– 10 feet.
C– 12 feet.

5-47. Answer A. JSGT 5C, AC 43.13-1B

Begin by finding the wire size on the bottom of the chart. From the #16, move upward to curve 3, which represents an intermittent load. From this point, project a horizontal line to the left until it reaches the column representing 28 volts with a 1 volt drop. The maximum length of a cable that can safely handle these requirements is 8 feet.

5-48   AMG015

(Refer to figure 39 on page 5-23.)

Determine the minimum wire size of a single cable in a bundle carrying a continuous current of 20 amperes 10 feet from the bus to the equipment in a 28-volt system with an allowable 1-volt drop.

A–No. 12.
B–No. 14.
C–No. 16.

5-48. Answer A. JSGT 5C, AC 43.13-1B

First, locate the column on the left side of the chart representing a 28V system with a 1 volt drop. Find the horizontal line representing a wire length of 10 feet and follow it to the right until it intersects the diagonal line for 20 amps. Because the wire is in a bundle and carries a continuous current, you must be at or above curve 1 on the chart. Follow along the diagonal line representing 20 amps until it intersects curve 1. From this point, drop down vertically to the bottom of the chart. The line falls between wire sizes #12 and #14. Whenever the chart indicates a wire size between two sizes, you must select the larger wire. In this case, a #12 wire is required.

5-49   AMG015

(Refer to figure 39 on page 5-23.)

Determine the maximum length of a No. 12 single cable that can be used between a 28-volt bus and a component utilizing 20 amperes continuous load in free air with a maximum acceptable 1-volt drop.

A–22.5 feet.
B–26.5 feet.
C–12.5 feet.

5-49. Answer B. JSGT 5C, AC 43.13-1B

Begin at the bottom of the chart and locate wire size #12. From this point, project a vertical line up until it intersects the diagonal line for 20 amps. Since the intersection of these two lines is above curve 2, the load requirements have been met. From the intersection, move left horizontally until you intersect the column for a 28-volt system with a 1 volt drop. The maximum length of cable that can be used is just over 25 feet, so 26.5 feet is just over 25 feet.

5-50   AMG011

(Refer to figure 40 on page 5-25.)

Determine the proper tension for a 1/8-inch cable (7 x 19) if the temperature is 80°F.

A–70 pounds.
B–75 pounds.
C–80 pounds.

5-50. Answer A. JSGT 5C, AC 65-15B

Begin by finding the temperature along the bottom of the chart. Follow this line up to the diagonal line representing 1/8-inch 7 x 19 cable. From this point, project a line horizontally to the right side of the chart. The rigging load is 70 pounds.

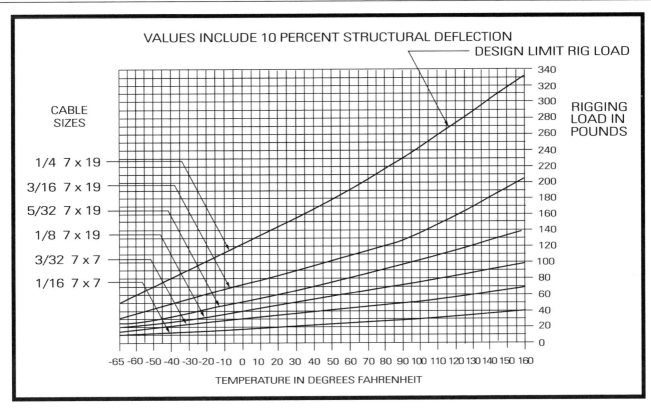

Figure 40. Cable Tension Chart.

5-51   AMG011
(Refer to figure 40 on page 5-25.)
Determine the proper tension for a 3/16-inch cable (7 x 19 extra flex) if the temperature is 87°F.

A– 135 pounds.
B– 125 pounds.
C– 140 pounds.

5-51. Answer B. JSGT 5C, FGH
Begin by locating the temperature along the bottom of the chart. From that point, move up vertically until you intersect the diagonal line representing a 3/16-inch 7 x 19 cable. From this intersection, project a line horizontally to the right side of the chart and read the rigging load. The proper rigging load is 125 pounds.

5-52   AMG016

(Refer to figure 41 on page 5-27.)

Determine how much fuel would be required for a 30-minute reserve operating at 2,300 RPM.

A– 25.3 pounds.
B– 35.5 pounds.
C– 49.8 pounds.

5-52. Answer A. JSGT 5C, FGH

To solve this problem you must first determine the specific fuel consumption. To do this, locate 2,300 RPM at the bottom of the chart and follow the vertical line up until it intersects the propeller load specific fuel consumption curve (use the full throttle curve only if full throttle operation is specified). From this point, extend a line horizontally to the right side of the chart and read the specific fuel consumption of .46 LB/BHP/HR. Now, determine the horsepower of the engine at 2,300 RPM. Again, begin at the bottom of the chart at the 2,300 RPM line and follow it up vertically to the propeller load horsepower curve. From this intersection, extend a line horizontally to the left side of the chart and read the brake horsepower (110 HP). To determine the fuel burn per hour, multiply the specific fuel consumption times the brake horsepower. The engine burns 50.6 pounds per hour (.46 x 110). Since this question asks for the fuel required for a 30-minute reserve, you must divide the fuel burn per hour by 2. The fuel required for a 30-minute reserve is 25.3 pounds (50.6 ÷ 2).

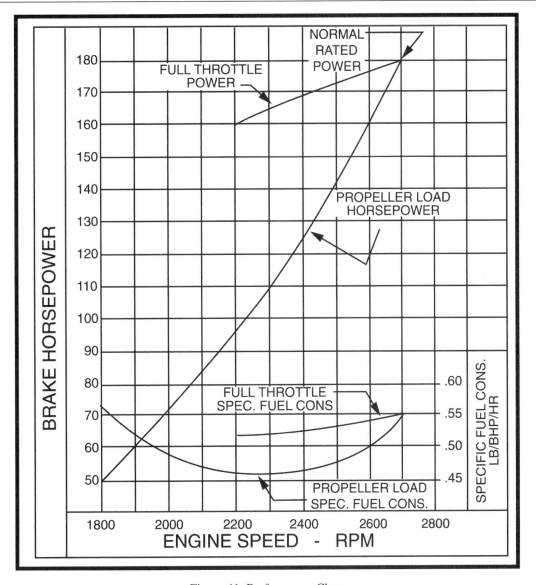

Figure 41. Performance Chart.

5-53   AMG016

(Refer to figure 41 on page 5-27.)
Determine the fuel consumption with the engine operating at cruise, 2,350 RPM.

A– 49.2 pounds per hour.
B– 51.2 pounds per hour.
C– 55.3 pounds per hour.

5-53. Answer C. JSGT 5C, FGH

To solve this problem, you must first determine the specific fuel consumption. To do this, locate 2,350 RPM on the bottom of the chart and follow the line up until it intersects the propeller load specific fuel consumption curve. From this intersection, extend a line to the right side of the chart and read a specific fuel consumption of .46 LB/BHP/HR. Now, determine the horsepower at 2,350 RPM. Again, begin at the bottom of the chart at the 2,350 RPM line and follow it up vertically to the propeller load horsepower curve. From this intersection, extend a line to the left side of the chart and read the brake horsepower (119 HP).To determine the fuel burn, multiply the specific fuel consumption times the brake horsepower. The engine burns 54.74 pounds per hour (.46 x 119 = 54.74). 55.3 pounds per hour is closest.

WEIGHT AND BALANCE

CHAPTER 6

SECTION A - WEIGHING PROCEDURES

In addition to examining the procedures for weighing an aircraft, Section A of Chapter 6 discusses the theory and methodology for calculating weight and balance information. Included are terminology used in weight and balance, information on how to determine an aircraft's empty weight and center of gravity, and the importance of weight and balance for aircraft.

6-1   AMG003
When computing weight and balance, an airplane is considered to be in balance when

A– the average moment arm of the loaded airplane falls within its CG range.
B– all moment arms of the plane fall within CG range.
C– the movement of the passengers will not cause the moment arms to fall outside the CG range.

6-1. Answer A. JSGT 6A, FGH
The CG can be thought of as the average moment arm for the aircraft. This value must fall within an allowable range to be considered safe for flight.

6-2   AMG003
What tasks are completed prior to weighing an aircraft to determine its empty weight?

A– Remove all items except those on the aircraft equipment list; drain fuel and hydraulic fluid.
B– Remove all items on the aircraft equipment list; drain fuel, compute oil and hydraulic fluid weight.
C– Remove all items except those on the aircraft equipment list; drain fuel and fill hydraulic reservoir.

6-2. Answer C. JSGT 6A, FGH
According to FAR Part 23, the empty weight of an aircraft includes all items on the aircraft's minimum equipment list, permanent ballast, unusable fuel, full hydraulics, and full oil (aircraft certified prior to March 1, 1978, are weighed with only the undrainable oil).

6-3   AMG003
The useful load of an aircraft consists of the

A– crew, usable fuel, passengers, and cargo.
B– crew, usable fuel, oil, and fixed equipment.
C– crew, passengers, usable fuel, oil, cargo, and fixed equipment.

6-3. Answer A. JSGT 6A, FGH
The useful load of an aircraft is the difference between the maximum gross weight and the empty weight. It includes items such as passengers and crew, usable fuel, and cargo.

6-4   AMG003
Which of the following can provide the empty weight of an aircraft if the aircraft's weight and balance records become lost, destroyed, or otherwise inaccurate?

A– Reweighing the aircraft.
B– The applicable Aircraft Specification or Type Certificate Data Sheet.
C– The applicable flight manual or pilot's operating handbook.

6-4. Answer A. JSGT 6A, FGH
If an aircraft's weight and balance records become lost or destroyed, the actual empty weight can only be established by reweighing the aircraft. The Aircraft Specification or Type Certificate Data Sheet is wrong because an aircraft's type certificate data sheet only lists maximum weights and not an empty weight, and the flight manual or pilot's operating handbook is wrong because an aircraft's flight manual contains an average empty weight for that model aircraft.

6-5   AMG003
In the theory of weight and balance, what is the name of the distance from the fulcrum to an object?

A– Lever arm.
B– Balance arm.
C– Fulcrum arm.

6-5. Answer A. JSGT 6A, FGH
In the theory of weight and balance, the name given to the distance from the fulcrum to any object is the lever arm. The lever arm is multiplied by the weight of the object to find the moment. In actual aircraft weight and balance problems, the arm is the distance from the datum to an item.

6-6   AMG089
(1) Private aircraft are required by regulations to be weighed periodically.
(2) Private aircraft are required to be weighed after making any alteration.
Regarding the above statements,

A– neither No. 1 nor No. 2 is true.
B– only No. 1 is true.
C– only No. 2 is true.

6-6. Answer A. JSGT 6A, FGH
Both of these statements are false. There is no regulation that requires private aircraft to be reweighed. Generally, after alterations, the weight changes are calculated and recorded in the aircraft's records. However, it's good operating practice to reweigh an aircraft whenever alterations may substantially affect an aircraft's weight and balance.

6-7   AMG003
To obtain useful weight data for purposes of determining the CG, it is necessary that an aircraft be weighed

A– in a level flight attitude.
B– with all items of useful load installed.
C– with at least minimum fuel (1/12-gallon per METO horsepower) in the fuel tanks.

6-7. Answer A. JSGT 6A, FGH
When an aircraft is weighed, it must be in a level flight attitude for the scale readings to be accurate. Weigh points, level points, and proper procedures for weighing are usually contained in the Type Certificate Data Sheets and are provided by the manufacturer's maintenance manual.

6-8   AMG003
What type of measurement is used to designate arm in weight and balance computation?

A– Distance.
B– Weight.
C– Weight/distance.

6-8. Answer A. JSGT 6A, FGH
Arm is the horizontal distance in inches or feet from the reference datum to an item of equipment.

6-9   AMG003

What determines whether the value of a moment is preceded by a plus (+) or a minus (-) sign in aircraft weight and balance?

A– The location of the weight in reference to the datum.

B– The result of a weight being added or removed and its location relative to the datum.

C– The location of the datum in reference to the aircraft CG.

6-9. Answer A. JSGT 6A, FGH

The location of items in an aircraft are given as positive or negative values according to their location relative to the reference datum. Items forward of the datum have a negative arm and items aft of the datum have a positive arm.

6-10   AMG003

What should be clearly indicated on the aircraft weighing form?

A– Minimum allowable gross weight.

B– Weight of unusable fuel.

C– Weighing points.

6-10. Answer C. JSGT 6A, FGH

The weighing points should be clearly indicated on the aircraft weighing forms because the arm values used for the scale readings are based on these locations.

6-11   AMG003

If the reference datum line is placed at the nose of an airplane rather than at the firewall or some other location aft of the nose,

A– all measurement arms will be in negative numbers.

B– all measurement arms will be in positive numbers.

C– measurement arms will be in both positive and negative numbers.

6-11. Answer B. JSGT 6A, FGH

All measurement arms aft of the datum carry a positive (+) value and arms in front of the datum carry a negative (–) value. When the datum is located in front of the aircraft, all measurement arms are positive.

6-12   AMG003

Zero fuel weight is the

A– dry weight plus the weight of full crew, passengers, and cargo.

B– basic operating weight without crew, fuel, and cargo.

C– maximum permissible weight of a loaded aircraft (passengers, crew, and cargo) without fuel.

6-12. Answer C. JSGT 6A, FGH

Zero fuel weight is the maximum permissible weight of a loaded aircraft, including the payload (passengers, crew, and cargo), but excluding the fuel load.

6-13   AMG003
The empty weight of an airplane is determined by

A– adding the net weight of each weighing point and multiplying the measured distance to the datum.
B– subtracting the tare weight from the scale reading and adding the weight of each weighing point.
C– multiplying the measured distance from each weighing point to the datum times the sum of scale reading less the tare weight.

6-13. Answer B. JSGT 6A, FGH
Tare weight includes the weight of extra items on the weighing scale that are not part of the aircraft. To determine the empty weight of an aircraft being weighed, add the weight of each scale reading and subtract out the tare weight.

6-14   AMG003
When dealing with weight and balance of an aircraft, the term "maximum weight" is interpreted to mean the maximum

A– weight of the empty aircraft.
B– weight of the useful load.
C– authorized weight of the aircraft and its contents.

6-14. Answer C. JSGT 6A, FGH
Maximum weight is the maximum authorized weight of the aircraft and its contents. This value may be found in the Aircraft Specifications or Type Certificate Data Sheet.

6-15   AMG003
Most modern aircraft are designed so that if all seats are occupied, full baggage weight is carried, and all fuel tanks are full, what will be the weight condition of the aircraft?

A– It will be in excess of maximum takeoff weight.
B– It will be at maximum basic operating weight (BOW).
C– It will be at maximum taxi or ramp weight.

6-15. Answer A. WBH
If all seats are occupied, all baggage allowed, and all fuel tanks full, most modern aircraft will be grossly overloaded. Excessive weight reduces the efficiency of an aircraft and the safety margin available if an emergency condition should arise.

6-16   AMG003
The major source of weight change for most aircraft as they age is caused by

A– accumulation of grime and debris in hard-to-reach areas of the structure, and moisture absorption in cabin insulation.
B– repairs and alterations.
C– installation of hardware and safety wire, and added layers of primer and paint on the structure.

6-16. Answer B. WBH
Repairs and alterations are the major sources of weight changes. The growth due to trash and dirt in hard-to-reach places is normally small.

6-17 AMG003
Use of which of the following generally yields the highest degree of aircraft leveling accuracy?

A–Electronic load cell(s).
B– Spirit level(s).
C– Plumb bob and chalk line.

6-17. Answer B. FGH
The most accurate method of leveling an aircraft is a plumb bob and grid plate and not a plumb bob and chalk line. Of the choices given, spirit levels are the most accurate method of leveling an aircraft.

6-18 AMG003
In the process of weighing an airplane toward obtaining the CG, the arms from the weighing points always extend

A–parallel to the centerline of the airplane.
B– straight forward from each of the landing gear.
C– directly from each weighing point to the others.

6-18. Answer A. FGH
An airplanes CG is determined from the distribution of weight along the centerline. Lateral distribution is not considered in an determining an airplanes CG.

6-19 AMG003
The useful load of an aircraft is the difference between

A–the maximum takeoff weight and basic empty weight.
B– maximum ramp or takeoff weight as applicable, and zero fuel weight.
C– (1) the weight of an aircraft with all seats filled, full baggage/cargo, and full fuel, and (2) aircraft weight with all seats empty, no baggage/cargo, and minimum operating fuel.

6-19. Answer A. JSGT 6A, FGH
The useful load of an aircraft is the difference between the maximum gross weight (maximum takeoff weight) and the empty weight. It includes items such as passengers and crew, usable fuel, and cargo.

6-20 AMG003
When determining the empty weight of an aircraft, certificated under current airworthiness standards (FAR Part 23), the oil contained in the supply tank is considered

A–a part of the empty weight.
B– a part of the useful load.
C– the same as the fluid contained in the water injection reservoir.

6-20. Answer A. JSGT 6A, FGH
Under current airworthiness standards (FAR Part 23), full oil is considered part of the empty weight of an aircraft. Until March 1, 1978, empty weight included only undrainable oil.

6-21   AMG003

The maximum weight as used in weight and balance control of a given aircraft can normally be found

A– by adding the weight of full fuel, pilot, passengers, and maximum allowable baggage to the empty weight.

B– in the Aircraft Specification or Type Certificate Data Sheet.

C– by adding the empty weight and payload.

6-21. Answer B. JSGT 6A, FGH

The maximum weight of a particular model of aircraft is found in the Aircraft Specification or Type Certificate Data Sheet. Empty weights and useful loads vary with the equipment installed on a particular aircraft. These values must be located in the permanent records for that aircraft.

6-22   AMG003

The amount of fuel used for computing empty weight and corresponding CG is

A– empty fuel tanks.

B– unusable fuel.

C– the amount of fuel necessary for 1/2 hour of operation.

6-22. Answer B. JSGT 6A, FGH

The empty weight of an aircraft includes only the weight of that fuel which remains in the sumps and plumbing of the aircraft and is termed unusable fuel.

6-23   AMG003

As weighed, the total empty weight of an aircraft is 5,862 pounds with a moment of 885,957. However, when the aircraft was weighed, 20 pounds of potable water were on board at +84 and 23 pounds of hydraulic fluid were in a tank located at +101. What is the empty weight CG of the aircraft?

A– 150.700
B– 151.700
C– 151.365

6-23. Answer C. JSGT 6A, FGH

The hydraulic fluid is part of the empty weight and may be ignored. Alcohol for alcohol/water injection is not part of the aircraft's empty weight and, therefore, must be subtracted out to determine the empty weight. It is typically easier to solve this type of problem if you enter the information into a table.

Item	Weight	Arm	Moment
Aircraft	5,862		885,957
Alcohol	-20	84	-1,680
Total	5,842		884,277

With the weight and moment of the alcohol subtracted out, divide the total moment by the total weight. The aircraft's empty weight CG is 151.365 inches (884,277 ÷ 5,852 = 151.365).

6-24 AMG002

Two boxes which weigh 10 pounds and 5 pounds are placed in an airplane so that their distance aft from the CG are 4 feet and 2 feet respectively. How far forward of the CG should a third box, weighing 20 pounds, be placed so that the CG will not be changed?

A– 3 feet.
B– 2.5 feet.
C– 8 feet.

6-24. Answer B. JSGT 6A, FGH

For the center of gravity to remain the same, the moments forward and aft of the CG must be equal. The two boxes added aft of the CG have moments of 40 foot/pounds (10 lbs x 4 ft = 40 ft/lbs) and 10 foot/pounds (5 lbs x 2 ft = 10 ft/lbs). This is a total moment of 50 foot/pounds. The box loaded forward must also have a moment of 50 foot/pounds to maintain balance. To determine the distance forward of the CG to maintain balance, divide 50 foot/pounds by 20 pounds. This results in a distance of 2.5 feet (50 ft/lbs ÷ 20 lbs = 2.5 ft).

6-25 AMG003

If a 40-pound generator applies +1400 inch-pounds to a reference axis, the generator is located

A– –35 from the axis.
B– +35 from the axis.
C– +25 from the axis.

6-25. Answer B. JSGT 6A, FGH

This question requires the application of the formula, Moment ÷ Weight = Arm. Substituting the values given, the arm is +35 inches from the axis (1,400 ÷ 40 = +35).

6-26 AMG003

In a balance computation of an aircraft from which an item located aft of the datum was removed, use

A– (–) weight x (+) arm (–) moment.
B– (–) weight x (–) arm (+) moment.
C– (+) weight x (–) arm (–) moment.

6-26. Answer A. JSGT 6A, FGH

Anytime you remove something from an aircraft, the weight is subtracted (–), and anytime an item is aft of the datum, it has a positive (+) arm. Therefore, a (–) weight times a (+) arm yield a (–) moment.

6-27 AMG003

Datum is forward of the main gear center point 30.24 in.

Actual distance between tail gear and main gear center points.....360.26 in.
Net weight at right main gear.....9,980 lb.
Net weight at left main gear.....9,770 lb.
Net weight at tail gear.....1,970 lb.

These items were in the aircraft when weighed:
1. Lavatory water tank full (34 pounds at +352).
2. Hydraulic fluid (22 pounds at 8).
3. Removable ballast (146 pounds at +380).

What is the empty weight CG of the aircraft described above?

A–62.92 inches.
B–60.31 inches.
C–58.54 inches.

6-27. Answer B. JSGT 6A, FGH

It is typically easier to solve this type of problem if you enter the information into a table.

Item	Weight	Arm	Moment
Tail Wt.	1,970	390.50	769,285.0
L.M. Wt.	9,770	30.24	295,444.8
R.M. Wt.	9,980	30.24	301,795.2
Water	−34	352.00	−11,968.0
Ballast	−146	380.00	−55,480.0
Total	21,540		1,299,077.0

Lavatory water and removable ballast are not part of the aircraft empty weight and must be removed. Therefore, you must subtract their weights and moments to determine the empty weight CG. On the other hand, full hydraulic fluid is considered part of the aircraft empty weight and, therefore, is not used for this calculation. To calculate the CG, divide the total moment by the total weight. The CG is 60.31 inches (1,299,077.0 ÷ 21,540 = 60.31).

6-28 AMG003

When an empty aircraft is weighed, the combined net weight at the main gears is 3,540 pounds with an arm of 195.5 inches. At the nose gear, the net weight is 2,322 pounds with an arm of 83.5 inches. The datum line is forward of the nose of the aircraft. What is the empty CG of the aircraft?

A–151.1
B–155.2
C–146.5

6-28. Answer A. JSGT 6A, FGH

It is typically easier to solve this type of problem if you enter the information into a table. The position of the datum has no bearing on this problem.

Item	Weight	Arm	Moment
Nose	2,322	83.5	193,887
Mains	3,540	195.5	692,070
Total	5,862		885,957

Calculate the CG by dividing the total moment by the total weight. The empty weight CG is 151.14 inches (885,957 ÷ 5,862 = 151.14).

6-29   AMG003

Find the empty weight CG location for the following tricycle-gear aircraft. Each main wheel weighs 753 pounds, nosewheel weighs 22 pounds, distance between nosewheel and main wheels is 87.5 inches, nosewheel location is +9.875 inches from datum, with 1 gallon of hydraulic fluid at –21.0 inches included in the weight scale.

A– +97.375 inches.
B– +95.61 inches.
C– +96.11 inches.

6-29. Answer C. JSGT 6A, FGH

It is typically easier to solve this type of problem if you enter the information into a table. Remember, hydraulic fluid is included in the empty weight of the airplane, therefore should not be subtracted out.

Item	Weight	Arm	Moment
Nose	22	9.875	217.25
Mains	1,506	97.375	146,646.75
Total	1,528		146,864.00

To determine the location of the main gear, you must add the distance between the nosewheel and main gear to the location of the nosewheel. The mains are located at 97.375 (87.5 + 9.875 = 97.375 inches). Calculate the new CG by dividing the total moment by the total weight. The empty weight CG is 96.11 inches (146,864 ÷ 1,528 = 96.11).

6-30   AMG003

The useful load of an aircraft is the difference between

A– the maximum takeoff weight and basic empty weight.
B– maximum ramp or takeoff weight as applicable, and zero fuel weight.
C– (1) the weight of an aircraft with all seats filled, full baggage/cargo, and full fuel, and (2) aircraft weight with all seats empty, no baggage/cargo, and minimum operating fuel.

6-30. Answer A. JSGT 6A, FGH

The useful load of an aircraft is the difference between the maximum gross weight (maximum takeoff weight) and the empty weight. It includes items such as passengers and crew, usable fuel, and cargo.

6-31   AMG003

If an aircraft CG is found to be at 24 percent of MAC, that 24 percent is an expression of the

A– distance from the TEMAC.
B– distance from the LEMAC.
C– average distance from the LEMAC to the wing center of lift.

6-31. Answer B. JSGT 6A, FGH

The mean aerodynamic chord (MAC) is determined from the leading edge to the trailing edge of the airfoil. The leading edge MAC (LEMAC) is the start, or 0% MAC. The trailing edge MAC (TEMAC) is 100% MAC. A CG that is 24% MAC is 24% of the distance from LEMAC to TEMAC.

6-32   AMG002
An aircraft's LEMAC and TEMAC are defined in terms of distance

A– from the datum.
B– from each other.
C– ahead of and behind the wing center of lift, respectively.

6-32. Answer A. JSGT 6A, FGH
An aircrafts leading edge mean aerodynamic chord (LEMAC) and trailing edge mean aerodynamic chord (TEMAC) are assigned fuselage or body station numbers representative of their distance from the datum. The actual MAC is the difference between the TEMAC and the LEMAC.

6-33   AMG003
When an aircraft is positioned for weighing on scales located under each landing gear wheel, which of the following may cause erroneous scale readings?

A– Gear downlocks installed.
B– Parking brakes set.
C– Parking brakes not set.

6-33. Answer B. JSGT 6A, FGH
When an aircraft is weighed, chocks should be used to prevent the aircraft from rolling and the weight of the chocks subtracted from the scale weight readings as tare weight. Setting the brakes may cause adverse side load to be applied to the scale, causing inaccurate readings.

6-34   AMG003
When accomplishing loading computations for a small aircraft, necessary information obtained from the weight and balance records would include

A– unusable fuel weight and distance from datum.
B– weight and location of permanent ballast.
C– current empty weight and empty weight CG.

6-34. Answer C. JSGT 6A, FGH
When accomplishing loading computations on a small aircraft, it's necessary to locate the empty weight and empty weight center of gravity in the weight and balance records to have a starting point from which to calculate the effect of added weights of useful load items.

6-35   AMG003
If it is necessary to weigh an aircraft with full fuel tanks, all fuel weight must be subtracted from the scale readings

A– except minimum fuel.
B– including unusable fuel.
C– except unusable fuel.

6-35. Answer C. JSGT 6A, FGH
When weighing an aircraft, only unusable fuel should be considered part of the aircraft's empty weight. If an aircraft is weighed with full fuel, all fuel weight must be subtracted from the scale weight readings except the unusable fuel, as specified in the aircraft's type certificate data sheet or specifications.

SECTION B - SHIFTING THE CG

As items are loaded into an aircraft, or when structural modifications are made, the center of gravity (CG) moves or shifts. At times, the CG will shift beyond its acceptable range. For this reason, you must understand how shifting weight in an aircraft changes the CG location.

6-36   AMG002

An aircraft with an empty weight of 2,100 pounds and an empty weight CG + 32.5 was altered as follows:

(1) two 18-pound passenger seats located +73 were removed;
(2) structural modifications were made at +77 increasing weight by 17 pounds;
(3) a seat and safety belt weighing 25 pounds were installed at +74.5; and
(4) radio equipment weighing 35 pounds was installed at +95.

What is the new empty weight CG?

A– +34.01
B– +33.68
C– +34.65

6-36. Answer B. JSGT 6B, FGH

It is typically easier to solve this type of problem if you enter the information into a table as seen below.

Item	Weight	Arm	Moment
Aircraft	2,100	32.5	68,250.0
2 Pass seats	–36	73.0	–2,628.0
Modification	17	77.0	1,309.0
Seat/belt	25	74.5	1,862.5
Radio	35	95.0	3,325.0
Total	2,141		72,118.5

First, multiply all weights by their arms to obtain the moments. Watch the negative sign on removed items. Total the weight and moment columns, then divide the new moment by the new weight. The new CG is 33.68 inches (72,118.5 ÷ 2,141 = 33.68).

6-37   AMG002

An aircraft as loaded weighs 4,954 pounds at a CG of +30.5 inches. The CG range is +32.0 inches to +42.1 inches. Find the minimum weight of the ballast necessary to bring the CG within the CG range. The ballast arm is +162 inches.

A– 61.98 pounds.
B– 30.58 pounds.
C– 57.16 pounds.

6-37. Answer C. JSGT 6B, FGH

Apply the ballast formula to the values given in the problem:

$$\text{BALLAST} = \frac{(\text{Aircraft weight as loaded}) \times (\text{Current CG - Desired CG})}{(\text{Desired CG}) - (\text{Arm of ballast})}$$

In the above formula, the aircraft weight is entered as 4,954 pounds. The current CG is +30.5 inches, and the desired CG is the forward limit of +32.0 inches. The arm of the ballast is +162.0 inches. A positive number requires addition of weight at the ballast point, and a negative number requires removal of weight.

$$\text{BALLAST} = \frac{4{,}954 \times (30.5 - 32.0)}{32.0 - 162.0} = \frac{-7{,}431}{-130.0} = 57.16 \text{ lbs.}$$

6-38   AMG002

An aircraft with an empty weight of 1,800 pounds and an empty weight CG of +31.5 was altered as follows:

(1) two 15-pound passenger seats located at +72 were removed;
(2) structural modifications increasing the weight 14 pounds were made at +76;
(3) a seat and safety belt weighing 20 pounds were installed at +73.5; and
(4) radio equipment weighing 30 pounds was installed at +30.

What is the new empty weight CG?

A– +30.61
B– +31.61
C– +32.69

6-38. Answer B. JSGT 6B, FGH

It is typically easier to solve this type of problem if you enter the information into a table.

Item	Weight	Arm	Moment
Aircraft	1,800	31.5	56,700
Seats	−30	72.0	−2,160
Mod	14	76.0	1,064
Seat/belt	20	73.5	1,470
Radio	30	30.0	900
Total	1,834		57,974

First multiply all weights by their arms to obtain the moments. Watch the negative sign on removed items. Total the weight and moment columns and divide the new moment by the new weight. The new CG is 31.61 inches (57,974 ÷ 1,834 = 31.61).

6-39   AMG002

An aircraft had an empty weight of 2,886 pounds with a moment of 101,673.78 before several alterations were made. The alterations included:

(1) removing two passengers seats (15 pounds each) at +71;
(2) installing a cabinet (97 pounds) at +71;
(3) installing a seat and safety belt (20 pounds) at +71; and
(4) installing radio equipment (30 pounds) at +94.

The alterations caused the new empty weight CG to move

A– 1.62 inches aft of the original empty weight CG.
B– 2.03 inches forward of the original empty weight CG.
C– 2.03 inches aft of the original empty weight CG.

6-39. Answer A. JSGT 6B, FGH

It is typically easier to solve this type of problem if you enter the information into a table.

Item	Weight	Arm	Moment
Aircraft	2,886	35.23	101,673.78
Seats	-30	71.00	−2,130.00
Cabinet	97	71.00	6,887.00
Seat/belt	20	71.00	1,420.00
Radio	30	94.00	2,820.00
Total	3,003		110,670.78

The old CG is calculated by dividing the original moment (101,673.78) by the original weight (2,886 lbs). The original CG was 35.23 (101,673.78 ÷ 2,886 = 35.23). The new CG is calculated by dividing the new moment (110,670.78) by the new weight (3,003 lbs). Because the new CG (36.85) is a larger number than the original (35.23), you know that the CG has shifted to the rear (aft). Subtracting the original CG from the new CG results in a difference of 1.62 inches (36.85 − 35.23 = 1.62). Therefore, the CG shifted aft 1.62 inches.

6-40   AMG002

When making a rearward weight and balance check to determine that the CG will not exceed the rearward limit during extreme conditions, the items of useful load which should be computed at their minimum weights are those located forward of the

A– forward CG limit.
B– datum.
C– rearward CG limit.

6-40. Answer C. JSGT 6B, FGH

When making a rearward extreme loading check, you must load the items of useful load behind the rearward CG limit to their maximum, and items of useful load ahead of the rearward CG limit to their minimum.

6-41   AMG002

An aircraft with an empty weight of 1,500 pounds and an empty weight CG of +28.4 was altered as follows:

(1) two 12-pound seats located at +68.5 were removed;
(2) structural modifications weighing +28 pounds were made at +73;
(3) a seat and safety belt weighing 30 pounds were installed at +70.5; and
(4) radio equipment weighing 25 pounds was installed at +85.

What is the new empty weight CG?

A–+23.51
B–+31.35
C–+30.30

6-41. Answer C. JSGT 6B, FGH

It is typically easier to solve this type of problem if you enter the information into a table.

Item	Weight	Arm	Moment
Aircraft	1,500	28.4	42,600
Seats	−24	68.5	−1,644
Mod	28	73.0	2,044
Seat/belt	30	70.5	2,115
Radio	25	85.0	2,125
Total	1,559		47,240

First, multiply all weights by their arms to obtain the moments. Watch the negative sign on removed items. Total the weight and moment columns and divide the new moment by the new weight. The new empty weight CG is 30.3 (47,240 ÷ 1,559 = 30.3).

6-42   AMG002

The following alteration was performed on an aircraft: A model B engine weighing 175 pounds was replaced by a model D engine weighing 185 pounds at a −62.00-inch station. The aircraft weight and balance records show the previous empty weight to be 998 pounds and an empty weight CG of 13.48 inches. What is the new empty weight CG?

A– 13.96 inches.
B– 14.25 inches.
C– 12.73 inches.

6-42. Answer C. JSGT 6B, FGH

It is typically easier to solve this type of problem if you enter the information into a table.

Item	Weight	Arm	Moment
Aircraft	998	13.48	13,453.04
Engine B	−175	-62.00	10,850.00
Engine D	185	-62.00	−11,470.00
Total	1,008		12,833.04

Calculate the new CG by dividing the total moment by the total weight. Upgrading to the model D engine increased the aircraft weight by 10 pounds at station −62.00. Since more weight is added ahead of the datum, the CG shifts forward to 12.73 inches (12,833.04 ÷ 1,008 = 12.73).

6-43   AMG002

If the empty weight CG of an airplane lies within the empty weight CG limits,

A– it is necessary to calculate CG extremes.
B– it is not necessary to calculate CG extremes.
C– minimum fuel should be used in both forward and rearward CG checks.

6-43. Answer B. JSGT 6B, FGH

Adverse loading checks are a deliberate attempt to load an aircraft in a manner that will create the most critical balance condition and still remain within the aircraft's design CG limits. If the empty weight CG falls within the empty weight CG range it is unnecessary to perform this check.

6-44   AMG002

When computing the maximum forward loaded CG of an aircraft, minimum weights, arms, and moments should be used for items of useful load that are located aft of the

A– rearward CG limit.
B– forward CG limit.
C– datum.

6-44. Answer B. JSGT 6B, FGH

A forward adverse-loading check is performed to determine if it is possible to load an airplane so that its CG will fall ahead of the forward CG limit. To perform this type of check, use maximum values for items of useful load that are forward of the forward limit, and minimum values for those items located aft of the forward CG limit.

6-45   AMG002

All other things being equal, if an item of useful load located aft of an aircraft's CG is removed, the aircraft's CG change will be

A– aft in proportion to the weight of the item and its location in the aircraft.
B– forward in proportion to the weight of the item and its location in the aircraft.
C– forward in proportion to the weight of the item, regardless of its location in the aircraft.

6-45. Answer B. JSGT 6B, FGH

When weight is added or removed to an aircraft, the CG is effected depending on on amount of weight and its location relative to the CG. When weight is added, it moves the CG toward the added weight. When weight is removed, the CG moves away from the location of the removed weight. Only when weight is added or removed at the CG does the CG remain constant.

SECTION C - HELICOPTER WEIGHT AND BALANCE

As an A&P technician, you must know how to compute weight and balance information on helicopters as well as airplanes. Fortunately, the theories and methodologies used for calculating weight and balance on airplanes apply to helicopters as well.

6-46   AMG002

Which statement is true regarding helicopter weight and balance?

A– Regardless of internal or external loading, lateral axis CG control is ordinarily not a factor in maintaining helicopter weight and balance.
B– The moment of tail-mounted components is subject to constant change.
C– Weight and balance procedures for airplanes generally also apply to helicopters.

6-46. Answer C. JSGT 6C, FGH

The same theory and methodology for calculating weight and balance applies to both helicopters and airplanes. The formula Weight x Arm = Moment applies in both cases.

6-47   AMG002

Improper loading of a helicopter which results in exceeding either the fore or aft CG limits is hazardous due to the

A– reduction or loss of effective cyclic pitch control.
B– Coriolis effect being translated to the fuselage.
C– reduction or loss of effective collective pitch control.

6-47. Answer A. JSGT 6C, FGH

Helicopters generally have a smaller CG envelope than airplanes, so extra caution must be observed during loading. Trimming of a helicopter which has less than ideal balance is done with the cyclic pitch control. In extreme out-of-balance conditions full fore or aft cyclic control may be insufficient to maintain control.

6-48   AMG002

The CG range in single-rotor helicopters is

A– much greater than for airplanes.
B– approximately the same as the CG range for airplanes.
C– more restricted than for airplanes.

6-48. Answer C. JSGT 6C, FGH

Most helicopters have a restricted CG range as compared to airplanes. In some cases, this range is less than 3 inches.

AIRCRAFT STRUCTURAL MATERIALS

CHAPTER 7

SECTION A - METALS

Section A of Chapter 7 discusses the characteristics, maintenance practices, and uses of ferrous and nonferrous metals such as steel and aluminum.

7-1   AMG019
Which of the following describe the effects of annealing steel and aluminum alloys?

1. decrease in internal stress.
2. softening of the metal.
3. improved corrosion resistance.

A– 1 and 2.
B– 1 and 3.
C– 2 and 3.

7-1. Answer A. JSGT 7A, FGH
The process of annealing softens a metal and decreases its internal stresses. Improved corrosion resistance is incorrect because annealing does not improve a metal's corrosion resistance.

7-2   AMG019
Which heat-treating process of metal produces a hard, wear-resistant surface over a strong, tough core?

A– Case hardening.
B– Annealing.
C– Tempering.

7-2. Answer A. JSGT 7A, FGH
Low-carbon and low-alloy steels may be case-hardened to give a wear resistant surface, and, at the same time, a tough internal core. This process is used on aircraft crankshafts and camshafts as well

7-3   AMG019
Which heat-treating operation would be performed when the surface of the metal is changed chemically by introducing a high carbide or nitride content?

A– Tempering.
B– Normalizing.
C– Case hardening.

7-3. Answer C. JSGT 7A, FGH
Case-hardening is usually accomplished in one of two ways. The first is a process known as carburizing, in which controlled amounts of carbon are added to the surface of the steel to form carbides. The second method, nitriding, introduces nitrogen to the surface of the steel.

7-4   AMG019
Normalizing is a process of heat treating

A– aluminum alloys only.
B– iron-base metals only.
C– both aluminum alloys and iron-base metals.

7-4. Answer B. JSGT 7A, FGH
Normalizing is used to relieve stresses in ferrous or iron-based metal parts. It is similar to annealing, but the particles of carbon that precipitate out are not as large as those formed during annealing. Normalizing also produces a harder and stronger material than that obtained by annealing.

7-5   AMG019
Which of the following occurs when a mechanical force is repeatedly applied to most metals at room temperature, such as rolling, hammering, or bending?
1. The metals become artificially aged.
2. The metals become stress corrosion cracked.
3. The metals become cold worked, strain or work hardened.

A– 2.
B– 1 and 3.
C– 3.

7-5. Answer B. JSGT 7A, FGH
Mechanically working metals at temperatures below their critical range results in strain, or work hardening of the material. Strain hardening can increase a metal part's strength and hardness. However, work hardening does reduce a material's flexibility.

7-6   AMG019
The reheating of a heat treated metal, such as with a welding torch

A– has little or no effect on a metal's heat treated characteristics.
B– can significantly alter a metal's properties in the reheated area.
C– has a cumulative enhancement effect on the original heat treatment.

7-6. Answer B. JSGT 7A, FGH
When a part is welded, internal stresses and strains set up in the surrounding structure that can significantly alter a metal's properties. In addition, the weld itself is a cast structure whereas the surrounding material is wrought. These two types of structures have different grain sizes and, therefore, are not very compatible. To refine the grain structure as well as relieve the internal stresses, all welded parts should be normalized after fabrication.

7-7   AMG019
Why is steel tempered after being hardened?

A– To increase its hardness and ductility.
B– To increase its strength and decrease its internal stresses.
C– To relieve its internal stresses and reduce its brittleness.

7-7. Answer C. JSGT 7A, FGH
When steel is hardened by quenching, it is usually too hard and brittle for use. Furthermore, rapid quenching causes stresses within the steel. Tempering involves reheating the material to a temperature below its critical temperature to draw out some of the hardness and relieve its internal stress.

7-8   AMG019

What aluminum alloy designations indicate that the metal has received no hardening or tempering treatment?

A– 3003-F.
B– 5052-H36.
C– 6061-O.

7-9   AMG019

Which material cannot be heat treated repeatedly without harmful effects?

A– Unclad aluminum alloy in sheet form.
B– 6061-T9 stainless steel.
C– Clad aluminum alloy.

7-10   AMG042

What is descriptive of the annealing process of steel during and after it has been annealed?

A– Rapid cooling; high strength.
B– Slow cooling; low strength.
C– Slow cooling; increased resistance to wear.

7-11   AMG019

What is generally used in the construction of aircraft engine firewalls?

A– Stainless steel.
B– Chrome-molybdenum alloy steel.
C– Titanium nickel alloy.

7-12   AMG019

Alclad is a metal consisting of

A– aluminum alloy surface layers and a pure aluminum core.
B– pure aluminum surface layers on an aluminum alloy core.
C– a homogeneous mixture of pure aluminum and aluminum alloy.

7-8. Answer A. JSGT 7A, FGH

The letter F following an alloy designation indicates that the metal is in an "as fabricated" condition, and has received no hardening or tempering treatment. An "H" on the other hand, indicates the alloy was hardened while a "O" indicates the metal was annealed.

7-9. Answer C. JSGT 7A, FGH

Because clad aluminum has a corrosion-resistant coating of pure aluminum over an alloy core, repeated heat-treatments can cause diffusion of the alloying agents into the pure aluminum, resulting in reduced corrosion resistance.

7-10. Answer B. JSGT 7A, FGH

Annealing of steel produces a fine-grained, soft metal. Annealing is accomplished by heating the metal to just above the critical temperature and cooling it very slowly in a furnace.

7-11. Answer A. JSGT 7A, FGH

Because of its corrosion resistant properties and high temperature performance, stainless steel is frequently used in firewalls, exhaust collectors, stacks, and manifolds.

7-12. Answer B. JSGT 7A, FGH

"Alclad" is a proprietary name, and refers to the practice of rolling a thin coating of pure aluminum onto both sides of the aluminum alloy core to improve corrosion resistance.

7-13   AMG019

The Society of Automotive Engineers (SAE) and the American Iron and Steel Institute use a numerical index system to identify the composition of various steels. In the number "4130", designating chromium molybdenum steel, the first digit indicates the

A– percentage of the basic element in the alloy.
B– percentage of carbon in the alloy in hundredths of a percent.
C– basic alloying element.

7-13. Answer C. JSGT 7A, FGH

The first digit of an SAE number indicates an alloy's basic alloying element. Percentage of the basic element in an alloy is wrong because it is indicated by the second digit in the SAE number. Percent of carbon in the alloy is incorrect because it is indicated by the third and fourth digits.

7-14   AMG019

The core material of Alclad 2024-T4 is

A– heat-treated aluminum alloy, and the surface material is commercially pure aluminum.
B– commercially pure aluminum, and the surface material is heat-treated aluminum alloy.
C– strain-hardened aluminum alloy, and the surface material is commercially pure aluminum.

7-14. Answer A. JSGT 7A, FGH

The term Alclad is used to identify a sheet where a pure aluminum coating is bonded to an aluminum alloy core. The designation 2024 indicates that the core is an aluminum alloy which uses copper as its primary alloying agent. The -T4 means that the sheet has been solution heat treated, followed by natural aging at room temperature.

7-15   AMG019

The aluminum code number 1100 identifies what type of aluminum?

A– Aluminum alloy containing 11 percent copper.
B– Aluminum alloy containing zinc.
C– 99 percent commercially pure aluminum.

7-15. Answer C. JSGT 7A, FGH

Commercially pure aluminum is assigned a code of 1100. It has a high degree of resistance to corrosion and is easily formed into intricate shapes. Pure aluminum is not used in structural applications because of its low tensile strength.

7-16   AMG019

In the four-digit aluminum index system number 2024, the first digit indicates

A– the major alloying element.
B– the number of different major alloying elements used in the metal.
C– the percent of alloying metal added.

7-16. Answer A. JSGT 7A, FGH

In the four digit aluminum index system, the first digit indicates the alloy type, or the major alloying element. The 2000 series alloys have copper as their major alloying element.

7-17   AMG019

Why is it considered good practice to normalize a part after welding?

A– To relieve internal stresses developed within the base metal.
B– To increase the hardness of the weld.
C– To remove the surface scale formed during welding.

7-17. Answer A. JSGT 7A, FGH

Steel that is forged, welded, or machined develops stresses within the structure that could cause failure. These stresses are typically relieved by a process known as normalizing. During the normalizing process, the part is heated above its critical temperature, then allowed to cool in still air.

7-18   AMG019

Parts are rinsed thoroughly in hot water after they have been heat treated in a sodium and potassium nitrate bath to

A– prevent corrosion.
B– prevent surface cracking.
C– retard discoloration.

7-18. Answer A. JSGT 7A, AC 43.13-1B

Some forms of heat treatment require immersion of parts in a heated sodium or potassium nitrate bath. Sodium and potassium nitrate are salts, and salt is a highly corrosive agent. Therefore, all parts bathed in sodium or potassium nitrate must be rinsed to prevent corrosion.

SECTION B - NONMETALLIC MATERIALS

While the greatest part of an aircraft's structure is made of metal, nonmetallic structural materials find wide use in aircraft and components. Section B of Chapter 7 covers the various types of nonmetallic materials you are likely to encounter as an aviation maintenance technician. Although the information discussed in this section is valuable, currently no FAA Test questions are based on this subject.

AIRCRAFT HARDWARE

SECTION A - AIRCRAFT RIVETS

Aircraft rivets are the single most common fastener used in aircraft fabrication. Chapter 8, Section A discusses the different types of aircraft rivets as well as several of the specialized fasteners used in aviation. Although this is an important subject, there are currently no FAA Test questions based on this material.

SECTION B - AIRCRAFT FASTENERS

Chapter 8, Section B covers the various kinds of aircraft fasteners that can be removed and reinstalled. These fasteners include bolts, nuts, washers, and screws.

8-1   AMG017

Unless otherwise specified, torque values for tightening aircraft nuts and bolts relate to

A– clean, dry threads.
B– clean, lightly oiled threads.
C– both dry and lightly oiled threads.

8-1. Answer A. JSGT 8B, FGH

Unless the table of torque values for a specific fastener specifies otherwise, the torque values given are for clean, dry threads.

8-2   AMG017

Unless otherwise specified or required, aircraft bolts should be installed so that the bolt head is

A– upward, or in a rearward direction.
B– upward, or in a forward direction.
C– downward, or in a forward direction.

8-2. Answer B. JSGT 8B, FGH

Bolts should always be placed in the direction specified by the aircraft or engine manufacturer. However, in the absence of specific instructions, bolt heads should be installed upward or in a forward direction. This helps prevent the bolt from slipping out if the nut comes off.

8-3   AMG017

A fiber-type, self-locking nut must never be used on an aircraft if the bolt is

A– under shear loading.
B– under tension loading.
C– subject to rotation.

8-3. Answer C. JSGT 8B, FGH

Self-locking nuts are used on aircraft to provide tight connections which will not shake loose under severe vibration. However, fiber-type, self-locking nuts will not remain secure at joints which are subject to rotation.

8-4   AMG017

Aircraft bolts with a cross or asterisk marked on the bolt head are

A– made of aluminum alloy.
B– close tolerance bolts.
C– standard steel bolts.

8-4. Answer C. JSGT 8B, FGH

AN standard steel bolts are identified by a cross or an asterisk on the head. An aluminum alloy bolt is identified by two dashes on opposite sides of the bolt head and close tolerance bolts are identified by an "X" inside a triangle.

8-5   AMG017

Which statement regarding aircraft bolts is correct?

A– Alloy bolts smaller than 1/4-inch diameter should not be used in primary structure.
B– When tightening castellated nuts on drilled bolts, if the cotter pin holes do not line up, it is permissible to tighten the nut up to 10 percent over recommended torque to permit alignment of the next slot with the cotter pin hole.
C– In general, bolt grip lengths should equal the material thickness.

8-5. Answer C. JSGT 8B, FGH
The grip length is the length of the unthreaded portion of the bolt shank. Generally the grip length should be equal to the thickness of the material being bolted together. However, bolts of slightly greater grip length may be used if washers are placed under the nut or the bolthead.

8-6   AMG017

Generally speaking, bolt grip lengths should be

A– equal to the thickness of the material which is fastened together, plus approximately one diameter.
B– equal to the thickness of the material which is fastened together.
C– one and one half times the thickness of the material which is fastened together.

8-6. Answer B. JSGT 8B, FGH
The grip length is the length of the unthreaded portion of the bolt shank. Generally the grip length should be equal to the thickness of the material being bolted together. However, bolts of slightly greater grip length may be used if washers are placed under the nut or the bolthead.

8-7   AMG017

When the specific torque value for nuts is not given, where can the recommended torque value be found?

A– AC 43.13-2B.
B– Technical Standard Order.
C– AC 43.13-1B.

8-7. Answer C. JSGT 8B, AC 43.13-1B
Standard torque tables are used as a guide in tightening nuts, studs, bolts, and screws whenever specific torque values are not called out in the maintenance procedures. These tables are found in AC 43.13-1B.

8-8   AMG017

A particular component is attached to the aircraft structure by the use of an aircraft bolt and a castellated tension nut combination. If the cotter pin hole does not align within the recommended torque range, the acceptable practice is to

A– exceed the torque range.
B– tighten below the torque range.
C– change washers and try again.

8-8. Answer C. JSGT 8B, AC 43.13-1B
When cotter pin holes don't line up with a nut castellation at the proper torque, you should vary the number of washers and try again. It is not acceptable to exceed a specified torque value.

8-9　AMG017

A bolt with a single raised dash on the head is classified as an

A– AN corrosion-resistant steel bolt.
B– NAS standard aircraft bolt.
C– NAS close tolerance bolt.

8-9. Answer A. JSGT 8B, FGH

A single raised dash on the head of a bolt identifies an AN corrosion-resistant standard steel bolt.

8-10　AMG017

How is a clevis bolt used with a fork-end cable terminal secured?

A– With a shear nut tightened to a snug fit, but with no strain imposed on the fork and safetied with a cotter pin.
B– With a castle nut tightened until slight binding occurs between the fork and the fitting to which it is being attached.
C– With a shear nut and cotter pin or a thin self-locking nut tightened enough to prevent rotation of the bolt in the fork.

8-10. Answer A. JSGT 8B, FGH

Because a clevis bolt is used only in shear loads, a shear nut is used, and is tightened only to a snug fit and secured with a cotter pin. Once installed there should be no strain imposed on the fork.

8-11　AMG017

Where is an AN clevis bolt used in an airplane?

A– For tension and shear load conditions.
B– Where external tension loads are applied.
C– Only for shear load applications.

8-11. Answer C. JSGT 8B, FGH

A clevis bolt is used only where shear loads occur and never under tension loads. Clevis bolts are commonly used to attach a cable to a control horn.

8-12　AMG017

A bolt with an X inside a triangle on the head is classified as an

A– NAS standard aircraft bolt.
B– NAS close tolerance bolt.
C– AN corrosion-resistant steel bolt.

8-12. Answer B. JSGT 8B, FGH

NAS close tolerance bolts are machined more accurately than a general purpose bolt. They are used in applications where a drive fit is required, and can be identified by an X inside a triangle on the head.

8-13　AMG017

Aircraft bolts are usually manufactured with a

A– class 1 fit for the threads.
B– class 2 fit for the threads.
C– class 3 fit for the threads.

8-13. Answer C. JSGT 8B, FGH

The class of a thread indicates the tolerance allowed in manufacturing. Class 1 is a loose fit, Class 2 is a free fit, Class 3 is a medium fit, and Class 4 is a close fit. Aircraft bolts are almost always manufactured to a Class 3 fit.

8-14   AMG017

How is the locking feature of the fiber-type locknut obtained?

A– By the use of an unthreaded fiber locking insert.
B– By a fiber insert held firmly in place at the base of the load carrying section.
C– By making the threads in the fiber insert slightly smaller than those in the load carrying section.

8-14. Answer A. JSGT 8B, FGH

A fiber-type lock nut is a standard nut with a fiberlocking collar. This collar is not threaded and its inside diameter is smaller than the largest diameter of the threaded portion.

8-15   AMG017

(Refer to figure 42 on page 8-5.)
Which of the bolt head code markings shown identifies a corrosion resistant AN standard steel bolt?

A– 1.
B– 2.
C– 3.

8-15. Answer C. JSGT 8B, FGH

A corrosion-resistant AN standard steel bolt is indicated by a single dash on the head. The raised cross indicates an AN standard steel bolt while a triangle with an "X" in it indicates a close tolerance bolt.

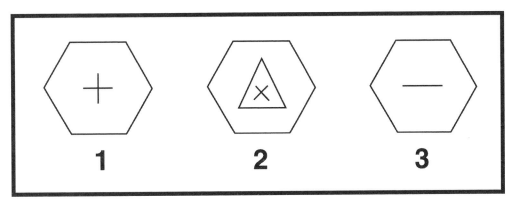

Figure 42. Aircraft Hardware.

8-16   AMG017

(Refer to figure 43 on page 8-6.)
Identify the clevis bolt illustrated.

A– 1.
B– 3.
C– 2.

8-16. Answer B. JSGT 8B, FGH

A clevis bolt resembles a screw in that the head of the bolt is either slotted to receive a common screwdriver or recessed to receive a crosspoint screwdriver. Clevis bolts are used only in shear applications, such as connecting a control cable to a control horn.

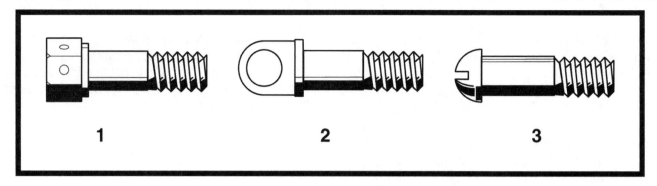

Figure 43. Aircraft Hardware.

8-17 AMG011

Which maintenance record entry best describes the action taken for a control cable showing approximately 20 percent wear on several of the individual outer wires at a fairlead?

A– Wear within acceptable limits, repair not necessary.
B– Removed and replaced the control cable and rerigged the system.
C– Cable repositioned, worn area moved away from fairlead.

8-17. Answer A. JSGT 8B, AC 43.13-1B

You should replace flexible and nonflexible cables when the individual wires in each strand appear to blend together or when the outer wires are worn 40 to 50 percent. In this example, the wear is within acceptable limits and no repair is necessary.

HAND TOOLS AND MEASURING DEVICES

SECTION A - HAND TOOLS

Section A of Chapter 9 discusses the hand tools that are typically used in the maintenance and repair of aircraft. As a technician, you must have a thorough knowledge of the the different kinds of hand tools and their correct use. There are no FAA Test questions taken from the material in this section.

SECTION B - MEASURING AND LAYOUT TOOLS

Chapter 9, Section B discusses the common measuring and layout tools used in aircraft manufacture and repair. Some of the measuring devices discussed in detail include micrometers, dial indicators, thickness gauges, telescoping gauges, and calipers.

9-1   AMG057

Which tool can be used to measure the alignment of a rotor shaft or the plane of rotation of a disk?

A– Dial indicator.
B– Shaft gauge.
C– Protractor.

9-1. Answer A. JSGT 9B, AC 43.13-1B

Dial indicators are precision measuring instruments that are used to measure end-play, and to check shaft alignments.

9-2   AMG057

Identify the correct statement.

A– An outside micrometer is limited to measuring diameters.
B– Tools used on certificated aircraft must be an approved type.
C– Dividers do not provide a reading when used as a measuring device.

9-2. Answer C. JSGT 9B, FGH

Dividers are a layout tool consisting of two legs with sharp points. They are used to scribe circles and arcs, and for transferring measurements. However, dividers have no way of indicating a measurement.

9-3   AMG057

Which tool is used to measure the clearance between a surface plate and a relatively narrow surface being checked for flatness?

A– Depth gauge.
B– Thickness gauge.
C– Dial indicator.

9-3. Answer B. JSGT 9B, FPH

A thickness gauge, often referred to as a feeler gauge, is often used to determine the clearance between a surface plate and a surface being checked for flatness. A depth gauge indicates the depth of something and a dial indicator allows you to check for shaft alignment and end play.

9-4   AMG057

Which number represents the vernier scale graduation of a micrometer?

A– .00001
B– .001
C– .0001

9-4. Answer C. JSGT 9B, FGH

A micrometer measures with a vernier scale on the barrel to the nearest ten-thousandths of an inch or .0001.

9-5   AMG057

Which tool is used to find the center of a shaft or other cylindrical work?

A–Combination set.
B–Dial indicator.
C–Micrometer caliper.

9-5. Answer A. JSGT 9B, FGH

A combination set consists of a steel scale, a stock head, a protractor head, and a centering head. The centering head is used to find the center of cylindrical pieces.

9-6   AMG057

If it is necessary to accurately measure the diameter of a hole approximately 1/4 inch in diameter, the mechanic should use a

A–telescoping gauge and determine the size of the hole by taking a micrometer reading of the adjustable end of the telescoping gauge.
B–0- to 1-inch inside micrometer and read the measurement directly from the micrometer.
C–small-hole gauge and determine the size of the hole by taking a micrometer reading of the ball end of the gauge.

9-6. Answer C. JSGT 9B, N/A

Small hole gauges are used to transfer the diameter measurement of a hole to a micrometer to determine the size. Telescoping gauges serve the same purpose, but are not generally available in sizes as small as 1/4".

9-7   AMG057

What tool is generally used to set a divider to an exact dimension?

A–Machinist scale.
B–Surface gauge.
C–Dial indicator.

9-7. Answer A. JSGT 9B, FGH

Dividers are a layout tool, not a precision measuring device. They are generally set using a machinist scale.

9-8   AMG057

What tool is generally used to calibrate a micrometer or check its accuracy?

A–Gauge block.
B–Dial indicator.
C–Machinist scale.

9-8. Answer A. JSGT 9B, N/A

Special gauge blocks are generally included when micrometers are purchased. They may be used to test the micrometer for accuracy, and to calibrate when required.

9-9   AMG057

What precision measuring tool is used for measuring crankpin and main bearing journals for out-of-round wear?

A–Dial gauge.
B–Micrometer caliper.
C–Depth gauge.

9-9. Answer B. JSGT 9B, AC 43.13-1B

In many cases, an outside micrometer is used to determine an out-of-round condition. To do this, take a measurement at one point and then rotate the micrometer 90 degrees and take a second measurement.

9-10   AMG057

The side clearances of piston rings are measured with a

A– micrometer caliper gauge.
B– thickness gauge.
C– dial gauge.

9-10. Answer B. JSGT 9B, FPH

Side clearance of piston rings is checked with a thickness gauge, or feeler gauge.

9-11   AMG057

How can the dimensional inspection of a bearing in a rocker arm be accomplished?

A– Depth gauge and micrometer.
B– Thickness gauge and push-fit arbor.
C– Telescopic gauge and micrometer.

9-11. Answer C. JSGT 9B, FPH

A telescoping gauge is used to transfer the diameter of the bearing to an outside micrometer.

9-12   AMG057

The twist of a connecting rod is checked by installing push-fit arbors in both ends, supported by parallel steel bars on a surface plate. Measurements are taken between the arbor and the parallel bar with a

A– dial gauge.
B– height gauge.
C– thickness gauge.

9-12. Answer C. JSGT 9B, FPH

To check for twisting in a connecting rod, install arbors in both ends of the connecting rod and lay it across parallel blocks on a surface plate. Then, check the clearance at the points where the arbors rest on the blocks with a thickness gauge.

9-13   AMG057

The clearance between the piston rings and the ring lands is measured with a

A– micrometer caliper.
B– thickness gauge.
C– depth gauge.

9-13. Answer B. JSGT 9B, FPH

The clearance between the piston rings and the ring lands is called side clearance and is easily checked using a thickness gauge.

9-14   AMG057

What may be used to check the stem on a poppet-type valve for stretch?

A– Dial indicator.
B– Micrometer.
C– Telescoping gauge.

9-14. Answer B. JSGT 9B, FPH

Valve stretch is indicated by a decrease in diameter near the neck of the valve stem. This is easily measured using a micrometer caliper.

9-15   AMG057

Which tool can be used to determine piston pin out-of-round wear?

A– Telescopic gauge.
B– Micrometer caliper.
C– Dial indicator.

9-15. Answer B. JSGT 9B

By taking measurements with an outside micrometer at 90 degrees to each other, an out-of-round condition may be determined.

9-16   AMG057

(Refer to figure 46 on page 9-5.)

The measurement reading on the illustrated micrometer is

A– 0.2851
B– 0.2911
C– 0.2901

9-16. Answer A. JSGT 9B, FGH

Each line on the barrel represents .025 inches. There are 11 lines showing, so you know the measurement is at least .275 (.025 x 11 = .275). Now look at the thimble. Each line represents .0010 inches. The line on the barrel is between the 10 and 11, which indicates the measurement is at least .010 inches longer, or .285 (.275 + .01 = .285). The number on the top of the barrel represents .0001 (ten-thousandth) inches. To identify the number of ten-thousandths, look for the line on the thimble that is aligned with a horizontal line on the barrel. In this case the line indicating 1 on the barrel is aligned with the 15 on the thimble. This means that .001 must be added to the measurement. The total measurement is .2851 (.285 + .0001 = .2851).

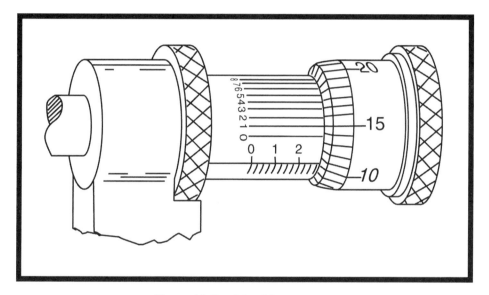

Figure 46. Precision Measurement.

9-17   AMG057

(Refer to figure 47 on page 9-6.)

What is the measurement reading on the venier caliper scale?

A– 1.411 inches.
B– 1.436 inches.
C– 1.700 inches.

9-17. Answer B. JSGT 9B, FGH

On a venier caliper inches, tenths of inches, and divisions of 25 thousands of an inch are taken from the top scale. The bottom scale represents thousandths of an inch. In this example, the zero mark on the bottom scale is between the 1-inch and 2-inch mark on the top scale indicating the measurement is greater than 1 inch. The zero mark is also beyond the 4 indicating the measurement is greater than 1.4 inches (1 + .4 = 1.4). The top scale also indicates that more than 25 thousandths must be added. This results in a measurement that is at least 1.425 inches (1.4 + .025 = 1.425). To determine how many thousandths greater than 25 thousandths, identify the line on the top scale that is aligned with a line on the bottom scale and read the number of thousandths off the bottom scale. An additional 11 thousandths must be added. The total measurement of 1.436 is correct (1.425 + .011 = 1.436).

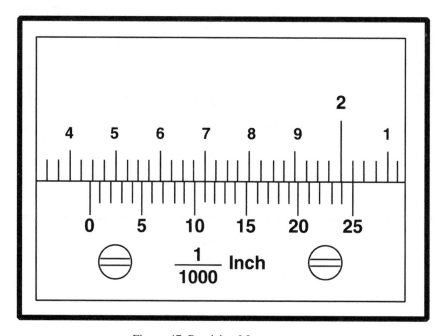

Figure 47. Precision Measurement.

9-18 AMG057

(Refer to figure 48 on page 9-7.)

What does the micrometer read?

A– .2974

B– .3004

C– .3108

9-18. Answer B. JSGT 9B, FGH

The micrometer is read as follows:

Barrel	.300
Thimble	.000
Vernier	.0004
Total	.3004

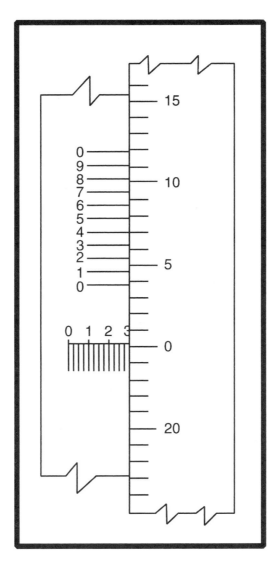

Figure 48. Precision Measurement.

9-19   AMG057

(Refer to figure 49 on page 9-8.)

The measurement reading on the micrometer is

A– .2758
B– .2702
C– .2792

9-19. Answer C. JSGT 9B, FGH

The micrometer reading is interpreted as follows:

Barrel	.275
Thimble	.004
Vernier	.0002
Total	.2792

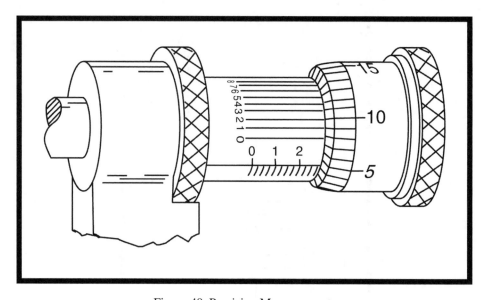

Figure 49. Precision Measurement.

FLUID LINES AND FITTINGS

SECTION A - RIGID FLUID LINES

Among other functions, rigid fluid lines and fittings supply fuel, hydraulic power, and breathing oxygen in modern aircraft. Therefore, as an aviation maintenance technician, it is important that you understand how to properly maintain and repair rigid tubing. Chapter 10, Section A presents important material on the rigid fluid lines you will most likely encounter.

10-1   AMG037

Which coupling nut should be selected for use with 1/2-inch aluminum oil lines which are to be assembled using flared tube ends and standard AN nuts, sleeves, and fittings?

A– AN-818-5.
B– AN-818-16.
C– AN-818-8.

10-1. Answer C. JSGT 10A, FGH

Since the coupling nut used must fit a 1/2-inch line, the final dash number in the AN-818 series coupling nut indicates the size tube that it will fit. The numbers are in 1/16 inch increments, so a -8 is equivalent to 8/16 or 1/2-inch (AN-818-16).

10-2   AMG037

Metal tubing fluid lines are sized by wall thickness and

A– outside diameter in 1/16 inch increments.
B– inside diameter in 1/16 inch increments.
C– outside diameter in 1/32 inch increments.

10-2. Answer A. JSGT 10A, FGH

All rigid metal fluid lines are sized by wall thickness and outside diameter in 1/16 inch increments. Inside diameter in 1/16 inch increments is incorrect because flexible fluid lines, not rigid fluid lines are sized by inside diameter. Outside diameter in 1/32 inch increments is wrong because no fluid lines are sized in 1/32 inch increments.

10-3 AMG036
From the following sequences of steps, indicate the proper order you would use to make a single flare on a piece of tubing:

1. Place the tube in the proper size hole in the flaring block.
2. Project the end of the tube slightly from the top of the flaring tool, about the thickness of a dime.
3. Slip the fitting nut and sleeve on the tube.
4. Strike the plunger several light blows with a lightweight hammer or mallet and turn the plunger one-half turn after each blow.
5. Tighten the clamp bar securely to prevent slippage.
6. Center the plunger or flaring pin over the tube.

A– 1, 3, 5, 2, 4, and 6.
B– 3, 1, 6, 2, 5, and 4.
C– 3, 2, 6, 5, 1, and 4.

10-3. Answer B. JSGT 10A, FGH
This question is geared to the impact-type single flaring tool. To prepare a tube for flaring, slip the fitting nut and sleeve on the tube (3) and place the tube in the proper size hole in the flaring tool (1). Center the plunger or flaring pin over the end of the tube (6). Then project the end of the tubing slightly from the top of the flaring tool, about the thickness of a dime (2), and tighten the clamp bar securely to prevent slippage (5). Make the flare by striking the plunger several light blows with a lightweight hammer or mallet (4). Turn the plunger a half turn after each blow and be sure it seats properly before removing the tube from the flaring tool.

10-4 AMG036
Hydraulic tubing, which is damaged in a localized area to such an extent that repair is necessary, may be repaired

A– by cutting out the damaged area and utilizing a swaged tube fitting to join the tube ends.
B– only by replacing the tubing section run (connection to connection) using the same size and material as the original.
C– by cutting out the damaged section and soldering in a replacement section of tubing.

10-4. Answer A. JSGT 10A, AC 43.13-1B
A severely damaged line is typically replaced; however, if the damage is localized, the line may be repaired by cutting out the damaged area and joining the tubing ends with swaged fittings.

10-5 AMG036
What is an advantage of a double flare on aluminum tubing?

A– Ease of construction.
B– More resistant to damage when the joint is tightened.
C– It is more resistant to the shearing effect of torque.

10-5. Answer C. JSGT 10A, FGH
A double flare should be used on soft aluminum tubing from 1/8" to 3/8" in diameter. The double flare is smoother and more concentric than a single flare, and is also more resistant to the shearing effects of torque.

10-6 AMG037
What is the color of an AN steel flared-tube fitting?

A– Black.
B– Blue.
C– Red.

10-6. Answer A. JSGT 10A, FGH
For identification purposes, all AN steel fittings are colored black, and all AN aluminum alloy fittings are colored blue.

10-7   AMG017

Which of the following statements is/are correct in reference to flare fittings?

1. AN fittings have an identifying shoulder between the end of the threads and the flare cone.
2. AC and AN fittings are considered identical except for material composition and identifying colors.
3. AN fittings are generally interchangeable with AC fittings of compatible material composition.

A– 1.
B– 1 and 3.
C– 1, 2, and 3.

10-7. Answer A. JSGT 10A, FGH

AN fittings have replaced AC fittings, but occasionally AC fittings are still found on older aircraft. The way to identify the AN fitting is by the shoulder between the ends of the flare and flare cone and by its blue dyed color. AC fittings do not have the shoulder and are dyed grey or yellow. AN and AC fittings are not interchangeable because the thread pitch is different and AN fittings have a 37 degree flare while AC fittings have a 35 degree flare.

10-8   AMG036

The primary purpose of providing suitable bends in fluid and pneumatic metal tubing runs is to

A– clear obstacles and make turns in aircraft structures.
B– provide for access within aircraft structures.
C– prevent excessive stress on the tubing.

10-8. Answer C. JSGT 10A, AC 43.13-1B

To prevent excessive stress on rigid tubing, bends must be provided to allow the tube to expand and contract with system usage, vibration, and temperature changes.

10-9   AMG036

Which statement(s) about Military Standard (MS) flareless fittings is/are correct?

1. During installation, MS flareless fittings are normally tightened by turning the nut a specified amount, rather than being torqued.
2. New MS flareless tubing/fittings should be assembled clean and dry without lubrication.
3. During installation, MS flareless fittings are normally tightened by applying a specified torque to the nut.

A– 1.
B– 1 and 2.
C– 3.

10-9. Answer A. JSGT 10A, FGH

Prior to installation of a new flareless tube assembly, the fitting must be preset. To do this, flareless fittings are tightened by turning the nut a specified amount after contact is made between the sleeve and fitting surface. For aluminum alloy tubing up to and including 1/2", tighten the nut from 1 to 1-1/6 turns. For steel tubing and aluminum alloy tubing over 1/2", tighten from 1-1/6 to 1-1/2 turns. When reattaching a flareless fitting that has been preset, you should tighten the nut by hand until it begins to bottom out. Once this occurs, tighten the nut with a wrench an additional one-sixth turn. If the connections leaks, it is permissible to tighten the nut an additional one-sixth turn.

10-10   AMG036

When flaring aluminum tubing for use with AN fittings, the flare angle should be

A– 37°.
B– 35°.
C– 45°.

10-10. Answer A. JSGT 10A, FGH

The flare angle used on aircraft fittings is 37°. Under no circumstances should you use an automotive type flaring tool since they produce a 45° flare angle. Use caution when selecting flaring tools as this difference is difficult to detect by eye.

10-11   AMG036
Scratches or nicks on the straight portion of aluminum alloy tubing may be repaired if they are no deeper than

A– 20 percent of the wall thickness.
B– 1/32 inch or 20 percent of wall thickness, whichever is less.
C– 10 percent of the wall thickness.

10-11. Answer C. JSGT 10A, FGH
Scratches or nicks in aluminum alloy tubing that are no deeper than 10 percent of the wall thickness and not in the heel of a bend may be repaired by burnishing with hand tools.

10-12   AMG036
A scratch or nick in aluminum tubing can be repaired, provided it does not

A– appear in the heel of a bend.
B– appear on the inside of a bend.
C– exceed 10 percent of the tube OD on a straight section.

10-12. Answer A. JSGT 10A, FGH
Scratches or nicks in aluminum tubing that are no deeper than 10 percent of the wall thickness and not in the heel of a bend may be repaired by burnishing with hand tools.

10-13   AMG037
Which tubings have the characteristics (high strength, abrasion resistance) necessary for use in a high-pressure (3,000 PSI) hydraulic system for operation of landing gear and flaps?

A– 2024-T or 5052-0 aluminum alloy.
B– Corrosion-resistant steel annealed or 1/4H.
C– 1100-1/2H or 3003-1/2H aluminum alloy.

10-13. Answer B. JSGT 10A, FGH
Corrosion resistant steel (stainless), either annealed or 1/4-hard, is used extensively in high-pressure hydraulic systems for the operation of landing gear, flaps, brakes, and the like.

10-14   AMG036
When installing bonded clamps to support metal tubing,

A– paint removal from tube is not recommended as it will inhibit corrosion.
B– paint clamp and tube after clamp installation to prevent corrosion.
C– remove paint or anodizing from tube at clamp location.

10-14. Answer C. JSGT 10A, FGH
Bonded clamps are used to secure metal hydraulic, fuel, and oil lines in place. Before installing these clamps you should remove any paint or anodizing from that portion of the tube the bonding clamp makes contact with. Any coatings on the line could defeat the purpose of the bonding clamp.

10-15   AMG036
In a metal tubing installation,

A– rigid straight line runs are preferable.
B– tension is undesirable because pressurization will cause it to expand and shift.
C– a tube may be pulled in line if the nut will start on the threaded coupling.

10-15. Answer B. JSGT 10A, FGH
Metal tubing should never be installed under tension. All rigid tubing should have at least one bend between the fittings to absorb vibrations, strains from vibrations, and strain from dimensional changes in the aircraft structure.

10-16   AMG036
(1) Bonded clamps are used for support when installing metal tubing.
(2) Unbonded clamps are used for support when installing wiring.
Regarding the above statements,

A– only No. 1 is true.
B– both No. 1 and No. 2 are true.
C– neither No. 1 nor No. 2 are true.

10-16. Answer B. JSGT 10A, FGH
Both statements are correct. Bonded clamps are used to secure metal hydraulic, fuel, and oil lines. Unbonded clamps are typically used to secure wiring.

10-17   AMG036
A scratch or nick in aluminum tubing can be repaired provided it does not

A– appear in the heel of a bend.
B– appear on the inside of a bend.
C– exceed 10 percent of the tube OD on a straight section.

10-17. Answer A. JSGT 10A, FGH
Scratches or nicks in aluminum tubing that are no deeper than 10 percent of the wall thickness and not in the heel of a bend may be repaired by burnishing with hand tools.

10-18   AMG036
Which statement is true regarding flattening of tubing in bends?

A– Flattening by a maximum of 20 percent of the original diameter is permissible.
B– Flattening by not more than 25 percent of the original diameter is permissible.
C– The small diameter portion in the bend cannot exceed more than 75 percent of the diameter of straight tubing.

10-18. Answer B. JSGT 10A, FGH
FGH states the small diameter of the flattened portion of the bend must not be less than 75% of the original diameter. Therefore the maximum amount of flattening allowed is 25%.

10-19   AMG036
The best tool to use when cutting aluminum tubing, or any tubing of moderately soft metal is a

A– hand operated wheel-type tubing cutter.
B– fine-tooth hacksaw.
C– circular-saw equipped with an abrasive cutting wheel.

10-19. Answer A. JSGT 10A, FGH
FGH states the preferred tool for cutting is the hand held tubing cutter. A fine-tooth hack saw may be used if a tubing cutter is unavailable, or the material is too hard for the tubing cutter.

10-20   AMG036

If a flared tube coupling nut is overtightened, where is the tube most likely to be weakened/damaged?

A– Along the entire length of the sleeve and tube interface.
B– At the edge of the sleeve and straight portion of the tube.
C– At the sleeve and flare junction.

10-20. Answer C. JSGT 10A, FGH

Overtightening a flared tube coupling will cause the sleeve to cut into the flare at their junction. This may damage the sleeve and flare or even cut the flare completely off the tube.

10-21   AMG037

Which statement is true regarding the variety of symbols utilized on the identifying color-code bands that are currently used on aircraft plumbing lines?

A– Symbols are composed of various single colors according to line content.
B– Symbols are always black against a white background regardless of line content.
C– Symbols are composed of one to three contrasting colors according to line content.

10-21. Answer B. JSGT 10A, FGH

Aircraft plumbing lines are identified using color coded tags with the name of the fluid and black on white geometric symbols. The black on white symbols are universal and allow identification worldwide.

10-22   AMG036

Which maintenance record entry best describes the action taken for a 0.125-inch deep dent in a straight section of 1/2-inch aluminum alloy tubing?

A– Dented section removed and replaced with identical new tubing flared to 45°.
B– Dent within acceptable limits, repair not necessary.
C– Dented section removed and replaced with identical new tubing flared to 37°.

10-22. Answer C. JSGT 10A, AC 43.13-1B

Dents less than 20 percent of the diameter of the tube are acceptable in straight sections. However, .125 is 25 percent of 1/2", so this dent must be repaired.

10-23   AMG036

Which of the following statements is true regarding minimum allowable bend radii for 1.5 inches OD or less aluminum alloy and steel tubing of the same size?

A– The minimum radius for steel is greater than for aluminum.
B– The minimum radius for steel is less than for aluminum.
C– The minimum radius is the same for both steel and aluminum.

10-23. Answer A. AC 43.13-1B

The minimum bend radius required for bending hard metals such as steel must be larger than that required for soft metals to prevent the tubing from kinking or flattening in the bend. Aluminum alloy tubing, being softer, is more malleable, and therefore capable of being bent around a tighter (smaller) bend radius.

10-24   AMG036

Which of the following defects are NOT acceptable for metal lines?

1. Cracked flare.
2. Seams.
3. Dents in the heel of a bend less than 20 percent of tube diameter.
4. Scratches/nicks on the inside of a bend less than 10 percent of wall thickness.
5. Dents in straight sections that are 20 percent of wall thickness.

A– 1, 2, 3, 4, and 5.
B– 1, 2, and 3.
C– 1, 2, 3, and 5.

10-24. Answer A. JSGT 10A, AC 43.13-1B

Damaged tubing must be replaced anytime cracks or seams appear in a flare or along the walls of the tubing. Tubing must also be replaced anytime there are dents, scratches, or nicks of any kind in a bend. Even though straight sections of tubing can be repaired when a dent does not exceed 20 percent of the tube's diameter (which 20 percent of the wall thickness is far under this limit) any dent in tubing is not acceptable and must be repaired or replaced.

SECTION B - FLEXIBLE FLUID LINES

Section B of Chapter 10 contains information on flexible fluid lines. Because many components in aircraft move or vibrate, flexible fluid lines are essential components in the construction of aircraft.

10-25   AMG036
A certain amount of slack must be left in a flexible hose during installation because, when under pressure, it

A– expands in length and diameter.
B– expands in length and contracts in diameter.
C– contracts in length and expands in diameter.

10-25. Answer C. JSGT 10B, FGH
When under pressure, flexible hose contracts in length and expands in diameter. Because of this, flexible hose installations should have 5 to 8 percent of the total length left as slack to allow for freedom of movement.

10-26   AMG036
The term "cold flow" is generally associated with

A– the effects of low temperature gasses or liquids flowing in the hose or tubing.
B– impressions left in natural or synthetic rubber hose material.
C– flexibility characteristics of various hose materials at low ambient temperatures.

10-26. Answer B. JSGT 10A, FGH
The term cold flow describes the deep, permanent impressions in rubber hose produced by the pressure of hose clamps or supports.

10-27   AMG036
Flexible lines must be installed with

A– enough slack to allow maximum flexing during operation
B– a slack of at least 10 to 12 percent of the length.
C– a slack of 5 to 8 percent of the length.

10-27. Answer C. JSGT 10B, FGH
Flexible fluid lines must have between 5 and 8 percent slack to allow for changes in dimension caused by pressure, vibration, and expansion and contraction of the airframe.

10-28   AMG036
The maximum distance between end fittings to which a straight hose assembly is to be connected is 50 inches. The minimum hose length to make such a connection should be

A– 54-1/2 inches.
B– 51 inches.
C– 52-1/2 inches.

10-28. Answer C. JSGT 10B, FGH
Flexible fluid lines must have between 5 and 8 percent slack to allow for changes in dimension caused by pressure, vibration, and expansion and contraction of the airframe. Therefore, you must add 2-1/2 inches to the length of the hose (50 ft. x .05 = 2.5 ft.). The minimum hose length is 52-1/2 inches.

10-29   AMG037

Flexible hose used in aircraft systems is classified in size according to the

A– outside diameter.
B– wall thickness
C– inside diameter.

10-29. Answer C. JSGT 10B, FGH

The size of flexible hose is determined by its inside diameter, whereas rigid fluid lines are determined by outside diameter.

10-30   AMG037

Which of the following hose materials are compatible with phosphate-ester base hydraulic fluids?

1. Butyl.
2. Teflon.
3. Buna-N.
4. Neoprene.

A– 1 and 2.
B– 2 and 4.
C– 1 and 3.

10-30. Answer A. JSGT 10B, FGH

Butyl and Teflon® hoses are compatible with phosphate-ester based hydraulic fluid (Skydrol®). Buna-N and Neoprene are compatible with petroleum products.

10-31   AMG037

A 3/8 inch aircraft high pressure flexible hose as compared to 3/8 inch metal tubing used in the same system will

A– have higher flow capabilities.
B– have equivalent flow characteristics.
C– usually have interchangeable applications.

10-31. Answer A. JSGT 10A, 10B

High pressure flexible hose is measured to its inside diameter, whereas tubing is measured to its outside diameter. Depending on the wall thickness of the tubing, the inside diameter of a 3/8 inch tube is somewhat smaller than the inside diameter of a 3/8 inch flexible line. Therefore, the tubing offers slightly more resistance to the flow of fluids.

CHAPTER 11

NONDESTRUCTIVE TESTING

SECTION A - VISUAL INSPECTIONS

Visual inspections are the most common and least expensive method of inspecting aircraft and their components. Chapter 11, Section A discusses the various types of visual inspections including dye penetrant, and magnetic particle inspections.

11-1   AMG019
Magnetic particle inspection is used primarily to detect

A– distortion.
B– deep subsurface flaws.
C– flaws on or near the surface.

11-1. Answer C. JSGT 11A, FGH
Because the magnetic fields generated within a material are weak, magnetic particle inspection is primarily used to detect surface flaws in ferromagnetic materials such as iron and steel. The magnetic field produced by distortions and deep subsurface flaws are typically not strong enough to attract the indicating medium.

11-2   AMG024
Liquid penetrant inspection methods may be used on which of the following?

1. porous plastics.
2. ferrous metals.
3. nonferrous metals.
4. smooth primer-sealed wood.
5. nonporous plastics.

A– 2, 3, and 4.
B– 1, 2, and 3.
C– 2, 3, and 5.

11-2. Answer C. JSGT 11A, FGH
Penetrant inspection is an effective nondestructive testing method for detecting defects that are open to the surface in materials such as ferrous metals, nonferrous metals, and nonporous materials. Even if the defects are too small for visual or other methods of detection, as long as the defect is open to the surface, dye penetrant inspection is effective. The magnetic characteristics of the material being checked have no bearing as to the effectiveness of dye penetrant inspection.

11-3   AMG019
What method of magnetic particle inspection is used most often to inspect aircraft parts for invisible cracks and other defects?

A– Residual.
B– Inductance.
C– Continuous.

11-3. Answer C. JSGT 11A, FGH
In the continuous method of magnetic particle inspection, a part is magnetized and the indicating medium applied while the magnetizing force is maintained. The continuous method is used in practically all circular and longitudinal magnetization procedures because it provides greater sensitivity than the residual method, particularly in locating subsurface defects.

11-4   AMG019

The testing medium that is generally used in magnetic particle inspection utilizes a ferromagnetic material that has

A– high permeability and low retentivity.
B– low permeability and high retentivity.
C– high permeability and high retentivity.

11-4. Answer A. JSGT 11A, FGH

In addition to being ferromagnetic, and finely divided, the testing medium used in magnetic particle inspection must conduct lines of magnetic flux easily (high permeability), and not retain a high degree of magnetism after the magnetizing current is removed (low retentivity).

11-5   AMG019

Which statement relating to the residual magnetizing inspection method is true?

A– Subsurface discontinuities are made readily apparent.
B– It is used in practically all circular and longitudinal magnetizing procedures.
C– It may be used only with steels which have been heat treated for stressed applications.

11-5. Answer C. JSGT 11A, FGH

The residual inspection procedure is used only with steels which have been heat treated for stressed applications. The continuous magnetizing inspection method is used on almost all circular and longitudinal magnetizing procedures. In either case, subsurface discontinuities are not made apparent using either method.

11-6   AMG019

What two types of indicating mediums are available for magnetic particle inspection?

A– Wet and dry process materials.
B– High retentivity and low permeability material.
C– Iron and ferric oxides.

11-6. Answer A. JSGT 11A, FGH

Magnetic particle inspection media are either wet or dry process materials. The dry process uses iron oxide powder poured or sprayed on the part being tested. The wet process requires mixing the oxide powder with kerosene or some other light oil. The part being inspected is then immersed in the oxide-oil bath. High retentivity and low permeability material is incorrect because the media used in magnetic particle inspection must have a low retentivity and a high permeability.

11-7   AMG019

Which of the following materials may be inspected using the magnetic particle inspection method?

1. Magnesium alloys.
2. Aluminum alloys.
3. Iron alloys.
4. Copper alloys.
5. Zinc alloys.

A– 1, 2, and 3.
B– 1, 2, 4, and 5.
C– 3.

11-7. Answer C. JSGT 11A, FGH

Magnetic particle inspection is limited to use on ferromagnetic materials such as iron and steel. Alloys containing primarily magnesium or aluminum are non-magnetic and, therefore, cannot be inspected using magnetic particle inspection.

11-8   AMG019

One way a part may be demagnetized after magnetic particle inspection is by

A–subjecting the part to high voltage, low amperage AC.
B–slowly moving the part out of an AC magnetic field of sufficient strength.
C–slowly moving the part into an AC magnetic field of sufficient strength.

11-8. Answer B. JSGT 11A, FGH

If a part is subjected to an AC magnetizing force and then slowly removed from the force while the current is still flowing, the domains within the material become disorganized and magnetization decreases.

11-9   AMG019

Which type crack can be detected by magnetic particle inspection using either circular or longitudinal magnetization?

A–45°.
B–Longitudinal.
C–Transverse.

11-9. Answer A. JSGT 11A, FGH

In order to locate a defect using magnetic particle inspection, it is essential that the lines of flux pass approximately perpendicular to the defect. Circular magnetization locates defects running approximately parallel to the axis of the part, while longitudinal magnetization locates defects running approximately 90° to the axis. If a defect is 45° to the axis of the part, either method should detect it.

11-10   AMG019

Which of the following methods may be suitable to use to detect cracks open to the surface in aluminum forgings and castings?

1. Dye penetrant inspection.
2. Magnetic particle inspection.
3. Metallic ring (coin tap) inspection.
4. Eddy current inspection.
5. Ultrasonic inspection.
6. Visual inspection.

A–1, 4, 5, and 6.
B–1, 2, 4, 5, and 6.
C–1, 2, 3, 4, 5, and 6.

11-10. Answer A. JSGT 11A, 11-B, FGH

If a crack is open to the surface on an aluminum forging, the crack can be detected through the use of dye penetrant, eddy current, ultrasonic, or visual inspections. Magnetic particle inspection is incorrect because it can only be used on ferrous metals and aluminum is not a ferrous metal. In addition, the metallic ring, or coin tap inspection is used primarily on composite structures.

11-11   AMG024

To detect a minute crack using dye penetrant inspection usually requires

A–that the developer be applied to a flat surface.
B–a longer-than-normal penetrating time.
C–the surface to be highly polished.

11-11. Answer B. JSGT 11A, FGH

Dye penetrant inspection is based on capillary attraction. In other words, dye is drawn into a crack or defect until developer is applied making the defect visible. A good rule to remember when using dye penetrant is that small defects require a longer penetrating time.

11-12   AMG019

When checking an item with the magnetic particle inspection method, circular and longitudinal magnetization should be used to

A– reveal all possible defects.
B– evenly magnetize the entire part.
C– ensure uniform current flow.

11-12. Answer A. JSGT 11A, FGH

Circular magnetization reveals defects running approximately parallel to the axis of the part, while longitudinal magnetization reveals defects that are approximately 90° to the axis. For this reason, it is best to use both methods to reveal all possible defects.

11-13   AMG019

In magnetic particle inspection, a flaw that is perpendicular to the magnetic field flux lines generally causes

A– a large disruption in the magnetic field.
B– a minimal disruption in the magnetic field.
C– no disruption in the magnetic field.

11-13. Answer A. JSGT 11A, FGH

When performing a magnetic particle inspection, defects that are perpendicular to the lines of flux are more easily detected because the flaw produces a large disruption in the magnetic field. A minimal disruption in the magnetic field is incorrect because defects that are parallel, not perpendicular, to the flux lines cause minimal disruptions in the magnetic field. No disruption in the magnetic field is wrong because, if a flaw exists perpendicular to the magnetic field, a disruption will exist.

11-14   AMG024

If dye penetrant inspection indications are not sharp and clear, the most probable cause is that the part

A– was not correctly degaussed before the developer was applied.
B– has no appreciable damage.
C– was not thoroughly washed before the developer was applied.

11-14. Answer C. JSGT 11A, FGH

It is very important to remove all excess penetrant from the surface of a part at the completion of the dwell time. Any remaining penetrant on the part may result in indications that are not clear, or are completely masked by the background indication.

11-15   AMG019

(1) An aircraft part may be demagnetized by subjecting it to a magnetizing force from alternating current that is gradually reduced in strength.
(2) An aircraft part may be demagnetized by subjecting it to a magnetizing force from direct current that is alternately reversed in direction and gradually reduced in strength.
Regarding the above statements,

A– both No. 1 and No. 2 are true.
B– only No. 1 is true.
C– only No. 2 is true.

11-15. Answer A. JSGT 11A, FGH

By introducing a part to a decreasing, alternating magnetic field, the magnetic poles constantly change direction as their strength decreases. This is continued until the part is no longer magnetized. Reversing the polarity of direct current makes it functionally the same as alternating current.

11-16   AMG019
The pattern for an inclusion is a magnetic particle buildup forming

A– a fernlike pattern.
B– a single line.
C– parallel lines.

11-16. Answer C. JSGT 11A, FGH
Inclusions are nonmetallic materials, such as slag, that have been trapped in a material. Large inclusions near the surface or open to the surface usually appear elongated or as parallel lines.

11-17   AMG024
A part which is being prepared for dye penetrant inspection should be cleaned with

A– a volatile petroleum-base solvent.
B– the penetrant developer.
C– water-base solvents only.

11-17. Answer A. JSGT 11A, FGH
The success of a penetrant inspection depends a great deal on the cleanliness of the part being tested. Pre-cleaning with vapor degreaser or a volatile petroleum base solvent is a necessary step. Many penetrant kits provide an aerosol can of cleaning solvent to be used before and after testing. Water-base solvents are typically not used for cleaning parts since they are not that effective on grease.

11-18   AMG019
Under magnetic particle inspection, a part will be identified as having a fatigue crack under which condition?

A– The discontinuity pattern is straight.
B– The discontinuity is found in a nonstressed area of the part.
C– The discontinuity is found in a highly stressed area of the part.

11-18. Answer C. JSGT 11A, FGH
Fatigue cracks are found in the highly stressed areas of a part, or where a stress concentration exists. The discontinuity pattern is straight is incorrect because, fatigue cracks offer clear, sharp patterns which are generally uniform and jagged in appearance.

11-19   AMG024
In performing a dye penetrant inspection, the developer

A– seeps into a surface crack to indicate the presence of a defect.
B– acts as a blotter to produce a visible indication.
C– thoroughly cleans the surface prior to inspection.

11-19. Answer B. JSGT 11A, FGH
The principle action of the developer is to "blot" or draw the penetrant out of a defect making the defect visible. It seeps into a surface crack to indicate the presence of a defect is incorrect because it is the penetrant, not the developer, that seeps into a surface crack to indicate the presence of a defect. It thoroughly cleans the surface prior to inspection is wrong because surface cleaning is left to a volatile petroleum-based solvent, not the developer.

11-20   AMG019
What defects will be detected by magnetizing a part using continuous longitudinal magnetization with a cable?

A– Defects perpendicular to the long axis of the part.
B– Defects parallel to the long axis of the part.
C– Defects parallel to the concentric circles of magnetic force within the part.

11-20. Answer A. JSGT 11A, FGH
In longitudinal magnetization, a magnetic field is produced that is parallel to the axis of the part. This type of magnetization detects faults that are perpendicular to the axis of the part. Defects parallel to the long axis of the part and to the concentric circles of magnetic force within the part are wrong because the lines of flux generated must intersect a defect at nearly a 90 degree angle.

11-21   AMG019
Circular magnetization of a part can be used to detect which defects?

A– Defects parallel to the long axis of the part.
B– Defects perpendicular to the long axis of the part.
C– Defects perpendicular to the concentric circles of magnetic force within the part.

11-21. Answer A. JSGT 11A, FGH
Circular magnetization is obtained by passing the current through the part, and indicates defects that are parallel to the axis of the part. Defects perpendicular to the long axis of the part and to the concentric circles of magnetic force within the part are wrong because the magnetic flux lines must intersect a defect at nearly a 90 degree angle.

11-22   AMG024
(1) In nondestructive testing, a discontinuity may be defined as an interruption in the normal physical structure or configuration of a part.
(2) A discontinuity may or may not affect the usefulness of a part.
Regarding the above statements,

A– only No. 1 is true.
B– only No. 2 is true.
C– both No. 1 and No. 2 are true.

11-22. Answer C. JSGT 11A, FGH
A discontinuity may be defined as an interruption in the normal physical structure or configuration of a part such as a crack, inclusion, seam, or change in cross-sectional area. A crack or inclusion would affect the usefulness of the part. However, a seam or change in the cross-sectional area would not effect the usefulness of the part.

11-23   AMG024
Which of the following is a main determinant of the dwell time to use when conducting a dye or fluorescent penetrant inspection?

A– The size and shape of the discontinuities being looked for.
B– The size and shape of the part being inspected.
C– The type and/or density of the part material.

11-23. Answer A. JSGT 11A, FGH
To find cracks open to the surface using a dye penetrant inspection requires the penetrant be drawn into the crack by capillary action. Small cracks require longer dwell times for the penetrant to be drawn into the crack.

11-24   AMG098

Holes and a few projecting globules are found in a weld. What action should be taken?

A– Thoroughly clean the area and reweld over the first bead to fill gaps and obtain uniform strength.
B– Remove all the old weld and reweld the joint.
C– Grind the rough surface smooth and reweld the joint.

11-24. Answer B. JSGT 11A, AC 43.13-1B
When checking the condition of a completed weld, there should be no signs of blowholes, porosity or projecting globules. If there is, the weld should be completely removed and the joint rewelded.

11-25   AMG098

Which condition indicates a part has cooled too quickly after being welded?

A– Cracking adjacent to the weld.
B– Discoloration of the base metal.
C– Gas pockets, porosity, and slag inclusions.

11-25. Answer A. JSGT 11A, FGH
Welding causes stresses to be set up in the material adjacent to the weld. In large parts, and in certain materials, these stresses can cause cracking if allowed to cool too rapidly.

11-26   AMG098

Select a characteristic of a good gas weld.

A– The depth of penetration shall be sufficient to ensure fusion of the filler rod.
B– The height of the weld bead should be 1/8 inch above the base metal.
C– The weld should taper off smoothly into the base metal.

11-26. Answer C. JSGT 11A, FGH
A good bead with proper penetration and good fusion is straight across the piece and has a smooth crowned surface that tapers off evenly into the base metal. The bead height should be 1/4 to 1/2 the thickness of the base metal.

11-27   AMG098

One characteristic of a good weld is that no oxide should be formed on the base metal at a distance from the weld of more than

A– 1/2 inch.
B– 1 inch.
C– 1/4 inch.

11-27. Answer A. JSGT 11A, AC 43.13-1B
On a good weld, no oxide should be on the base metal more than 1/2 inch from the weld.

11-28   AMG098

On a fillet weld, the penetration requirement includes what percentage(s) of the base metal thickness?

A– 100 percent.
B– 25 to 50 percent.
C– 60 to 80 percent.

11-28. Answer B. JSGT 11A, FGH
A fillet weld is made along the joint of two metals that meet at a 90 degree angle. A fillet weld must penetrate 25 to 50 percent of the thickness of the base metal.

11-29   AMG098
(Refer to figure 44 on page 11-8.)
Identify the weld caused by an excessive amount of acetylene.

A– 4.
B– 1.
C– 3.

11-29. Answer C. JSGT 11A, FGH
When an excessive amount of acetylene is used, the puddle has a tendency to boil. This often leaves slight bumps along the center, and craters at the finish of the weld. Cross-checks are apparent if the body of the weld is sound. If the weld were crosssectioned, pockets and porosity would be visible. This condition is illustrated in selection 3 is correct.

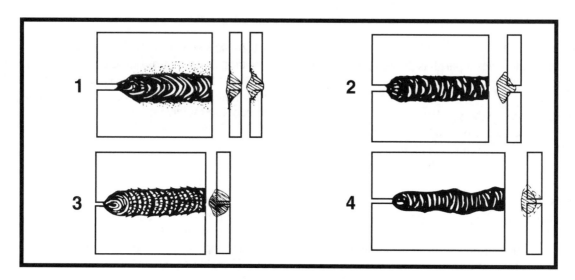

Figure 44. Welds.

11-30   AMG098
(Refer to figure 44 on page 11-8.)
Select the illustration which depicts a cold weld.

A– 3.
B– 2.
C– 4.

11-30. Answer B. JSGT 11A, FGH
A weld that is done with insufficient heat (a cold weld) appears rough and irregular and its edges will not feather into the base metal. This is illustrated in selection 2.

11-31   AMG098
(Refer to figure 45 on page 11-9.)
What type weld is shown at A?

A– Fillet.
B– Butt.
C– Lap.

11-31. Answer B. JSGT 11A, FGH
Area A illustrates a butt weld. This type of weld is made by placing two pieces of material edge to edge, so that there is no overlap.

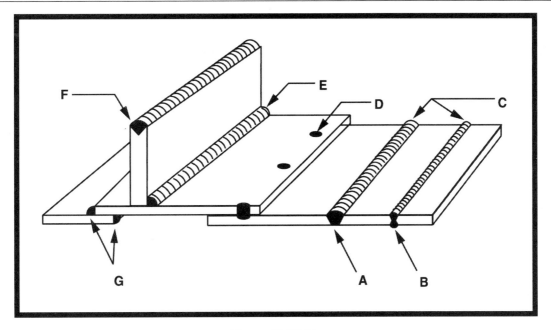

Figure 45. Welds.

11-32   AMG098
(Refer to figure 45 on page 11-9.)
What type weld is shown at B?

A– Butt.
B– Double butt.
C– Fillet.

11-33   AMG098
(Refer to figure 45 on page 11-9.)
What type of weld is shown at G?

A– Lap.
B– Butt.
C– Joint.

11-34   AMG098
Why should an aircraft maintenance technician be familiar with weld nomenclature?

A– So that accurate visual (pictorial) comparisons can be made.
B– In order to gain familiarity with the welding technique, filler material, and temperature range used.
C– In order to compare welds with written (non-pictorial) description standards.

11-32. Answer B. JSGT 11A, FGH
Area B illustrates a double butt weld. On this type of weld a bead is applied on both sides of the joint. A single butt weld is illustrated in area A.

11-33. Answer A. JSGT 11A, FAH
Area G illustrates a lap weld. A lap weld is used when two pieces of material are overlapped and welded at the joint.

11-34. Answer A. JSGT 11A, AC 43.13-1B
An aircraft maintenance technician must be familiar with basic weld nomenclature in order to determine the airworthiness of welds when performing visual inspections on aircraft parts. If the technician is certified to perform weld repairs on aircraft parts, then they must be familiar with welding techniques including the types of filler materials and the proper heat ranges for different types of base metals.

SECTION B - ELECTRONIC INSPECTIONS

Section B of Chapter 11 discusses the various types of electronic inspections currently used in aircraft maintenance. These methods include eddy current, ultrasonic, radiological, and pulse-echo inspections.

11-35   AMG024

Which of these nondestructive testing methods is suitable for the inspection of most metals, plastics, and ceramics for surface and subsurface defects?

A–Eddy current inspection.
B–Magnetic particle inspection.
C–Ultrasonic inspection.

11-35. Answer C. JSGT 11B, FGH

Only ultrasonic inspection meets all of the criteria listed in the question. Eddy current inspection is eliminated because it requires a material that conducts electricity. Magnetic particle inspection requires a ferromagnetic material and, therefore, will not work on plastic or ceramics.

11-36   AMG019

What nondestructive testing method requires little or no part preparation, is used to detect surface or near-surface defects in most metals, and may also be used to separate metals or alloys and their heat-treat conditions?

A–Eddy current inspection.
B–Ultrasonic inspection.
C–Magnetic particle inspection.

11-36. Answer A. JSGT 11B, FGH

Eddy current inspection meets all the criteria of the question. Neither ultrasonic inspection nor magnetic particle inspection can distinguish between different alloys or heat-treat conditions.

11-37   AMG024

How many of these factors are considered essential knowledge for x-ray exposure?

1. Processing of the film.
2. Material thickness and density.
3. Exposure distance and angle.
4. Film characteristics.

A–One.
B–Three.
C–Four.

11-37. Answer B. JSGT 11B, FGH

The factors affecting radiographic (x-ray) exposure include:

(a) material thickness and density
(b) shape and size of the object
(c) type of defect to be detected
(d) characteristics of x-ray machine used
(e) the exposure distance
(f) the exposure angle
(g) film characteristics
(h) types of intensifying screen, if used

Three of these factors are listed in the question. Although film processing is an important procedure to ensure a valid inspection, it does not affect exposure.

11-38   AMG024

A mechanic has completed a bonded honeycomb repair using the potted compound repair technique. What nondestructive testing method is used to determine the soundness of the repair after the repair has cured?

A– Eddy current test.
B– Metallic ring test.
C– Ultrasonic test.

11-38. Answer B. JSGT 11B, FAH

The metallic ring test is the simplest way to inspect honeycomb structures for delamination. When a coin (25-cent piece) is lightly bounced against a solid structure, a clear metallic ring is heard. If delamination is present a dull thud is heard. Eddy current is incorrect because it requires the material being tested to accept an electric charge and composites are not conductive. Ultrasonic testing is incorrect because ultrasound works only on solid structures and bonded honeycomb is not a solid structure.

CLEANING AND CORROSION

SECTION A - AIRCRAFT CLEANING

Since most aircraft contain some metal, they require constant inspection and cleaning to minimize the destructive effects of corrosion. However, to prevent damaging an aircraft, specific procedures must be adhered to when cleaning various aircraft components. Section A of Chapter 12 looks at procedures and compounds used to clean aircraft.

12-1   AMG009

A primary reason why ordinary or otherwise nonapproved cleaning compounds should not be used when washing aircraft is because their use can result in

A– hydrogen embrittlement in metal structures.
B– hydrogen embrittlement in nonmetallic materials.
C– a general inability to remove compound residues.

12-1. Answer A. JSGT 12A, AC 43-4A

Washing an aircraft with nonapproved cleaning compounds can cause a chemical reaction known as hydrogen embrittlement. This results when a chemical reaction produces hydrogen gas that is absorbed by the base metal. This process causes the metal to become more brittle, allowing cracks and stress corrosion to occur. The most vulnerable metals are high-strength steels, titanium alloys and aluminum alloys.

12-2   AMG009

How may magnesium engine parts be cleaned?

A– Soak in a 20 percent caustic soda solution.
B– Spray with MEK (methyl ethyl ketone).
C– Wash with a commercial solvent, decarbonize, and scrape or grit blast.

12-2. Answer C. JSGT 12A, FPH

Magnesium engine parts may be cleaned using commercial solvents, scrapers, and grit blasting. However, extreme care must be taken to make certain that the chemical cleaner used is safe for use on magnesium.

12-3   AMG009

Select the solvent recommended for wipe down of cleaned surfaces just before painting.

A– Aliphatic naphtha.
B– Dry-cleaning solvent.
C– Aromatic naphtha.

12-3. Answer A. JSGT 12A, FPH

Aliphatic naphtha is the solvent recommended for wipe down on cleaned surfaces just before painting. In addition to metals, aliphatic naphtha is also safe to use on acrylic plastics and rubber.

12-4   AMG009
Which of the following are acceptable to use when utilizing chemical cleaning and/or depainting/stripping agents on aircraft?

1. Synthetic fiber wiping cloths when using a flammable agent.
2. Cotton fiber wiping cloths when using a flammable agent.
3. Atomizing spray equipment.

A–2 and 3.
B–2.
C–1.

12-4. Answer B. JSGT 12A, AC 43-205
Do not use synthetic wiping cloths with flammable agents. Wiping cloths made of natural materials such as cotton should be used. Chemical agents should not be applied with atomizing spray equipment. This is not only hazardous, but violates environmental regulations in most areas.

12-5   AMG009
Select the solvent used to clean acrylics and rubber.

A–Aliphatic naphtha.
B–Methyl ethyl ketone.
C–Aromatic naphtha.

12-5. Answer A. JSGT 12A, FGH
Aliphatic naphtha, which is typically used to wipe down surfaces prior to painting, is also used to clean acrylics and rubber. Methyl ethyl ketone or aromatic naphtha will harm acrylics and rubber.

12-6   AMG009
Fayed surfaces cause concern in chemical cleaning because of the danger of

A–forming passive oxides.
B–entrapping corrosive materials.
C–corrosion by imbedded iron oxide.

12-6. Answer B. JSGT 12A, FGH
Faying surfaces exist at joints that are fitted or joined tightly, as in a riveted seam. When using chemical cleaners around fayed surfaces, corrosive chemical residue can get into the small openings of the fayed surface. If possible, cover fayed surfaces to prevent corrosive chemicals from entering. Remove or neutralize all chemicals to prevent any trapped residue from causing corrosion.

12-7   AMG009
Caustic cleaning products used on aluminum structures have the effect of producing

A–passive oxidation.
B–improved corrosion resistance.
C–corrosion.

12-7. Answer C. JSGT 12A, FGH
The term caustic means having the ability to burn, corrode, or eat away. By definition these are cleaners that can produce corrosion.

12-8   AMG009

Which of the following is an acceptable first step procedure to help prevent scratching when cleaning a transparent plastic surface?

A–Gently wipe the surface with a clean, dry, soft cloth.
B–Flush the surface with clean water.
C–Gently wipe the surface with a clean, soft cloth moistened with de-mineralized or distilled water.

12-8. Answer B. JSGT 12A, FGH

Before applying soap and water to plastic surfaces, flush the plastic with fresh water to dissolve salt deposits and wash away dust particles. This helps prevent scratching when the surface is washed.

12-9   AMG009

What should be done to prevent rapid deterioration when oil or grease come in contact with a tire?

A–Wipe the tire thoroughly with a dry cloth, and then rinse with clean water.
B–Wipe the tire with a dry cloth followed by a wash down and rinse with soap and water.
C–Wipe the tire with a cloth dampened with aromatic naphtha and then wipe dry with a clean cloth.

12-9. Answer B. JSGT 12A, FGH

Lubricating oil causes deterioration of rubber tires and should be removed as soon as it is detected. To do this, wipe the oil from the tire with a dry cloth and wash the tire with soap and water.

SECTION B - TYPES OF CORROSION

Aircraft are subject to attack by a number of different kinds of corrosion. In fact, as aircraft age, the prevention of corrosion becomes a primary concern. Section B of Chapter 12 discusses the different types of corrosion found on aircraft.

12-10   AMG012

What type of corrosion attacks grain boundaries of aluminum alloys which are improperly or inadequately heat treated?

A– Filiform.
B– Intergranular.
C– Fretting.

12-10. Answer B. JSGT 12B, FGH

Intergranular corrosion is a type of dissimilar metal corrosion along the grain boundaries of aluminum that has been improperly heat treated.

12-11   AMG012

Fretting corrosion is most likely to occur

A– when two surfaces fit tightly together but can move relative to one another.
B– only when two dissimilar metals are in contact.
C– when two surfaces fit loosely together and can move relative to one another.

12-11. Answer A. JSGT 12B, FGH

Fretting corrosion occurs when two surfaces are held tightly together, but are still subject to a small amount of relative movement. When the movement between the parts is small, the debris created by the rubbing action remains between the surfaces and acts as an abrasive to cause further erosion.

12-12   AMG012

The rust or corrosion that occurs with most metals is the result of

A– a tendency for them to return to their natural state.
B– blocking the flow of electrons in homogenous metals, or between dissimilar metals.
C– electron flow in or between metals from cathodic to anodic areas.

12-12. Answer A. JSGT 12B, AC 43-4A

Corrosion occurs because of the tendency of metals to return to their natural state. Noble metals such as gold and platinum do not corrode because they are chemically uncombined in their natural state.

12-13   AMG012

Which of the listed conditions is NOT one of the requirements for corrosion to occur?

A– The presence of an electrolyte.
B– Electrical contact between an anodic area and cathodic area.
C– The presence of a passive oxide film.

12-13. Answer C. JSGT 12B, AC 43-4A

Four conditions must exist before corrosion can occur: (1) Presence of a metal that will corrode (anode), (2) Presence of a dissimilar metal (cathode), (3) Presence of an electrolyte, and (4) Electrical contact between anode and cathode. The presence of a passive oxide film is not necessary for corrosion to occur.

12-14   AMG012
The lifting or flaking of the metal at the surface due to delamination of grain boundaries caused by the pressure of corrosion residual product buildup is called

A– brinelling.
B– granulation.
C– exfoliation.

12-14. Answer C. JSGT 12B, FGH
The pressure of corrosion residual product buildup can cause delamination of grain boundaries resulting in lifting or flaking, and is called exfoliation.

12-15   AMG012
Which of the following may not be detectable even by careful visual inspection of the surface of aluminum alloy parts or structures?

A– Filiform corrosion.
B– Intergranular corrosion.
C– Uniform etch corrosion.

12-15. Answer B. JSGT 12B, FGH
Intergranular corrosion occurs within the metal rather than on the surface. It is difficult to detect without the use of ultrasonic or eddy-current equipment.

12-16   AMG012
A primary cause of intergranular corrosion is

A– improper heat treatment.
B– dissimilar metal contact.
C– improper application of primer.

12-16. Answer A. JSGT 12B, FGH
The primary cause of intergranular corrosion is a lack of uniformity in an alloy's structure, which is usually a result of improper heat treatment. The corrosion is an attack along the grain boundaries of the dissimilar metals and may show no surface indications. However, very severe intergranular corrosion may cause the surface to flake or exfoliate.

12-17   AMG012
Corrosion caused by galvanic action is the result of

A– excessive anodization.
B– contact between two unlike metals.
C– excessive etching.

12-17. Answer B. JSGT 12B, FGH
Contact between dissimilar metals in the presence of moisture creates an electrolytic action. This is usually referred to as galvanic, electrolytic, or dissimilar metal corrosion.

12-18   AMG012
Which of these materials is the most anodic?

A– Cadmium.
B– 7075-T6 aluminum alloy.
C– Magnesium.

12-18. Answer C. JSGT 12B, FGH
Magnesium is the most anodic metal on the Electrochemical Series of metals chart. In other words, magnesium corrodes very easily.

12-19   AMG012
Which of these materials is the most cathodic?

A– Zinc.
B– 2024 aluminum alloy.
C– Stainless steel.

12-19. Answer C. JSGT 12B, AC 43-4A
Zinc and aluminum are higher than stainless steel on the Electrochemical Series of metals chart, therefore stainless steel is more cathodic (less anodic) than the other answer choices.

12-20   AMG012
Galvanic corrosion is likely to be most rapid and severe when

A– the surface area of the cathodic metal is smaller than surface area of the anodic metal.
B– the surface areas of the anodic and cathodic metals are approximately the same.
C– the surface area of the anodic metal is smaller than the surface area of the cathodic metal.

12-20. Answer C. JSGT 12B, AC 43-4A
Galvanic corrosion occurs when two dissimilar metals make electrical contact in the presence of an electrolyte. If the surface area of the anode (the corroding metal) is smaller than the cathode, corrosion will be rapid and severe.

12-21   AMG012
One way of obtaining increased resistance to stress corrosion cracking is by

A– relieving compressive stresses (via heat treatment) on the metal surface.
B– creating compressive stresses (via shot peening) on the metal surface.
C– producing nonuniform deformation while cold working during the manufacturing process.

12-21. Answer B. JSGT 12B, AC 43.13-1B
Shot peening metal surfaces increases their resistance to stress-corrosion cracking, fatigue failures, and hydrogen embrittlement by creating compressive stresses on the surface. Stress corrosion cracking cannot occur in an area of compressive stress because compressive stresses effectively overcome the surface tensile stresses that cause stress corrosion.

12-22   AMG012
(1) In the corrosion process, it is the cathodic area or dissimilar cathodic material that corrodes.
(2) In the Galvanic or Electro-Chemical Series for metals, the most anodic metals are those that will give up electrons most easily.
Regarding the above statements,

A– only No. 1 is true.
B– only No. 2 is true.
C– both No. 1 and No. 2 are true.

12-22. Answer B. JSGT 12B, AC 43-4A, FGH
Only statement number 2 is true. In the galvanic series of metals, the anodic metals give up electrons most easily. Therefore, the anode metal corrodes.

12-23   AMG012
Spilled mercury on aluminum

A– greatly increases susceptibility to hydrogen embrittlement.
B– may cause impaired corrosion resistance if left in prolonged contact.
C– causes rapid and severe corrosion that is very difficult to control.

12-23. Answer C. JSGT 12B, AC 43-4A
Mercury attacks aluminum through a process called amalgamation. It causes pitting and intergranular corrosion and is very difficult to control.

12-24   AMG012

Of the following, when and/or where is galvanic corrosion most likely to occur?

A– When an electrolyte (water) covers the surface of an aluminum skin, seeps into the cracks between lap joints, and oxygen is excluded from the area.

B– At the interface of a steel fastener and aluminum alloy inspection plate in the presence of an electrolyte.

C– In an area of unprotected metal exposed to an atmosphere containing battery fumes, exhaust gases, or industrial contaminants.

12-24. Answer B. JSGT 12B, FGH

Galvanic corrosion, also called dissimilar metal corrosion, occurs when two dissimilar metals come into electrical contact in the presence of an electrolyte.

SECTION C - CORROSION DETECTION

Section C of Chapter 12 presents methods of detecting corrosion once it has become established in an aircraft structure. In addition, several of the common areas where corrosion typically occurs are discussed. There are no FAA Test questions taken from the information presented in this section.

SECTION D - TREATMENT OF CORROSION

Once corrosion is found on an aircraft structure it must be removed. Furthermore, the corroded area must be protected from further attack. Chapter 12 Section D discusses the various methods of corrosion removal and control used in aviation.

12-25   AMG012

When an anodized surface coating is damaged in service, it can be partially restored by

A– use of a metal polish.
B– chemical surface treatment.
C– a suitable mild cleaner.

12-25. Answer B. JSGT 12D, FGH

Anodizing is a common surface treatment of aluminum alloys. It is an electrolytic process requiring special equipment and is not generally done in the repair shop. When this coating is damaged in service, it can only be partially restored by chemical surface treatment.

12-26   AMG012

Which of the following are the desired effects of using Alodine on aluminum alloy?

1. A slightly rough surface.
2. Relieved surface stresses.
3. A smooth painting surface.
4. Increased corrosion resistance.

A– 3 and 4.
B– 1, 2, and 4.
C– 1 and 4.

12-26. Answer C. JSGT 12D, FGH

Alodizing is a simple chemical treatment for all aluminum alloys to increase their corrosion resistance and to improve paint-bonding qualities.

12-27   AMG012

A nonelectrolytic chemical treatment for aluminum alloys to increase corrosion resistance and paint-bonding qualities is called

A– anodizing.
B– alodizing.
C– dichromating.

12-27. Answer B. JSGT 12D, FGH

Alodizing is a chemical treatment for all aluminum alloys to increase their corrosion resistance and improve their paint-bonding qualities.

12-28   AMG012

Corrosion should be removed from magnesium parts with a

A– silicon carbide brush.
B– carborundum abrasive.
C– stiff, hog-bristle brush.

12-28. Answer C. JSGT 12D, FGH

Magnesium is a highly-active metal, and contact with most other metals will result in dissimilar metal corrosion. To avoid the danger of residue from metal abrasive or wire brushes, a stiff hog-bristle brush is typically used to remove corrosion from magnesium.

12-29   AMG012

Why is it important not to rotate the crankshaft after the corrosion preventive mixture has been put into the cylinders on engines prepared for storage?

A–Fuel may be drawn into one or more cylinders and dilute or wash off the corrosion preventive mixture.
B–The seal of corrosion preventive mixture will be broken.
C–Engine damage can occur from hydraulic lock.

12-29. Answer B. JSGT 12D, FGH

When preparing an engine for long term storage, a corrosion preventive mixture is sprayed into the cylinders to form a seal against oxidation. After this mixture is applied, the propeller shaft should not be moved. Any movement causes the pistons to move which breaks the seal of the corrosion preventive mixture.

12-30   AMG012

The interior surface of sealed structural steel tubing would be best protected against corrosion by which of the following?

A–Charging the tubing with dry nitrogen prior to sealing.
B–Evacuating moisture from the tubing before sealing.
C–A coating of linseed oil.

12-30. Answer C. AC 43.13-1B

A small amount of water entrapped in a tube can corrode through the tubing in a very short time. To protect tubing, hot linseed oil is used to coat the interior surfaces.

12-31   AMG012

For which of the following reasons would a water break test be conducted?

A–To make certain that a newly alodized aluminum surface is sufficiently coated.
B–To make certain that a bare metal surface is thoroughly clean.
C–To make certain that an anodizing coating has been sufficiently removed before an electrical bonding connection can be made.

12-31. Answer B. JSGT 12D, FGH

When water is poured over a surface, contaminants such as oil or grease will cause water to bead. Absence of beading indicates the part is clean.

GROUND HANDLING AND SERVICING

SECTION A - SHOP SAFETY

Section A of Chapter 13 discusses safety in the shop. Included is information regarding fire safety, the importance of protective clothing, including safety goggles, and the safety precautions that should be taken when jacking or hoisting an aircraft. While shop safety is critical, no FAA Test questions are taken from this subject area.

SECTION B - FLIGHT LINE SAFETY

Chapter 13, Section B discusses the hazards of working around aircraft on the flight line. Flight line safety is especially critical because of the risks ground personnel are exposed to in the vicinity of spinning propellers and idling turbine engines.

13-1   AMG094

During starting of a turbine powerplant using a compressed air starter, a hung start occurred. Select the proper procedure.

A–Shut the engine down
B–Re-engage the starter
C–Advance power level to increase RPM

13-1. Answer A. JSGT 13B, FGH

A hung start is one in which the engine starts but does not accelerate to normal starting RPM. If a hung start occurs, the engine should be shut down.

13-2   AMG094

A hung start in a jet engine is often caused by

A–malfunctions in the ignition system.
B–the starter cutting off too soon.
C–an excessively rich fuel/air mixture.

13-2. Answer B. JSGT 13B, FGH

Hung starts are often the result of insufficient power to the starter, or the starter cutting off before the engine starts self-accelerating. To help prevent a hung start, many operators insist on ground power assistance when starting.

13-3   AMG045

Which statement(s) below reflect(s) the typical requirement(s) when towing some aircraft?

1. Discharge all hydraulic pressure to prevent accidental operation of the nosewheel steering mechanism.
2. Tailwheel aircraft should be towed backwards.
3. If the aircraft has a steerable nosewheel, the torque-link lock should be set to full swivel.

A–1 and 2.
B–2.
C–3.

13-3. Answer C. JSGT 13B, FGH

Ground handling should be done according to the aircraft manufacturer's instructions. When towing an aircraft with a steerable nosewheel, you should verify that the locking scissors are set to full swivel. Tailwheel aircraft are usually towed forward, but in some cases may be towed backward. While discharging hydraulic pressure may help prevent accidental operation of the nosewheel steering, it also makes the brake system inoperative.

13-4   AMG045

Which statement(s) is/are true regarding tiedown of small aircraft?

1. Manila (hemp) rope has a tendency to stretch when it gets wet.
2. Nylon or dacron rope is preferred to manila rope.
3. The aircraft should be headed downwind in order to eliminate or minimize wing lift.
4. Leave the nosewheel or tailwheel unlocked.

A– 1, 2, 3, and 4.
B– 1 and 2.
C– 2.

13-4. Answer C. JSGT 13B, FGH

When tieing down an aircraft, nylon or Dacron rope is preferred because it won't shrink, mildew, or rot.

13-5   AMG045

When approaching the front of an idling jet engine, the hazard area extends forward of the engine approximately

A– 10 feet.
B– 15 feet.
C– 25 feet.

13-5. Answer C. JSGT 13B, FGH

Whether at idle or at full thrust, the hazard area in front of a jet engine extends out 25 feet. In the rear, the hazard area may extend from 100 to 200 feet, depending on the power setting.

13-6   AMG045

Which of the following is the most satisfactory extinguishing agent for use on a carburetor or intake fire?

A– Dry chemical.
B– A fine, water mist.
C– Carbon dioxide.

13-6. Answer C. JSGT 13B, FGH

Carbon dioxide is the most satisfactory extinguishing agent for carburetor or intake fires. CO_2 is preferred because it leaves no residue.

13-7   AMG045

If a radial engine has been shut down for more than 30 minutes, the propeller should be rotated through at least two revolutions to

A– check for hydraulic lock.
B– check for leaks.
C– prime the engine.

13-7. Answer A. JSGT 13B, FGH

Oil seeping past the piston rings or incomplete scavenging of oil in the cylinders of a radial engine may result in an accumulation of oil in the lower cylinders. Before starting a radial engine that has been shut down for more than 30 minutes, you should check for hydraulic lock by turning the propeller three or four complete revolutions. If liquid is present in the cylinders it is indicated by a resistance to turn, or by the prop stopping abruptly. All liquid must be cleared from the cylinders before attempting to start the engine.

13-8   AMG094

The priming of a fuel injected horizontally opposed engine is accomplished by placing the fuel control lever in the

A– IDLE-CUTOFF position.
B– AUTO-RICH position.
C– FULL-RICH position.

13-8. Answer C. JSGT 13B, FGH

To prime most fuel injection systems installed on horizontally opposed engines, you place the mixture control in the full-rich position. If the fuel control lever is placed in the idle-cutoff position no fuel can flow to the engine and there is no such thing as an auto-rich position on a horizontally opposed piston engine.

13-9   AMG094

The most important condition to be monitored during start after fuel flow begins in a turbine engine is the

A– EGT, TIT, or ITT.
B– RPM.
C– oil pressure.

13-9. Answer A. JSGT 13B, FGH

Light-off of a turbine engine is indicated by an increase in exhaust gas temperature (EGT), turbine inlet temperature (TIT), and interstage and turbine temperature (ITT). These temperatures should be monitored closely during start to prevent engine damage. In a piston engine, oil pressure is the most important condition to monitor.

13-10   AMG094

How is a flooded engine, equipped with a float-type carburetor, cleared of excessive fuel?

A– Crank the engine with the starter or by hand, with the mixture control in cutoff, ignition switch off, and the throttle fully open, until the fuel charge has been cleared.
B– Turn off the fuel and the ignition. Discontinue the starting attempt until the excess fuel has cleared.
C– Crank the engine with the starter or by hand, with the mixture control in cutoff, ignition switch on, and the throttle fully open, until the excess fuel has cleared or until the engine starts.

13-10. Answer A. JSGT 13B, FGH

The best way to clear a flooded engine is to crank the engine with the mixture in the cutoff position, ignition turned off, and the throttle fully open. This purges the excess fuel from the cylinders.

13-11   AMG094

Generally, when an induction fire occurs during starting of a reciprocating engine, the first course of action should be to

A– direct carbon dioxide into the air intake of the engine.
B– continue cranking and start the engine if possible.
C– close the throttle.

13-11. Answer B. JSGT 13B, FGH

Induction fires during starting are surprisingly common and you should be ready to deal with them at anytime. If a fire occurs during the start, you should continue cranking and attempt to start the engine. This draws the fire into the engine. If the engine does not start and the fire continues, discontinue the start attempt. A carbon dioxide fire extinguisher may then be discharged into the engine's intake.

13-12 AMG045

When starting and ground operating an aircraft's engine, the aircraft should be positioned to head into the wind primarily

A– to aid in achieving and maintaining the proper air flow into the engine induction system.
B– to help cancel out engine torque effect.
C– for engine cooling purposes.

13-12. Answer C. FGH
A headwind will aid in engine cooling during ground operations.

13-13 AMG045

When approaching the rear of an idling turbojet engine, the hazard area extends aft of the engine approximately

A– 200 feet.
B– 100 feet.
C– 50 feet.

13-13. Answer B. JSGT 13B, FGH
An idling turbojet engine creates high velocity gases that extend 100 feet aft of the engine. At takeoff power, the hazard area extends back 200 feet.

13-14 AMG094

During starting of a turbojet powerplant using a compressed air starter, a hot start occurrence was recorded. Select what happened from the following.

A– The pneumatic starting unit overheated.
B– The powerplant was preheated before starting.
C– The fuel/air mixture was excessively rich.

13-14. Answer C. JSGT 13B, FGH
A hot start is characterized by excessive turbine inlet or exhaust gas temperatures. This condition is the result of an excessively RICH fuel/air mixture.

13-15 AMG045

When towing a large aircraft

A– a person should be in the cockpit to watch for obstructions.
B– persons should be stationed at the nose, each wingtip, and the empennage at all times.
C– a person should be in the cockpit to operate brakes.

13-15. Answer C. JSGT 13B, FGH
When towing an aircraft, a qualified person should be in the cockpit to operate the aircraft's brakes, because the brakes on most tow vehicles are insufficient to stop the momentum of a large aircraft.

13-16 AMG045

A tailwheel-type airplane has a greater tendency to weathervane during taxi than a nosewheel-type because on a tailwheel airplane, the

A– vertical stabilizer to fuselage proportion is greater.
B– surface area ratio behind the pivot point (main gear) is greater.
C– surface area ratio behind the pivot point (main gear) is less.

13-16. Answer B. JSGT 13B, FAA-H-8083-3
A tailwheel aircraft has a greater surface area behind the main gear (pivot point) than a nosewheel-type aircraft. Because of this, a tailwheel aircraft has a greater tendency to weathervane.

13-17   AMG045

When taxiing (or towing) an aircraft, a flashing red light from the control tower means

A– stop and wait for a green light.
B– move clear of the runway/taxiway immediately.
C– return to starting point.

13-17. Answer B. JSGT 13B, FGH

A flashing red light from the control tower indicates that you should taxi clear of the runway/taxiway immediately. A steady red light means that you should stop and a flashing white light means you should return to the starting point.

13-18   AMG045

A person should approach or leave a helicopter in the pilot's field of vision whenever the engine is running in order to avoid

A– the tail rotor.
B– the main rotor.
C– blowing dust or debris caused by rotor downwash.

13-18. Answer A. JSGT 13B, AC 91-32A

When approaching a helicopter, you should be aware of propellers, rotors, and jet engine intakes and exhausts. One way to help ensure you remain clear of the tail rotor on a helicopter is to approach and leave the helicopter in the pilot's field of vision.

13-19   AMG045

When taxiing (or towing) an aircraft, a flashing white light from the control tower means

A– move clear of the runway/taxiway immediately.
B– OK to proceed but use extreme caution.
C– return to starting point.

13-19. Answer C. JSGT 13B, FGH

A flashing white light from the control tower is a signal for you to return to the place you started from. An alternating red and green light indicates you should proceed with extreme caution, whereas, a flashing red light indicates you should move clear of the runway or taxiway you are on.

13-20   AMG045

When taxiing (or towing) an aircraft, an alternating red and green light from the control tower means

A– move clear of the runway/taxiway immediately.
B– OK to proceed but use extreme caution.
C– return to starting point.

13-20. Answer B. JSGT 13B, FGH

Alternating red and green flashes from the tower indicate that it's O.K. to proceed but use extreme caution. A flashing red light indicates you should move clear of the runway or taxiway immediately, and a flashing white light indicates you should return to where you started.

13-21   AMG045

When stopping a nosewheel-type airplane after taxiing (or towing), the nosewheel should be left

A– unlocked.
B– turned at a small angle.
C– pointed straight ahead.

13-21. Answer C. JSGT 13B, FGH

When stopping a nose-wheel type aircraft, the nose-wheel should be left in the straight ahead position so the aircraft cannot move from side-to-side in the wind.

13-22   AMG045

When first starting to move an aircraft while taxiing, it is important to

A– test the brakes.
B– closely monitor the instruments.
C– notify the control tower.

13-22. Answer A. JSGT 13B, FGH

After the engine is started and immediately after the aircraft begins moving, the brakes should be tested. If braking is unsatisfactory, the engine should be shut down immediately.

13-23   AMG094

Which of the following conditions has the most potential for causing engine damage when starting or attempting to start a turbine engine?

A– Hung start.
B– False start.
C– Hot start.

13-23. Answer C. JSGT 13B, FGH

When excessive fuel and/or insufficient air is delivered to the combustor of a turbine engine, the exhaust temperature may rise above the engine's maximum limit, causing engine damage. This condiiton is known as a hot start. A hung start can lead to a hot start, but a hung start alone will not cause damage to the engine if corrective action is taken before a hot start condition occurs.

13-24   AMG045

(Refer to figure 50 on page 13-7.)
Identify the signal to engage rotor on a rotorcraft.

A– 1.
B– 3.
C– 2.

13-24. Answer B. JSGT 13B, FGH

Use of standard hand signals is important for communication in high noise areas. Pointing one hand at the rotor and moving the other hand in a circle, indicates that it is safe to engage the rotor.

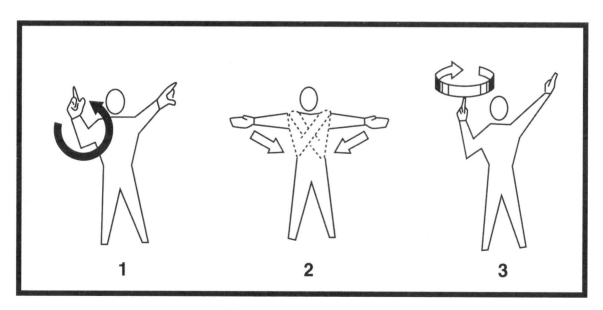

Figure 50. Marshalling Signals.

13-25   AMG045
(Refer to figure 51 on page 13-8.)
Which marshalling signal should be given if a taxiing aircraft is in imminent danger of striking an object?

A–1.
B–2.
C–3.

13-25. Answer C. JSGT 13B, FGH
Anyone working around moving aircraft should know the standard FAA hand signals. Hands over the head and moving from shoulder width to crisscross is the signal for an emergency stop as in No. 3.

Figure 51. Marshalling Signals.

13-26   AMG045
(Refer to figure 51 on page 13-8.)
Which marshalling signal should be given if a taxiing aircraft is in imminent danger of striking an object?

A–1 or 3.
B–2.
C–3.

13-26. Answer C. JSGT 13B, FGH
Anyone working around moving aircraft should know the standard FAA hand signals. Hands over the head and moving from shoulder width to crisscross is the signal for an emergency stop as in No. 3.

13-27   AMG053
How much current does a 30-volt 1/2-horsepower motor that is 85-percent efficient draw from the bus?
(Note: 1 horsepower = 746 watts)

A–14.6 amperes.
B–12.4 amperes.
C–14.3 amperes.

13-27. Answer A. JSGT 3A, FGH
A 1/2 horsepower motor delivers 373 watts. With an 85% efficiency, the motor draws 439 watts. By using the equation P=EI where P is watts, E is voltage, and I is amperes, we can solve the equation by substituting the known values.

373/.85 = 438.82

438.82 = 30 × I

438.82/30 = I

14 .6 = I

13-28 AMG045

Weathervaning tendency is greatest when taxiing

A– a tailwheel-type airplane in a direct crosswind.
B– a nosewheel-type airplane in a quartering headwind.
C– both nosewheel and tailwheel-type airplanes in a
     quartering tailwind.

13-28. Answer A. JSGT 13B

When taxiing a tailwheel airplane in a strong
crosswind, the wind pushing against the vertical
stabilizer and side of the fuselage causes the aircraft
to pivot around the main wheels to align into the wind.
Although a nosewheel airplane is also affected by
crosswinds during taxi, a tailwheel airplane is more
prone to the weathervaning tendency.

13-29 AMG045

When approaching the rear of an idling turbojet or
turbofan engine, the hazard area extends aft of the
engine approximately

A– 200 feet.
B– 100 feet.
C– 50 feet.

13-29. Answer B. JSGT 13B, FGH

Turbojet aircraft are hazardous from both the front and
rear. At idle, the jet thrust can adversely affect persons
or objects as far away as 100 feet from the engine
outlet. At takeoff power, the jet blast can adversely
affect objects up to 200 feet away.

SECTION C - SERVICING AIRCRAFT

Section C of Chapter 13 discusses the maintenance practices used when servicing aircraft. Included is information on fueling and defueling, as well as things to watch for when operating ground power units (GPUs).

13-30   AMG040

What effect, if any, will aviation gasoline mixed with jet fuel have on a turbine engine?

A– No appreciable effect.
B– The tetraethyl lead in the gasoline forms deposits on the turbine blades.
C– The tetraethyl lead in the gasoline forms deposits on the compressor blades.

13-30. Answer B. JSGT 13C, FGH

When turbine engines are operated on a mixture of jet fuel and aviation gasoline, the TEL (lead) in the gasoline forms deposits on the turbine blades and vanes. Continuous use of mixed fuel typically causes a loss in engine efficiency. The tetraethyl lead in the gasoline forms deposits on the compressor blades is incorrect because the exhaust gases containing the tetraethyl lead do not pass through the compressor blades.

13-31   AMG040

1. Jet fuel is of higher viscosity than aviation gasoline and therefore holds contaminants more readily.
2. Viscosity has no relation to contamination of fuel.

Regarding the above statements,

A– only No. 1 is true.
B– both No. 1 and No. 2 are true.
C– neither No. 1 nor No. 2 is true.

13-31. Answer A. JSGT 13C, FGH

The higher the viscosity of a fuel, the greater its ability to hold contaminants in suspension. Jet fuel does have a high viscosity and, therefore, is more susceptible to contamination than aviation gasoline. Only statement number 1 is true.

13-32   AMG040

The color of 100LL fuel is

A– blue.
B– colorless or straw.
C– red.

13-32. Answer A. JSGT 13C, FGH

100LL aviation fuel is colored blue, jet A is colorless or may have a straw tint, and 80/87 is dyed red.

13-33   AMG040

How are aviation fuels, which possess greater anti-knock qualities than 100 octane, classified?

A– According to the milliliters of lead.
B– By reference to normal heptane.
C– By performance numbers.

13-33. Answer C. JSGT 13C, FGH

Octane and performance numbers designate the anti-knock value of a fuel. The higher the grade, the more compression the fuel can withstand without detonating. The octane scale goes to 100, which represents the anti-knock characteristics of pure iso-octane. For fuels with higher anti-knock characteristics, performance numbers are used.

13-34   AMG040

Why is ethylene dibromide added to aviation gasoline?

A–To remove zinc silicate deposits from the spark plugs.
B–To scavenge lead oxide from the cylinder combustion chambers.
C–To increase the anti-knock rating of the fuel.

13-34. Answer B. JSGT 13C, FGH
Ethylene dibromide is added to aviation gasoline to scavenge lead oxide from the cylinders. The ethylene dibromide combines with the lead oxide in aviation fuels to form a lead bromide that passes out the exhaust.

13-35   AMG040

Both gasoline and kerosene have certain advantages for use as turbine fuel. Which statement is true in reference to the advantages of each?

A–Kerosene has a higher heat energy/value per unit weight than gasoline.
B–Gasoline has a higher heat energy/value per unit volume than kerosene.
C–Kerosene has a higher heat energy/value per unit volume than gasoline.

13-35. Answer C. JSGT 13C, AST Spec. D-910, D-1655
Aviation gasoline (100LL) has a heat energy of 18,720 BTU/lb. Jet A fuel (kerosene) has a heat energy of 18,439 BTU/lb. Since Jet A weighs 6.7 lbs/gal, its heat energy is 123,541 BTU/gal. 100LL weighs 6 lbs/gal and, therefore, has a heat energy of 112,320 BTU/gal. Therefore, kerosene has a higher heat energy per unit volume.

13-36   AMG040

What must accompany fuel vaporization?

A–An absorption of heat.
B–A decrease in vapor pressure.
C–A reduction in volume.

13-36. Answer A. JSGT 13C, FGH
When any material, including fuel, changes from a liquid to a vapor state, it must absorb heat from its surroundings.

13-37   AMG040

Characteristics of detonation are

A–cylinder pressure remains the same, excessive cylinder head temperature, and a decrease in engine power.
B–rapid rise in cylinder pressure, excessive cylinder head temperature, and a decrease in engine power.
C–rapid rise in cylinder pressure, cylinder head temperature normal, and a decrease in engine power.

13-37. Answer B. JSGT 13C, FGH
Detonation is also known as engine knock and is caused by an abrupt explosion of the fuel/air mixture in the cylinder. This causes a rapid rise in cylinder pressures, an increase in cylinder head temperature, and a decrease in power. Detonation can cause damage to the cylinder head and/or piston.

13-38   AMG040

A fuel that vaporizes too readily may cause

A–hard starting.
B–detonation.
C–vapor lock.

13-38. Answer C. JSGT 13C, FGH
Volatility is a measure of the tendency of a liquid to vaporize under given conditions. If gasoline vaporizes too readily, vapor lock may occur. If it does not vaporize readily, hard starting may result.

13-39   AMG040

Jet fuel number identifiers are

A– performance numbers to designate the volatility of the fuel.

B– performance numbers and are relative to the fuel's performance in the aircraft engine.

C– type numbers and have no relation to the fuel's performance in the aircraft engine.

13-39. Answer C. JSGT 13C, FGH

The numbers and letters used to identify different types of jet fuel have no relation to the fuel's rating or performance in the engine.

13-40   AMG040

The main differences between grades 100 and 100LL fuel are

A– volatility and lead content.

B– volatility, lead content, and color.

C– lead content and color.

13-40. Answer C. JSGT 13C, FGH

The primary differences between 100 and 100LL fuel are the color and lead content. 100 grade aviation fuel (old designation 100/130) is green in color and contains more tetraethyl lead than the newer 100LL which is dyed blue.

13-41   AMG040

Characteristics of aviation gasoline are

A– high heat value, high volatility.

B– high heat value, low volatility.

C– low heat value, low volatility.

13-41. Answer A. JSGT 13C, FGH

Aviation gasoline has a high heat value (approximately 18,720 BTUs per pound) and is highly volatile (5.5 to 7 PSI at 100F).

13-42   AMG040

Tetraethyl lead is added to aviation gasoline to

A– retard the formation of corrosives.

B– improve the gasoline's performance in the engine.

C– dissolve the moisture in the gasoline.

13-42. Answer B. JSGT 13C, FGH

Tetraethyl lead (TEL) is added to gasoline to improve the performance (anti-knock rating). The addition of TEL allows the engine to develop more power without knocking.

13-43   AMG040

A fuel that does not vaporize readily enough can cause

A– vapor lock.

B– detonation.

C– hard starting.

13-43. Answer C. JSGT 13C, FGH

A fuel that does not vaporize readily can cause hard starting; whereas, a fuel that vaporizes too readily can cause vapor lock.

MAINTENANCE PUBLICATIONS, FORMS, AND RECORDS

SECTION A - MAINTENANCE PUBLICATIONS

Having and using the proper maintenance publications are every bit as important as having the correct tools for a given job. Chapter 14, Section A presents information on government publications such as Airworthiness Directives, Advisory Circulars, Type Certificate Data Sheets, and manufacturer's manuals.

14-1   AMG089

What FAA-approved document gives the leveling means to be used when weighing an aircraft?

A– Type Certificate Data Sheet.
B– AC 43.13-1B.
C– Manufacturer's maintenance manual.

14-1. Answer A. JSGT 14A, FGH

The FAA-approved leveling means for an aircraft is found in the Type Certificate Data Sheet for that particular model of aircraft. Although the manufacturer's maintenance manual also includes the leveling means for the aircraft, the manual is not FAA approved.

14-2   AMG062

What is the means by which the FAA notifies aircraft owners and other interested persons of unsafe conditions and prescribes the condition under which the product may continue to be operated?

A– Airworthiness Directives.
B– Airworthiness Alerts.
C– Aviation Safety Data.

14-2. Answer A. JSGT 14A, FGH

Airworthiness Directives (ADs) are issued by the FAA to notify aircraft owners of an unsafe condition. Compliance with ADs is mandatory, and the conditions for compliance are listed in the AD itself.

14-3   AMG079

Which is an appliance major repair?

A– Overhaul of a hydraulic pressure pump.
B– Repairs to a propeller governor or its control.
C– Troubleshooting and repairing broken circuits in landing lights circuits.

14-3. Answer A. JSGT 14A, FAR 43, Appendix A

Specific criteria to determine whether a job is a major or minor repair is found in FAR Part 43, Appendix A. Major repairs to appliances consist of 1. calibration and repair of instruments. 2. calibration of radio equipment. 3. rewinding the field coil of an electrical accessory. 4. complete disassembly of complex hydraulic power valves. 5. overhaul of pressure type carburetors, and pressure type fuel, oil and hydraulic pumps.

14-4   AMG079
Which maintenance action is an airframe major repair?

A–Changes to the wing or to fixed or movable
   control surfaces which affect flutter and vibration
   characteristics.
B–Rewinding the field coil of an electrical accessory.
C–The repair of portions of skin sheets by making
   additional seams.

14-4. Answer C. JSGT 14A, FAR 43, Appendix A
According to Part 43, Appendix A, the repair of portions
of skin sheets by making additional seams is

14-5   AMG085
An aircraft was not approved for return to service after
an annual inspection and the owner wanted to fly the
aircraft to another maintenance base. Which statement
is correct?

A–The owner must obtain a special flight permit.
B–The aircraft may be flown without restriction up to
   10 hours to reach another maintenance base.
C–The owner must obtain a restricted category type
   certificate.

14-5. Answer A. JSGT 14A, FAR 21.197
If an owner desires to fly an aircraft that is in an
unairworthy condition to another maintenance facility
where repairs, alterations, or maintenance can be
performed, a special flight permit (ferry permit) must be
issued.

14-6   AMG024
Each person performing an annual or 100-hour
inspection shall use a checklist that contains at least
those items in the appendix of

A–14 CFR Part 43.
B–14 CFR Part 65.
C–AC 43.13-3.

14-6. Answer A. JSGT 14A, FAR 43.15
Each person performing an annual or 100-hour
inspection shall use a checklist while performing the
inspection. The checklist may be of the person's
own design, one provided by the manufacturer of the
equipment being inspected, or one obtained from
another source. However, the checklist used must
include at least the scope and detail of the items
contained in Appendix D of FAR Part 43.

14-7   AMG085
When a discrepancy list is provided to an aircraft
owner or operator after an inspection is completed, it
says in effect that

A–the item inspected is unairworthy.
B–except for these discrepancies, the item inspected is
   airworthy.
C–the item inspected may or may not be airworthy
   depending on the discrepancies found.

14-7. Answer B. JSGT 14B, FAR 43.11
Part 43.11 states that if an aircraft is inspected and
items are found to be unairworthy, the following or
similar statement is entered into the logbook: "I certify
that this aircraft has been inspected in accordance
with (insert type) inspection and a list of discrepancies
and unairworthy items dated (date) has been provided
for the aircraft owner or operator." The inspector is
essentially saying that the item is airworthy except for
the listed discrepancies.

14-8 AMG062
Airworthiness Directives are issued primarily to

A– provide information about malfunction or defect trends.
B– present recommended maintenance procedures for correcting potentially hazardous defects.
C– correct an unsafe condition.

14-8. Answer C. JSGT 14A, FGH
Airworthiness Directives (ADs) are used to notify aircraft owners and other interested persons of unsafe conditions as well as methods for correcting the condition.

14-9 AMG097
(1) A Supplemental Type Certificate may be issued to more than one applicant for the same design change, providing each applicant shows compliance with the applicable airworthiness requirement.
(2) An installation of an item manufactured in accordance with the Technical Standard Order system requires no further approval for installation in a particular aircraft.

Regarding the above statements,

A– both No. 1 and No. 2 are true.
B– neither No. 1 nor No. 2 is true.
C– only No. 1 is true.

14-9. Answer C. JSGT 14A, FAR 21.115
Only statement number 1 is true. Providing the applicant can show compliance with applicable airworthiness requirements, an STC may be issued to any number of applicants for the same design change. Even though an item is manufactured according to a Technical Standard Order, it is not to be interpreted as an approval for installation on any particular aircraft.

14-10 AMG062
Primary responsibility for compliance with Airworthiness Directives lies with the

A– Aircraft owner or operator.
B– certificated mechanic holding an Inspection Authorization who conducts appropriate inspections.
C– certificated mechanic who maintains the aircraft.

14-10. Answer A. FGH
Although a mechanic is responsible for determining compliance with ADs during certain airworthiness inspections, the owner or operator of the aircraft is required by Part 91.403 to maintain their aircraft in an airworthy condition, including compliance with applicable ADs.

14-11 AMG097
An aircraft Type Certificate Data Sheet contains

A– maximum fuel grade to be used.
B– control surface adjustment points.
C– location of the datum.

14-11. Answer C. JSGT 14A, FGH
The only item listed that is on the Type Certificate Data Sheet (TCDS) is the location of the datum. The TCDS also includes, among other things, the minimum fuel grade to be used, and the control surface movements.

14-12   AMG025
When an airworthy (at the time of sale) aircraft is sold, the Airworthiness Certificate

A– becomes invalid until the aircraft is reinspected and returned to service.
B– is voided and a new certificate is issued upon application by the new owner.
C– is transferred with the aircraft.

14-12. Answer C. JSGT 14A, FAR 21.179
The Airworthiness Certificate is valid as long as the aircraft is maintained in accordance with FAA regulations, and is considered part of the permanent records of the aircraft. When the aircraft is sold, the Airworthiness Certificate is transferred to the new owner.

14-13   AMG021
Specifications pertaining to an aircraft model manufactured under a type certificate, of which less than 50 are shown on the FAA Aircraft Registry, can be found in the

A– Aircraft Listing.
B– Annual Summary of Deleted and Discontinued Aircraft Specifications.
C– FAA Statistical Handbook of Civil Aircraft Specifications.

14-13. Answer A. JSGT 14A, AFS 613 Vol VI
Older aircraft of which fewer than 50 remain in service, or any aircraft of which fewer than 50 were produced or remain in service, are found in the Aircraft Listing.

14-14   AMG097
Where are technical descriptions of certificated propellers found?

A– Applicable Airworthiness Directives.
B– Aircraft Specifications.
C– Propeller Type Certificate Data Sheet.

14-14. Answer C. FAR 21.41
All specifications for a certificated propeller can be found in the Propeller Type Certificate Data Sheet.

14-15   AMG097
What information is generally contained in Aircraft Specifications or Type Certificate Data Sheets?

A– Empty weight of the aircraft.
B– Useful load of aircraft.
C– Control surface movements.

14-15. Answer C. JSGT 14A, FGH
Of the items listed, only the Control Surface Movements are found on the Type Certificate Data Sheet.

14-16   AMG072
Placards required on an aircraft are specified in

A– AC 43.13-1B.
B– FAR's under which the aircraft was type certificated.
C– Aircraft Specifications or Type Certificate Data Sheets.

14-16. Answer C. JSGT 14A, FGH
The required placards for a particular model aircraft are found in the Aircraft Specifications or Type Certificate Data Sheet for that model.

14-17   AMG021
Technical information about older aircraft models, of which no more than 50 remain in service, can be found in the

A– Aircraft Listing.
B– Annual Summary of Deleted and Discontinued Aircraft Specifications.
C– Alphabetical Index of Antique Aircraft.

14-17. Answer A. JSGT 14A
Specifications on aircraft of which fewer than 50 were produced, or fewer than 50 remain in service are found in the Aircraft Listing.

14-18   AMG063
(1) The FARs require approval after compliance with the data of a Supplemental Type Certificate.
(2) An installation of an item manufactured in accordance with the Technical Standard Order system requires no further approval for installation in a particular aircraft.

Regarding the above statements,

A– only No. 2 is true.
B– neither No.1 nor No. 2 is true.
C– only No. 1 is true.

14-18. Answer C. JSGT 14A, FAR 21 Subpart E
Only statement number 1 is correct. Complying with the data of a Supplemental Type Certificate (STC) is a major alteration that must be approved with a Form 337. Installation of an item manufactured under a Technical Standard Order always requires approval.

14-19   AMG066
Which regulation provides the airworthiness standards for an airplane certificated in the normal category?

A– 14 CFR Part 27.
B– 14 CFR Part 25.
C– 14 CFR Part 23.

14-19. Answer C. JSGT 14A, FAR 23
Airworthiness standards for airplanes certificated in the normal, utility, and acrobatic categories are covered in 14 CFR Part 23.

14-20   AMG082
(1) Propellers are NOT included in the Airworthiness Directive system.
(2) A certificated powerplant mechanic may make a minor repair on an aluminum propeller and approve for return to service.

Regarding the above statements,

A– only No. 2 is true.
B– both No. 1 and No. 2 are true.
C– neither No. 1 nor No. 2 is true.

14-20. Answer A. JSGT 14A, FGH/FAR 65.87
Only statement number 2 is true. A certificated powerplant mechanic with the necessary experience may make minor repairs on aircraft propellers and return them to service. Statement number 1 is incorrect because an Airworthiness Directive may be issued on any product that affects safety. This includes aircraft, engines, propellers, and appliances.

14-21   AMG051

An aircraft mechanic is privileged to perform major alterations on U. S. certificated aircraft; however, the work must be done in accordance with FAA-approved technical data before the aircraft can be returned to service. Which is NOT approved data?

A– Airworthiness Directives.
B– AC 43.13-2B.
C– Supplemental Type Certificates.

14-21. Answer B. JSGT 14A, AC 43.9-1E

Airworthiness Directives, Type Certificates, and FAA-approved data provided by the manufacturer are all approved data. AC 43.13-2B provides acceptable methods of performing aircraft alterations but is not considered approved data. A good practice when planning an alteration that is not specifically covered by an AD, STC, or other approved data is to outline your work and submit a pencil copy of a 337 Form to your local FAA maintenance inspector for approval.

14-22   AMG062

What is the maintenance recording responsibility of the person who complies with an Airworthiness Directive?

A– Advise the aircraft owner/operator of the work performed.
B– Make an entry in the maintenance record of that equipment.
C– Advise the FAA district office of the work performed, by submitting an FAA Form 337.

14-22. Answer B. FGH

Compliance with Airworthiness Directives is required, and a record of the action taken to comply with an AD must be included in the permanent records of the equipment affected by the AD.

14-23   AMG051

(1) Manufacturer's data and FAA publications such as Airworthiness Directives, Type Certificate Data Sheets, and advisory circulars are all approved data.
(2) FAA publications such as Technical Standard Orders, Airworthiness Directives, Type Certificate Data Sheets, and Aircraft Specifications and Supplemental Type Certificates are all approved data.

Regarding the above statements,

A– both No. 1 and No. 2 are true.
B– only No. 1 is true.
C– only No. 2 is true.

14-23. Answer C. AC 43.9-1E

Only statement number 2 is true. Items such as Technical Standard Orders, Airworthiness Directives, Type Certificate Data Sheets, and Aircraft Specifications and Supplemental Type Certificates are all approved data. Items such as advisory circulars are not considered approved data.

14-24 AMG026

The Air Transport Association of America (ATA) Specification No. 100

(1) establishes a standard for the presentation of technical data in maintenance manuals.

(2) divides the aircraft into numbered systems and subsystems in order to simplify locating maintenance instructions.

Regarding the above statements,

A– both No. 1 and No. 2 are true.
B– neither No. 1 nor No. 2 is true.
C– only No. 1 is true.

14-24. Answer A. JSGT 14A, FGH

Both statements are correct. The ATA Specification 100 is a standard for the presentation of technical information. Because of this specification, maintenance information from any of the manufacturers of transport aircraft is arranged in the same way.

14-25 AMG051

Aviation Maintenance Alerts (formerly General Aviation Airworthiness Alerts)

A– provide mandatory procedures to prevent or correct serious aircraft problems.
B– provide information about aircraft problems and suggested corrective actions.
C– provide temporary emergency procedures until Airworthiness Directives can be issued.

14-25. Answer B. JSGT 14A, AC 43.16

The Aviation Maintenance Alert system (AC 43.16) is published monthly to inform maintenance personnel about aircraft problems and suggested corrective actions. This publication was formerly called General Aviation Airworthiness Alerts.

14-26 AMG077

Which of the following includes all the regulatory definitions of "maintenance"?

A– Overhaul, repair, parts replacement, and preservation, and preventive maintenance.
B– Overhaul, repair, parts replacement, preservation, inspection, and preventive maintenance.
C– Overhaul, repair, parts replacement, inspection, and preservation.

14-26. Answer C. JSGT 14A, FAR 1.1

Part 1.1 defines maintenance as inspection, overhaul, repair, preservation, and the replacement parts, but excludes preventive maintenance.

14-27 AMG097

What does the Type Certificate Data Sheet designation code "2 PCSM" mean?

A– Two place (number of seats), closed, sea, monoplane.
B– Two wing (biplane), primary category, semi-monocoque (airframe).
C– Neither of the other two choices.

14-27. Answer A. FAA-G-8082-11, FGH

This designation is broken down in four segments. The first segment indicates the number of seats (2P = two place aircraft). The second segment is the type of cockpit/cabin design (C = closed cockpit). The third segment is the basic type of aircraft (S = seaplane). The fourth segment indicates the wing design (M = monoplane). This airplane is a two place, closed cockpit, seaplane, monoplane.

14-28   AMG097

Type Certificate Data Sheets are issued for which of the following products?

A– Aircraft, engines, and propellers.
B– Aircraft, engines, and appliances.
C– Aircraft, engines, propellers, and appliances.

14-28. Answer A. FAR 21.11

Part 21.11 includes the applicability for procedural requirements of Type Certificate Data Sheets (TCDSs) for aircraft, engines, and propellers. Part 21, subpart K describes the requirements for approval of appliances, which are not issued TCDSs.

14-29   AMG048

The action required by an AD may take what form?

1. Inspection.
2. Part(s) replacement.
3. Design modification.
4. Change in operating procedure(s).
5. Overall change in the content, form and disposition of aircraft maintenance records.

A– 1, 2, 3, and/or 4.
B– 1, 2, 3, and/or 5.
C– 1, 2, 3, 4, and/or 5.

14-29. Answer A. AC 39-7C

Advisory Circular 39-7C describes Airworthiness Directives (ADs) and what they may prescribe, which includes inspections, parts replacements, modifications, and changes in operating procedures.

14-30   AMG062

The following words are an example of what kind of statement in an AD? "Required within the next 25 hours time-in-service after the effective date of this AD, unless already accomplished."

A– Amendment.
B– Compliance.
C– Applicability.

14-30. Answer B. JSGT 14A, AC 39-7C

Advisory Circular 39-7C describes Airworthiness Directives (ADs) and how to interpret the information. It states that the compliance section of an AD describes the time or date by which compliance must be met.

14-31   AMG066

Which of the following are sometimes used as authorization to deviate from an aircraft's original type design?

1. FAA Form 337.
2. Supplemental Type Certificate.
3. Airworthiness Directive.
4. Technical Standard Order.

A– 1, 2, 3, and 4.
B– 1, 2, and 4.
C– 1, 2, and 3.

14-31. Answer C. AC 43.9-1E

A deviation from an aircraft's type design requires an FAA Form 337, a Supplemental Type Certiciate (STC), or an Airworthiness Directive (AD). A Technical Standard Order is issued to approved parts, but those parts cannot be installed unless they were part of the original type certificate or the installation is approved by an FAA Form 337, STC, or AD.

14-32   AMG072

The following is a table of airspeed limits as given in an FAA-issued aircraft specification.

Normal operating speed.....260 knots
Never-exceed speed.....293 knots
Maximum landing gear operating speed.....174 knots
Maximum flap extended speed.....139 knots

The high end of the white arc on the airspeed instrument would be at

A– 260 knots.
B– 174 knots.
C– 139 knots.

14-32. Answer C. FAR 23.1545

According to Part 23, the flap operating speed range on an airspeed indicator is marked with a white arc. The high end of this arc designates the maximum flap extension speed.

14-33   AMG062

(Refer to figure 63 on page 14-9.)
An aircraft has a total time in service of 468 hours. The Airworthiness Directive given was initially complied with at 454 hours in service. How many additional hours in service may be accumulated before the Airworthiness Directive must again be complied with?

A– 46.
B– 200.
C– 186.

14-33. Answer C. JSGT 14A, FGH

Although compliance wasn't required until 500-hours total time, the AD was complied with at 454-hours total time. Once the AD is complied with, you are required to abide by the repetitive 200-hour inspection. The aircraft has been in service for 14 hours (468 – 454 = 14) since the AD was complied with, and, therefore, the AD must again be complied with in 186 hours (200 – 14 = 186).

The following is the compliance portion of an Airworthiness Directive. "Compliance required as indicated, unless already accomplished:

I.   Aircraft with less than 500-hours' total time in service: Inspect in accordance with instructions below 500-hours' total time,   or within the next 50-hours' time in service after the effective date of this AD,   and repeat after each subsequent 200 hours in service.

II.   Aircraft with 500-hours' through 1,000-hours' total time in service: Inspect in accordance with instructions below within the next 50-hours' time in service after the effective date of this AD, and repeat after each subsequent 200 hours in service.

III.   Aircraft with more than 1,000-hours' time in service: Inspect in accordance with instructions below within the next 25-hours' time in service after the effective date of this AD, and repeat after each subsequent 200 hours in service."

Figure 63. Airworthiness Directive Excerpt

14-34   AMG076

A repair, as performed on an airframe, shall mean

A– the upkeep and preservation of the airframe including the component parts thereof.
B– the restoration of the airframe to a condition for safe operation after damage or deterioration.
C– simple or minor preservation operations and the replacement of small standard parts not involving complex assembly operations.

14-34. Answer B. JSGT 14A, FAR 43, Appendix A
Restoration after damage or deterioration is a repair (answer B). The upkeep and preservation, as well as simple replacement of small parts are preventive maintenance (answers A and C).

14-35   AMG079

The replacement of fabric on fabric-covered parts such as wings, fuselages, stabilizers, or control surfaces is considered to be a

A– minor repair unless the new cover is different in any way from the original cover.
B– minor repair unless the underlying structure is altered or repaired.
C– major repair even though no other alteration or repair is performed.

14-35. Answer C. FAR 43, Appendix A
It is clearly stated in Part 43, Appendix A that replacement of fabric covering is a major repair.

14-36   AMG079

Which is classified as a major repair?

A– The splicing of skin sheets.
B– Installation of new engine mounts obtained from the aircraft manufacturer.
C– Any repair of damaged stressed metal skin.

14-36. Answer A. JSGT 14A, FAR 43, Appendix A
Making additional seams or splicing skin sheets to repair a portion of the skin is a major repair. Installation of new engine mounts obtained from the aircraft manufacturer and any repair of damaged stressed metal skin are incorrect because they are both considered minor repairs.

14-37   AMG079

The replacement of a damaged vertical stabilizer with a new identical stabilizer purchased from the aircraft manufacturer is considered a

A– minor alteration.
B– major repair.
C– minor repair.

14-37. Answer C. JSGT 14A, FAR 43, Appendix A
Generally, the replacement of a complete assembly with an identical assembly purchased from the manufacturer is a minor repair, regardless of the size of the part. One way to determine if something constitutes a major or minor repair is that if the action is not included in Part 43, Appendix A, it is a minor repair or alteration.

14-38   AMG063

Who is responsible for determining that materials used in aircraft maintenance and repair are of the proper type and conform to the appropriate standards?

A– The installing person or agency.
B– The owner of the aircraft.
C– The manufacturer of the aircraft.

14-38. Answer A. FAR 43.13
Whenever maintenance is being performed, it is the responsibility of the technician performing the work to ensure that the parts being used meet appropriate standards.

14-39   AMG051

Which of these publications contains standards for protrusion of bolts, studs, and screws through self-locking nuts?

A– AC 43.13-2B.
B– Aircraft Specifications or Type Certificate Data Sheets.
C– AC 43.13-1B.

14-39. Answer C. AC 43.13-1B

AC 43.13-1B provides a wealth of information on standard applications for hardware, as well as torque charts and other information.

14-40   AMG079

The replacement of a damaged engine mount with a new identical engine mount purchased from the aircraft manufacturer is considered a

A– minor alteration.
B– major repair.
C– minor repair.

14-40. Answer C. JSGT 14A, FAR 43, Appendix A

Generally, if you are replacing a part with an identical new part, the operation is a minor repair. This could change if the part required welding or riveting for installation.

14-41   AMG062

The following words are an example of what kind of statement in an AD? "Model 172 airplanes (serial numbers 36216 through 36769) that have not been modified with Cessna Service Kit SK-172-10 or SK-172-10A, certificated in any category."

A– Amendment.
B– Compliance.
C– Applicability.

14-41. Answer C. JSGT 14A, FGH

The applicability section of an airworthiness directive provides the make, model, serial number, or other relevant information to identify the equipment affected by the AD.

14-42   AMG076

What is the regulatory definition of "preventive maintenance"?

A– Simple or minor preservation operations and the replacement of small standard parts not involving complex assembly operations.
B– All preservation operations and the replacement of standard parts, including any required assembly operations.
C– All preservation operations and the replacement of standard parts not involving complex assembly operations.

14-42. Answer A. JSGT 14A, FAR 1

The definition of preventive maintenance is the performance of simple or minor preservation operations and the replacement of small standard parts not involving complex assembly operations.

SECTION B - FORMS AND RECORDS

Section B of Chapter 14 discusses the steps required to properly document aircraft maintenance. Included is information on inspection checklists, aircraft logbooks, and common phraseology used to sign off an aircraft and return it to service.

14-43   AMG076

Where is the record of compliance with Airworthiness Directives or manufacturers' service bulletins normally indicated?

A– FAA Form 337.
B– Aircraft maintenance records.
C– Flight manual.

14-43. Answer B. JSGT 14B, FGH

Record of compliance with Airworthiness Directives and manufacturer's service bulletins must be entered into the aircraft's maintenance records.

14-44   AMG086

If work performed on an aircraft has been done satisfactorily, the signature of an authorized person on the maintenance records for maintenance or alterations performed constitutes

A– approval of the aircraft for return to service.
B– approval for return to service only for the work performed.
C– verification that the maintenance or alterations were performed referencing approved maintenance data.

14-44. Answer B. JSGT 14B, FAR 43.9

The signature of the person approving the work constitutes approval for return to service only for the work performed.

14-45   AMG085

During an annual inspection, if a defect is found which makes the aircraft unairworthy, the person disapproving must

A– void the aircraft's Airworthiness Certificate.
B– submit a Malfunction or Defect Report.
C– provide a written notice of the defect to the owner.

14-45. Answer C. JSGT 14B, FAR 43.11

If a defect is found during an inspection that renders the aircraft unairworthy, regulations require the person disapproving the inspection to provide a signed and dated list of discrepancies to the owner.

14-46   AMG076

Where should you find this entry? "Removed right wing from aircraft and removed skin from outer 6 feet. Repaired buckled spar 49 inches from tip in accordance with figure 8 in the manufacturer's structural repair manual No. 28-1."

A– Aircraft engine maintenance record.
B– Aircraft minor repair and alteration record.
C– FAA Form 337

14-46. Answer C. JSGT 14B, FAR 43, Appendix A & B

This entry is describing a major repair based on FAR Part 43, Appendix A criteria. All major repairs must be recorded on an FAA Form 337, or reference made in the maintenance release to work order number if the repair was made by a certified repair station.

14-47   AMG076

Which aircraft record entry is the best description of the replacement of several damaged heli-coils in a casting?

A–Eight 1/4 - 20 inch standard heli-coils were replaced. The damaged inserts were extracted, the tapped holes gauged, then new inserts installed, and tangs removed.

B–Eight 1/4 - 20 inch standard heli-coils were installed in place of damaged ones.

C–Eight 1/4 - 20 inch standard heli-coil inserts were repaired by replacing the damaged inserts with a lock-type insert, after the tapped holes were checked for corrosion.

14-47. Answer A. JSGT 14B, FGH

This question is somewhat subjective. However, when making logbook entries you should describe the work accomplished so that the reader will know, without a doubt, what you did, and what parts you used in the process. Eight 1/4 - 20 inch standard Heli-Coil® inserts were replaced. The damaged inserts were extracted, the tapped holes gauged, then new inserts installed, and tangs removed provides the most complete description of the operations involved in replacing a standard Heli-Coil insert.

14-48   AMG076

Which aircraft record entry best describes a repair of a dent in a tubular steel structure dented at a cluster?

A–Removed and replaced the damaged member.

B–Welded a reinforcing plate over the dented area.

C–Filled the damaged area with a molten metal and dressed to the original contour.

14-48. Answer B. JSGT 14B, AC 43.13-1B

To repair dents at a steel-tube cluster-joint, weld a specially formed steel patch plate over the dented area and surrounding tubes.

14-49   AMG076

If more space is needed for a work description entered on FAA Form 337, what information should be included on the attached sheet(s), in addition to the rest of the work description?

A–Make, model, and serial number of the aircraft.

B–Aircraft nationality and registration mark, and the date the work was accomplished.

C–Name, date, and office designator of the FAA inspector from the supervising district office.

14-49. Answer B. JSGT 14B, AC 43.9-1E

The FAA has issued Advisory Circular 43.9-1E which provides instruction for completion of FAA Form 337. This AC states "If additional space is needed to describe the repair or alteration, attach sheets bearing the aircraft nationality and registration mark and the date the work was completed."

14-50   AMG076
For aircraft operated under part 91, what difference is there, if any, between the record entry requirements for maintenance (e.g., repair or alteration) and the record entry requirements for inspections (beyond the description of the work performed and the type and extent of inspection)?

A– There is no difference.
B– Aircraft total time is required to be included only in the maintenance entry.
C– Aircraft total time is required to be included only in the inspection entry.

14-50. Answer C. JSGT 14B, FAR 43.9 - 43.11
This requires a comparison between Part 43.9 and Part 43.11. A close examination reveals that aircraft total time is the only additional information required for an inspection entry.

14-51   AMG076
For aircraft operated under part 91, when is aircraft total time required to be recorded in aircraft maintenance records?

A– After satisfactorily completing maintenance, preventive maintenance, rebuilding, and alteration (except inspections).
B– After satisfactorily completing inspections.
C– After satisfactorily completing maintenance, preventive maintenance, rebuilding, and alteration (including inspections).

14-51. Answer B. JGST 14-B, FAR 43.9 - 43.11
Part 43.11 requires that aircraft total time in service be recorded after an inspection. Part 43.9 which pertains to maintenance, preventive maintenance, rebuilding, and alteration does not require a record of aircraft total time in service.

14-52   AMG076
When a 100-hour inspection is completed, if separate maintenance records for the airframe, powerplant(s), and propeller(s) are maintained, where is the entry for the inspection recorded?

A– In each record.
B– In the airframe record only.
C– In any one of the records.

14-52. Answer A. FAR 43.11
Part 43.11 requires that a person approving or disapproving for return to service an aircraft, airframe, aircraft engine, propeller, appliance, or component part after any inspection performed shall make an entry in the maintenance record of that equipment.

14-53   AMG076
Which statement is true regarding the requirements for maintenance record format?

A– Any format that provides record continuity and includes the required information may be used.
B– The format provided by the manufacturer of the aircraft must be retained.
C– Any desired change from manufacturer provided format requires approval from the Federal Aviation Administration.

14-53. Answer A. JSGT 14B, FAR 43.9, AC 61-23C
Part 43.9 — Content, form, and disposition of maintenance, preventive maintenance, rebuilding, and alteration records does not require a specific format. Any format which provides record continuity and includes the required information may be used.

14-54 AMG076

Which statement is true regarding the use of FAA Form 337?

A– FAA Form 337 is authorized for use with both U.S. and foreign registered aircraft.

B– FAA Form 337 is authorized for use with U.S. registered aircraft, and foreign registered aircraft when located in the United States.

C– FAA Form 337 is not authorized for use with other than U.S. registered aircraft.

14-54. Answer C. JSGT 14B, AC 43.9-1E

Advisory Circular 43.9-1E provides instruction for completion of FAA Form 337 Major Alternations and Repairs. Paragraph 6 (d) states FAA Form 337 is not authorized for use on other than U. S. Registered aircraft.

14-55 AMG076

Who is responsible for making the entry in the maintenance records after an annual, 100 hour, or progressive inspection?

A– The owner or operator of the aircraft.

B– The person approving or disapproving for return to service.

C– The designee or inspector representing the FAA Administrator.

14-55. Answer B. JSGT 14B, FAR 43.11

Regardless of how many mechanics there are working on an aircraft, the person responsible for the logbook entry is the person approving or disapproving the aircraft for return to service.

14-56 AMG086

When approving for return to service after maintenance or alteration, the approving person must enter in the maintenance record of the aircraft

A– the date the maintenance or alteration was begun, a description (or reference to acceptable data) of work performed, the name of the person performing the work (if someone else), signature, and certificate number.

B– a description (or reference to acceptable data) of work performed, date of completion, the name of the person performing the work (if someone else), signature, and certificate number.

C– a description (or reference to acceptable data) of work performed, date of completion, the name of the person performing the work (if someone else), signature, certificate number, and kind of certificate held.

14-56. Answer C. JSGT 14B, FAR 43.9

Each person who maintains, performs preventative maintenance, rebuilds, or alters an aircraft airframe, aircraft engine, propeller, appliance, or component shall make an entry in the maintenance record containing the following information.

1. A description (or reference to acceptable data) of work performed.
2. Date the work was completed.
3. The name of the person performing the work (if someone else).
4. Signature.
5. Certificate number.
6. Kind of certificate held.

14-57   AMG079

What action is required when a minor repair is performed on a certificated aircraft?

A–An FAA Form 337 must be completed.
B–An entry in the aircraft's maintenance record is required.
C–The owner of the aircraft must annually report minor repairs to the FAA.

14-57. Answer B. JSGT 14B, FAR 43.9; FAR 43, Appendix B
All major repairs and major alterations must be accompanied by an FAA Form 337 and entered in the aircraft's permanent records. However, minor repairs and minor alterations only need to be entered in the aircraft's permanent records.

14-58   AMG076

After making a certain repair to an aircraft engine that is to be returned to service, an FAA Form 337 is prepared. How many copies are required and what is the disposition of the completed forms?

A–Two; one copy for the aircraft owner and one copy for the FAA.
B–Two; one copy for the FAA and one copy for the permanent records of the repairing agency or individual.
C–Three; one copy for the aircraft owner, one copy for the FAA, and one copy for the permanent records of the repairing agency or individual.

14-58. Answer A. JSGT 14B, FAR 43, Appendix B
The key here is that the question asks for the required number of copies. Regulations require that you give a signed copy to the aircraft owner and forward a copy to the local Flight Standards District Office (FSDO) within 48 hours after the part is approved for return to service.

14-59   AMG076

Who is responsible for upkeep of the required maintenance records for an aircraft?

A–The maintaining repair station or authorized inspector.
B–The maintaining certificated mechanic.
C–The aircraft owner.

14-59. Answer C. JSGT 14B, FAR 91.417
The person ultimately responsible for maintaining an aircraft in an airworthy condition, including its maintenance records, is the aircraft owner.

14-60   AMG076
An FAA Form 337 is used to record and document

A–preventive and unscheduled maintenance, and special inspections.
B–major and minor repairs, and major and minor alterations.
C–major repairs and major alterations.

14-60. Answer C. JSGT 14B, FAR 43, Appendix B
FAA Form 337 is used to document any major repair or major alteration to an aircraft, engine, propeller, or appliance.

14-61   AMG086

After a mechanic holding an airframe and powerplant rating completes a 100-hour inspection, what action is required before the aircraft is returned to service?

A–Make the proper entries in the aircraft's maintenance record.
B– An operational check of all systems.
C– A mechanic with an inspection authorization must approve the inspection.

14-61. Answer A. JSGT 14B, FAR 43.11

Once a 100-hour inspection is complete, the mechanic must make the appropriate entries in the aircraft's maintenance records before the aircraft can be returned to service.

14-62   AMG051

What is the status of data used as a basis for approving major repairs or alterations for return to service?

A–Data must be least FAA-acceptable when it is used for that purpose.
B–Data must be FAA-approved prior to its use for that purpose.
C–Data may be FAA-approved after its use for that purpose.

14-62. Answer B. JSGT 14B, AC 43.9-1E

Advisory Circular 43.9-1 provides instruction for completion of FAA Form 337 Major Repairs and Alternations. Paragraph 5 (h)(2) states that data used as a basis for approving major alternations or repairs for return to service must be FAA-approved prior to its use for that purpose.

14-63   AMG076

When work is performed on an aircraft that necessitates the use of FAA Form 337, who should prepare the form?

A–The person who performs or supervises the work.
B–The person who approves for return to service.
C–Either the person who approves for return to service, or aircraft owner or operator.

14-63. Answer A. JSGT 14B, AC 43.9-1E

Advisory Circular 43.9-1E provides instructions for completing FAA Form 337. Paragraph 5 states that the person who performs or supervises the work should prepare the form.

14-64   AMG076

What is/are the appropriate action(s) concerning minor repairs performed on a certified aircraft?

1. FAA Form 337's must be completed.
2. Entries must be made in the aircraft's maintenance record.
3. The owner of the aircraft must submit a record of all minor repairs to the FAA at least annually.

A–1 and 2.
B–2.
C–2 and 3.

14-64. Answer B. JSGT 14A, FAR 43.11, AC 43.9C

Minor repairs and alterations must be recorded in the aircraft's permanent maintenance records.

14-65   AMG022

In order to reconstruct lost or destroyed aircraft maintenance records, what is it necessary to establish?

A– Dates of all maintenance, preventive maintenance and alterations.

B– Dates and/or times of all 100-hour, annual, or progressive inspections.

C– Total time-in-service of the airframe.

14-65. Answer C. JSGT 14B, AC 43-9C

Advisory Circular 43-9C, paragraph 12 states that when aircraft maintenance records are lost or destroyed, they can be reconstructed by determining the aircraft's total time-in-service.

14-66   AMG082

A certificated mechanic without an inspection authorization who signs the appropriate block on FAA Form 337 is doing what?

A– Certifying that the work was done in accordance with the requirements of 14 CFR part 43.

B– Approving the work for return to service.

C– Certifying the maintenance information used as FAA-approved data.

14-66. Answer A. JSGT 14B, AC 43.9-1E

This is known as the "Conformity Statement" on a Form 337. Directly under this block it states "I certify that the repair and/or alteration made to the unit(s) identified in item 4 above and described on the reverse or attachments hereto have been made in accordance with the requirements of Part 43 of the U.S. Federal Aviation Regulations and that the information furnished herein is true and correct to the best of my knowledge."

14-67   AMG076

For aircraft operated under part 91, which of the following records must be retained and transferred with the aircraft when it is sold?

A– Records of maintenance, alterations, preventive maintenance, 100-hour, annual, and progressive inspections.

B– Records of inspections performed in accordance with 14 CFR part 43, Appendix D.

C– Records of the current status of applicable ADs, and date and time when recurring ADs are next due.

14-67. Answer C. JSGT 14B, FAR 91.419

Part 91.419 — Transfer of Maintenance Records states that records of the current status of applicable airworthiness directives (AD) including, for each, the method of compliance, the AD number, and revision date. If the AD involves recurring action, the time and date when the next action is required.

14-68   AMG062

How long are AD compliance records required to be kept?

A– Until the work is repeated or superseded by other work.

B– For one year after the work is performed, or until the work is repeated or superseded by other work.

C– They shall be retained, and then transferred with the aircraft when it is sold.

14-68. Answer C. JSGT 14B, FAR 91.417

Part 91.417 lists the length of time records must be kept. It states ADs shall be retained, and then transferred with the aircraft when it is sold.

14-69   AMG062

When is a mechanic responsible for checking AD compliance?

A– Never, the owner or operator is solely responsible.
B– When performing an inspection required under part 91, 125, or 135.
C– Anytime an aircraft or portion thereof is returned to service.

14-69. Answer B. AC 39-7C

Advisory Circular 39-7C describes Airworthiness Directives (ADs) and who is responsible for AD compliance. Paragraph 13 (b) states that maintenance persons have a direct responsibility for determining AD compliance when performing an inspection under parts 91, 121, or 135.

MECHANIC PRIVILEGES AND LIMITATIONS

CHAPTER 15

SECTION A - THE MECHANIC CERTIFICATE

Chapter 15 discusses the privileges and limitations associated with Mechanic's Certificates, Repairman's Certificates, and the Inspection Authorization.

15-1 AMG082
An aircraft owner was provided a list of discrepancies on an aircraft that was not approved for return to service after an annual inspection. Which of the following statements is/are true concerning who may correct the discrepancies?

1. Only a mechanic with an inspection authorization.
2. An appropriately rated mechanic.
3. Any certificated repair station.

A– 1.
B– 2.
C– 2 & 3.

15-1. Answer C. JSGT 15A, FAR 43.3
An A&P technician must hold an inspection authorization to perform an annual inspection. However, discrepancies may be corrected by any mechanic who is appropriately rated for the work required to correct the discrepancy. Likewise, a certificated repair station may perform maintenance or alterations on any article for which it is rated, within the limitations in its operations specifications.

15-2 AMG082
Which of the following may a certificated airframe and powerplant mechanic perform on aircraft and approve for return to service?

1. A 100-hour inspection.
2. An annual inspection, under specified circumstances.
3. A progressive inspection, under specified circumstances.

A– 1 and 3.
B– 1, 2, and 3.
C– 1 and 2.

15-2. Answer A. JSGT 15A, FAR 65
Provided airframe and powerplant mechanics are current and have the necessary experience, they may return an aircraft to service following a 100-hour inspection or a progressive inspection. To return an aircraft to service following an annual inspection, the mechanic must hold an Inspection Authorization.

15-3   AMG054

What is the maximum penalty for cheating or other unauthorized conduct when taking an FAA mechanic test?

A– Ineligibility to receive any certificate or rating for one year.

B– Ineligibility to receive any certificate or rating for one year, and suspension or revocation of any certificate held.

C– Ineligibility to receive any certificate or rating for one year, and suspension of any certificate held.

15-3. Answer B. JSGT 15A, FAR 65.18

According to Part 65.18 (b), no person who commits a prohibited act when taking a written test is eligible for any airman or ground instructor certificate or rating under this chapter for a period of one year after the date of that act. In addition, the commission of that act is a basis for suspending or revoking any airman or ground instructor certificate or rating held by that person.

15-4   AMG082

Certificated mechanics with a powerplant rating may perform the

A– any inspection required by the Federal Aviation Regulations on a powerplant or propeller or any component thereof, and may release the same to service.

B– 100-hour and/or annual inspections required by the Federal Aviation Regulations on powerplants, propellers, or any components thereof, and may release the same to service.

C– 100-hour inspection required by the Federal Aviation Regulations on a powerplant, propeller, or any component thereof, and may release the same to service.

15-4. Answer C. JSGT 15A, FAR 65.87

A certificated mechanic with a powerplant rating may approve and return to service a powerplant or propeller or any related part or appliance, after performing a 100-hour inspection required by Part 91.

15-5   AMG082

The 100-hour inspection required by FARs for certain aircraft being operated for hire may be performed by

A– persons working under the supervision of an appropriately rated mechanic, but the aircraft must be approved by the mechanic for return to service.

B– appropriately rated mechanics only if they have an inspection authorization.

C– appropriately rated mechanics and approved by them for return to service.

15-5. Answer C. JSGT 15A, FAR 65.85, FAR 65.87

According to FAR Part 65, aircraft mechanics with Airframe and Powerplant ratings may perform a 100-hour inspection and return an aircraft to service. Persons working under the supervision of an appropriately rated mechanic may not, according to FAR 43.3, conduct a 100-hour inspection. Appropriately rated mechanics and approved by them for return to service is incorrect because you do not need an inspection authorization to conduct a 100-hour inspection.

15-6 AMG081

A person working under the supervision of a certificated mechanic with an airframe and powerplant rating is not authorized to perform

A– repair of a wing brace strut by welding.
B– a 100-hour inspection.
C– repair of an engine mount by riveting.

15-6. Answer B. JSGT 15A, FAR 43.3

A person working under the supervision of a certificated mechanic may perform the maintenance, preventive maintenance, and alterations that his supervisor is authorized to perform. However, this authorization is not extended to any inspections required by Part 91 or Part 125. This includes 100-hour inspections.

15-7 AMG082

Certificated mechanics, under their general certificate privileges, may

A– perform minor repairs to instruments.
B– perform 100-hour inspection of instruments.
C– perform minor alterations to instruments.

15-7. Answer B. JSGT 15A, FAR 43, Appendix D; FAR 65.81

Instrument repairs and alterations must be accomplished by an appropriately rated repair station. The mechanic can only inspect the instruments within the scope of the 100-hour inspection. This includes inspecting for poor condition, mounting, marking, and where practicable, for improper operation.

15-8 AMG081

An Airworthiness Directive requires that a propeller be altered. Certificated mechanics could

A– perform and approve the work for return to service if it is a minor alteration.
B– not perform the work because it is an alteration.
C– not perform the work because they are not allowed to perform and approve for return to service, repairs or alterations to propellers.

15-8. Answer A. JSGT 15A, FAR 65.81, FAR 65.87

Powerplant certificated mechanics may perform minor repairs and minor alterations on propellers and return them to service.

15-9 AMG082

FAA certificated mechanics may

A– approve for return to service a major repair for which they are rated.
B– supervise and approve a 100-hour inspection.
C– approve for return to service a minor alteration they have performed appropriate to the rating(s) they hold.

15-9. Answer C. JSGT 15A, FAR 65.81

FAA-certificated mechanics are authorized to perform minor alterations appropriate to the rating(s) they hold, and return them to service.

15-10   AMG081

A certificated mechanic with a powerplant rating may perform the

A– annual inspection required by the FAR's on a powerplant or any component thereof and approve and return the same to service.

B– 100-hour inspection required by the FAR's on a powerplant or any component thereof and approve and return the same to service.

C– 100-hour inspection required by the FAR's on an airframe, powerplant, or any component thereof and approve and return the same to service.

15-10. Answer B. JSGT 15A, FAR 65.87

FAR Part 65 authorizes the powerplant certificated mechanic to perform a 100-hour inspection on a powerplant, propeller, and component parts thereof, and approve the items for return to service.

15-11   AMG082

What part of the FAR's prescribes the requirements for issuing mechanic certificates and associated ratings and the general operating rules for the holders of these certificates and ratings?

A– 14 CFR Part 43.

B– 14 CFR Part 91.

C– 14 CFR Part 65.

15-11. Answer C. JSGT 15A, FAR 65.1

FAR Part 65 covers the certification requirements for all airmen other than flight crewmembers. This includes mechanics and repairmen.

15-12   AMG082

A certificated mechanic shall not exercise the privileges of the certificate and rating unless, within the preceding 24 months, the Administrator has found that the certificate holder is able to do the work or the certificate holder has

A– served as a mechanic under the certificate and rating for at least 18 months.

B– served as a mechanic under the certificate and rating for at least 12 months.

C– served as a mechanic under the certificate and rating for at least 6 months.

15-12. Answer C. JSGT 15A, FAR 65.83

To be considered current, a certificated mechanic must, for at least 6 months out of 24, serve as a mechanic under his certificate and rating.

15-13   AMG081

(1) Certificated mechanics with an airframe rating may perform a minor repair to an airspeed indicator providing they have the necessary tools and equipment available.
(2) Certificated mechanics with a powerplant rating may perform a major repair to a propeller providing they have the necessary tools and equipment available. Regarding the above statements,

A– only No. 1 is true.
B– neither No. 1 nor No. 2 is true.
C– only No. 2 is true.

15-13. Answer B. JSGT 15A, FAR 65.81
Neither of these statements is true. Even minor repairs to instruments must be accomplished by a certified instrument repair station and certificated powerplant mechanics may only perform MINOR repairs to propellers.

15-14   AMG086

Who has the authority to approve for return to service a powerplant or propeller or any part thereof after a 100-hour inspection?

A– A mechanic with a powerplant rating.
B– Any certificated repairman.
C– Personnel of any certificated repair station.

15-14. Answer A. JSGT 15A, FAR 65.87
A certificated mechanic with the powerplant rating is authorized to perform a 100-hour inspection and return to service a powerplant, propeller, or any part thereof.

15-15   AMG081

Instrument repairs may be performed

A– by the instrument manufacturer only.
B– by an FAA-approved instrument repair station.
C– on airframe instruments by mechanics with an airframe rating.

15-15. Answer B. JSGT 15A, AC 43.13-1B
Repair and overhaul of aircraft instruments must be made by an FAA-approved facility having proper test equipment, adequate manufacturer's maintenance manuals and service bulletins, and qualified personnel.

15-16   AMG082

Which of the following statements is true for a certificated and appropriately rated mechanic regarding repairs and alterations?

A– He/she may perform an airframe major repair or major alteration, but cannot approve the work for return to service.
B– He/she may perform airframe minor repairs and minor alterations and approve the work for return to service, but cannot perform an airframe major repair or major alteration.
C– He/she may perform an airframe major repair or major alteration and approve the work, but not the entire aircraft, for return to service.

15-16. Answer A. JSGT 15A, FAR 65.85
Part 65.85 states that a certificated mechanic with an airframe rating may approve and return to service an airframe, or any related part or appliance, after he has performed, supervised, or inspected its maintenance or alteration (excluding major repairs and major alterations).

15-17   AMG082
When may an otherwise qualified mechanic who does not read, write, speak, and understand the English language be eligible to apply for a mechanic certificate?

A– When a special authorization has been issued by the supervising FAA Flight Standards District Office.
B– When employed outside the United States by a U.S. air carrier.
C– When employed outside the United States.

15-17. Answer B. JSGT 15A, FAR 65.71
Part 65.71 (a) (2) says that an applicant who does not read, write, speak, and understand English must be employed outside of the United States by a U.S. air carrier, and have his certificate endorsed "Valid only outside the United States."

15-18   AMG082
What is the maximum duration of a temporary airman certificate?

A– 60 days.
B– 90 days.
C– 120 days.

15-18. Answer C. JSGT 15A, FAR 65.13
Part 65.13 provides for a certificate and ratings effective for a period of not more than 120 days to be issued to a qualified applicant.

15-19   AMG082
Why is a mechanic applicant issued a temporary certificate after successful completion of the required tests?

A– To allow for review of his/her application and supplementary documents.
B– So that a background check/investigation may be completed.
C– Both of the other two choices.

15-19. Answer A. JSGT 15A, FAR 65.13
Part 65.13 provides for a temporary certificate to be issued pending review of the application and supplementary documents.

15-20   AMG082
What is the normal duration a mechanic certificate with airframe and/or powerplant ratings?

A– Until the holder is relieved of duties for which the holder was employed and certificated.
B– Until surrendered, suspended, or revoked.
C– Until 24 months after the holder has last exercised the privileges of the certificate.

15-20. Answer B. JSGT 15A, FAR 65.15
Part 65.15 (a) indicates that certificate a certificate or rating issued under this part is effective until it is surrendered, suspended, or revoked.

15-21   AMG067
How long does the holder of a certificate issued under 14 CFR part 65 have to notify the FAA after any change in permanent mailing address?

A– 30 days.
B– 60 days.
C– 90 days.

15-21. Answer A. JSGT 15A, FAR 65.21
Part 65.21 states that certificate holders shall notify the FAA within 30 days after any change in permanent mailing address.

15-22   AMG054
Under Title 14 of the Code of Federal Regulations, what is the maximum penalty for falsification, alteration, or fraudulent reproduction of certificates, logbooks, reports, and records?

A– Ineligibility to receive any certificate or rating for one year.
B– Imprisonment for one year and a $5,000.00 fine.
C– Suspension or revocation of any certificate held.

15-22. Answer C. JSGT 15A, FAR 65.20
According to Part 65.20 (b), the acts listed in the question is a basis for suspending or revoking any airman or ground instructor certificate or rating held by that person.

15-23   AMG082
Under the Federal Aviation Regulations, an aviation maintenance technician is required to perform maintenance on an aircraft so that it

A– always meets its original type design.
B– is at least equal to its original or properly altered condition.
C– exceeds minimum standards with regard to aerodynamic function, structural strength, resistance to vibration, and other qualities affecting airworthiness.

15-23. Answer B. FAR 43.13
Each person maintaining, altering, or performing preventive maintenance, shall do that work in such a manner and use materials of such a quality, that the condition of the aircraft, airframe, aircraft engine, propeller, or appliance worked on will be at least equal to its original or properly altered condition.

LEARNING STATEMENT CODES AND LEARNING STATEMENTS

Learning Statement Codes and Learning Statements for Inspection Authorization

Code	Learning Statement
IAR001	Calculate alteration specification
IAR002	Calculate center of gravity
IAR003	Calculate electrical load
IAR004	Calculate proof loading
IAR005	Calculate repair specific
IAR006	Calculate sheet metal repair
IAR007	Calculate temperature conversion
IAR008	Calculate weight and balance - adjust weight / fuel
IAR009	Determine alteration parameters
IAR010	Determine alteration requirements
IAR011	Determine Correct data
IAR012	Determine data application
IAR013	Determine design specific
IAR014	Determine fabrication specification
IAR015	Determine process specific
IAR016	Determine regulatory requirement
IAR017	Determine regulatory requirements
IAR018	Determine repair parameters
IAR019	Determine repair requirements
IAR020	Interpret data
IAR021	Interpret regulations
IAR022	Recall alteration / design fundamentals
IAR023	Recall engine repair fundamentals
IAR024	Recall fundamental inspection principles - airframe / engine
IAR025	Recall MEL requirements
IAR026	Recall principles of corrosion control
IAR027	Recall principles of sheet metal forming
IAR028	Recall principles of system fundamentals
IAR029	Recall principles of weight and balance
IAR030	Recall regulatory requirements
IAR031	Recall regulatory specific

Code	Learning Statement
IAR032	Recall repair fundamentals

Learning Statement Codes and Learning Statements for Aviation Mechanic - General Exams

Code	Learning Statement
AMG001	Ability to draw / sketch repairs / alterations
AMG002	Calculate center of gravity
AMG003	Calculate weight and balance
AMG004	Determine correct data
AMG005	Determine regulatory requirement.
AMG006	Interpret drag ratio from charts
AMG007	Recall aerodynamic fundamentals
AMG008	Recall air density
AMG009	Recall aircraft cleaning - materials / techniques
AMG010	Recall aircraft component markings
AMG011	Recall aircraft control cables - install / inspect / repair / service
AMG012	Recall aircraft corrosion - principles / control / prevention
AMG013	Recall aircraft drawings - detail / assembly
AMG014	Recall aircraft drawings / blueprints - lines / symbols / sketching
AMG015	Recall aircraft electrical system - install / inspect / repair / service
AMG016	Recall aircraft engines - performance charts
AMG017	Recall aircraft hardware - bolts / nuts / fasteners / fittings / valves
AMG018	Recall aircraft instruments - tachometer indications / dual tachometers
AMG019	Recall aircraft metals - inspect / test / repair / identify / heat treat
AMG020	Recall aircraft metals - types / tools / fasteners
AMG021	Recall aircraft publications - aircraft listings
AMG022	Recall aircraft records - required / destroyed
AMG023	Recall aircraft repair - major
AMG024	Recall airframe - inspections
AMG025	Recall airworthiness certificates - validity / requirements
AMG026	Recall ATA codes
AMG027	Recall basic physics - matter / energy / gas
AMG028	Recall data - approved
AMG029	Recall dissymmetry
AMG030	Recall effects of frost / snow on airfoils
AMG031	Recall electrical system - components / operating principles / characteristics/ symbols
AMG032	Recall environmental factors affecting maintenance performance
AMG033	Recall external loading
AMG034	Recall flight characteristics - autorotation / compressibility
AMG035	Recall flight operations - air taxi
AMG036	Recall fluid lines - install / inspect / repair / service
AMG037	Recall fluid lines - material / coding
AMG038	Recall forces acting on aircraft - angle of incidence
AMG039	Recall forces acting on aircraft - yaw / adverse yaw
AMG040	Recall fuel - types / characteristics / contamination / fueling / defueling / dumping
AMG041	Recall fundamental inspection principles - airframe / engine
AMG042	Recall fundamental material properties

Code	Learning Statement
AMG043	Recall generator system - components / operating principles / characteristics
AMG044	Recall geometry
AMG045	Recall ground operations - start / move / service / secure aircraft
AMG046	Recall helicopter engine control system
AMG047	Recall helicopter flight controls
AMG048	Recall information on an Airworthiness Directive
AMG049	Recall instrument panel mounting
AMG050	Recall maintenance error management
AMG051	Recall maintenance publications - service / parts / repair
AMG052	Recall maintenance resource management
AMG053	Recall mathematics - percentages / decimals / fractions / ratio / general
AMG054	Recall penalties - falsification / cheating
AMG055	Recall physics - work forces
AMG056	Recall pitch control - collective / cyclic
AMG057	Recall precision measuring tools - meters / gauges / scales / calipers
AMG058	Recall reciprocating engine - components / operating principles / characteristics
AMG059	Recall regulations - aircraft inspection / records / expiration
AMG060	Recall regulations - aircraft operator certificate
AMG061	Recall regulations - aircraft registration / marks
AMG062	Recall regulations - Airworthiness Directives
AMG063	Recall regulations - airworthiness requirements / responsibilities
AMG064	Recall regulations - certificate of maintenance review requirements
AMG065	Recall regulations - Certificate of Release
AMG066	Recall regulations - certification of aircraft and components
AMG067	Recall regulations - change of address
AMG068	Recall regulations - check periods
AMG069	Recall regulations - determine mass and balance
AMG070	Recall regulations - display / inspection of licences and certificates
AMG071	Recall regulations - emergency equipment
AMG072	Recall regulations - flight / operating manual marking / placard
AMG073	Recall regulations - housing and facility requirements
AMG074	Recall regulations - instrument / equipment requirements
AMG075	Recall regulations - maintenance control / procedure manual
AMG076	Recall regulations - maintenance reports / records / entries
AMG077	Recall regulations - maintenance requirements
AMG078	Recall regulations - minimum equipment list
AMG079	Recall regulations - minor / major repairs
AMG080	Recall regulations - persons authorized for return to service
AMG081	Recall regulations - persons authorized to perform maintenance
AMG082	Recall regulations - privileges / limitations of maintenance certificates / licences
AMG083	Recall regulations - privileges of approved maintenance organizations
AMG084	Recall regulations - reapplication after revocation / suspension
AMG085	Recall regulations - reporting failures / malfunctions / defects
AMG086	Recall regulations - return to service
AMG087	Recall regulations - special airworthiness certificates / requirements

Code	Learning Statement
AMG088	Recall regulations - special flight permit
AMG089	Recall regulations - weighing an aircraft
AMG090	Recall repair fundamentals - turnbuckles
AMG091	Recall rotor system - components / operating principles / characteristics
AMG092	Recall rotorcraft vibration - characteristics / sources
AMG093	Recall starter / ignition system - components / operating principles / characteristics
AMG094	Recall starter system - starting procedures
AMG095	Recall turbine engines - components / operational characteristics / associated instruments
AMG096	Recall turbine engines - install / inspect / repair / service / hazards
AMG097	Recall type certificate data sheet (TCDS) / supplemental type certificate (STC)
AMG098	Recall welding types / techniques / equipment
AMG099	Recall work / power / force / motion

Learning Statement Codes and Learning Statements for Aviation Mechanic - Airframe Exam

Code	Learning Statement
AMA001	Recall aerodynamic fundamentals
AMA002	Recall air conditioning system - components / operating principles / characteristics
AMA003	Recall aircraft component markings
AMA004	Recall aircraft components material - flame resistant
AMA005	Recall aircraft cooling system - charging / leaking / oil / pressure / water
AMA006	Recall aircraft cooling system - components / operating principles / characteristics
AMA007	Recall aircraft corrosion - principles / control / prevention
AMA008	Recall aircraft engines - indicating system
AMA009	Recall aircraft exterior lighting - systems / components
AMA010	Recall aircraft flight indicator system
AMA011	Recall aircraft hardware - bolts / nuts / fasteners / fittings / valves
AMA012	Recall aircraft heating system - exhaust jacket inspection
AMA013	Recall aircraft instruments - install / inspect / adjust / repair / markings
AMA014	Recall aircraft instruments - types / components / operating principles / characteristics
AMA015	Recall aircraft lighting - install / inspect / repair / service
AMA016	Recall aircraft metals - inspect / test / repair / identify
AMA017	Recall aircraft metals - types / tools / fasteners
AMA018	Recall aircraft warning systems - navigation / stall / takeoff
AMA019	Recall airframe - inspections
AMA020	Recall airframe - repair / component installation
AMA021	Recall airframe design - structures / components
AMA022	Recall alternators - components / operating principles / characteristics
AMA023	Recall antenna system - install / inspect / repair / service
AMA024	Recall anti-icing / deicing - methods / systems
AMA025	Recall autopilot - components / operating principles / characteristics
AMA026	Recall autopilot - install / inspect / repair / service
AMA027	Recall avionics - components / operating principles / characteristics
AMA028	Recall avionics - install / inspect / repair / service
AMA029	Recall basic hand tools / torque values
AMA030	Recall batteries - capacity / charging / types / storage / rating / precautions
AMA031	Recall brake system - components / operating principles / characteristics
AMA032	Recall brake system - install / inspect / repair / service
AMA033	Recall carburetor - icing / anti-icing
AMA034	Recall chemical rain repellant
AMA035	Recall combustion heaters - components / operating principles / characteristics
AMA036	Recall compass - components / operating principles / characteristics
AMA037	Recall composite materials - types / repairs / techniques / processes
AMA038	Recall control cables - install / inspect / repair / service
AMA039	Recall DC electric motors - components / operating principles / characteristics
AMA040	Recall dope and fabric - materials / techniques / hazards
AMA041	Recall electrical system - components / operating principles / characteristics / symbols
AMA042	Recall electrical system - install / inspect / repair / service

Code	Learning Statement
AMA043	Recall electronic test equipment
AMA044	Recall Emergency Locator Transmitter (ELT) - operation / battery / testing
AMA045	Recall fiberglass - install / troubleshoot / service / repair
AMA046	Recall fire detection system - types / components / operating principles / characteristics
AMA047	Recall fire detection systems - install / inspect / repair / service
AMA048	Recall fire extinguishing systems - components / operating principles / characteristics
AMA049	Recall flap overload valve
AMA050	Recall flight characteristics - longitudinal stability / instability
AMA051	Recall fluid lines - material / coding
AMA052	Recall fuel - types / characteristics / contamination / fueling / defueling / dumping
AMA053	Recall fuel / oil - anti-icing / deicing
AMA054	Recall fuel system - components / operating principles / characteristics
AMA055	Recall fuel system - install / troubleshoot / service / repair
AMA056	Recall fuel system - types
AMA057	Recall fuel/air mixture - idle rich mixture - RPM rise
AMA058	Recall fundamental material properties
AMA059	Recall fuselage stations
AMA060	Recall helicopter control system
AMA061	Recall helicopter control system - collective
AMA062	Recall helicopter drive system - free wheeling unit
AMA063	Recall hydraulic systems - components / operating principles / characteristics
AMA064	Recall hydraulic systems - fluids
AMA065	Recall hydraulic systems - install / inspect / repair / service
AMA066	Recall instrument panel installation - shock mounts
AMA067	Recall instruments - manifold pressure indicating system
AMA068	Recall landing gear system - components / operating principles / characteristics
AMA069	Recall landing gear system - install / inspect / repair / service
AMA070	Recall maintenance publications - service / parts / repair
AMA071	Recall navigation / communication systems - types / operational characteristics
AMA072	Recall oxygen system - components / operating principles / characteristics
AMA073	Recall oxygen system - install / inspect / repair / service / precautions
AMA074	Recall oxygen system - quality / types / contamination / cylinders / pressure
AMA075	Recall physics - work forces
AMA076	Recall pitot-static system - components / operating principles / characteristics
AMA077	Recall pitot-static system - install / inspect / repair / service
AMA078	Recall plastic fundamentals - installation / cleaning / repair / characteristics
AMA079	Recall pneumatic system - components / operating principles / characteristics
AMA080	Recall pressurization system - components / operating principles / characteristics
AMA081	Recall primary flight controls - inspect / adjust / repair
AMA082	Recall primary flight controls - types / purpose / functionality
AMA083	Recall radar altimeter - indications
AMA084	Recall radar altimeter - signals
AMA085	Recall radio system - components / operating principles / characteristics
AMA086	Recall radio system - install / inspect / repair / service
AMA087	Recall radio system - licence requirements / frequencies

Code	Learning Statement
AMA088	Recall regulations - airworthiness requirements / responsibilities
AAM089	Recall regulations - maintenance reports / records / entries
AMA090	Recall regulations - privileges / limitations of maintenance certificates / licences
AAM091	Recall rotor system - components / operating principles / characteristics
AMA092	Recall secondary flight control system - inspect / adjust / repair
AMA093	Recall secondary flight control system - types / purpose / functionality
AMA094	Recall sheet metal fabrication - blueprints / shaping / construction
AMA095	Recall smoke detection systems - types / components / operating principles / characteristics
AMA096	Recall static pressure system - install / inspect / repair / service
AMA097	Recall tires - install / inspect / repair / service / storage
AMA098	Recall turbine engines - components / operational characteristics / associated instruments
AMA099	Recall type certificate data sheet (TCDS) / supplemental type certificate (STC)
AMA100	Recall weight and balance - equipment installation / CG / general principles
AMA101	Recall welding / soldering - types / techniques / equipment
AMA102	Recall wooden components - failures / decay / patching / gluing / substitutions

Learning Statement Codes and Learning Statements for Aviation Mechanic - Powerplant Exam

Code	Learning Statement
AMP001	Recall aircraft alternators - components / operating principles / characteristics
AMP002	Recall aircraft batteries - capacity / charging / types / storage / rating / precautions
AMP003	Recall aircraft carburetor - icing / anti-icing
AMP004	Recall aircraft component markings
AMP005	Recall aircraft cooling system - components / operating principles / characteristics
AMP006	Recall aircraft electrical system - install / inspect / repair / service
AMP007	Recall aircraft engine - inspections / cleaning
AMP008	Recall aircraft engines - components / operating principles / characteristics
AMP009	Recall aircraft engines - indicating system
AMP010	Recall aircraft fire classifications
AMP011	Recall aircraft hydraulic systems - components / operating principles / characteristics
AMP012	Recall aircraft instruments - types / components / operating principles / characteristics / markings
AMP013	Recall airflow systems - Bellmouth compressor inlet
AMP014	Recall airframe - inspections
AMP015	Recall altitude compensator / aneroid valve
AMP016	Recall anti-icing / deicing - methods / systems
AMP017	Recall Auxiliary Power Units - components / operating principles / characteristics
AMP018	Recall Auxiliary Power Units - install / inspect / repair / service
AMP019	Recall axial flow compressor - components / operating principles / characteristics
AMP020	Recall basic physics - matter / energy / gas
AMP021	Recall carburetor - effects of carburetor heat / heat control
AMP022	Recall carburetors - components / operating principles / characteristics
AMP023	Recall carburetors - install / inspect / repair / service
AMP024	Recall data - approved
AMP025	Recall DC electric motors - components / operating principles / characteristics
AMP026	Recall electrical system - components / operating principles / characteristics
AMP027	Recall engine cooling system - components / operating principles / characteristics
AMP028	Recall engine cooling system - install / inspect / repair / service
AMP029	Recall engine lubricating oils - function / grades / viscosity / types
AMP030	Recall engine lubricating system - components / operating principles / characteristics
AMP031	Recall engine lubricating system - install / inspect / repair / service
AMP032	Recall engine operations - thrust / thrust reverser
AMP033	Recall engine pressure ratio - EPR
AMP034	Recall fire detection system - types / components / operating principles / characteristics
AMP035	Recall fire detection systems - install / inspect / repair / service
AMP036	Recall fire extinguishing systems - components / operating principles / characteristics
AMP037	Recall float type carburetor - components / operating principles / characteristics
AMP038	Recall float type carburetor - install / inspect / repair / service
AMP039	Recall fuel - types / characteristics / contamination / fueling / defueling / dumping
AMP040	Recall fuel / oil - anti-icing / deicing
AMP041	Recall fuel system - components / operating principles / characteristics
AMP042	Recall fuel system - install / troubleshoot / service / repair

Code	Learning Statement
AMP043	Recall fuel system - types
AMP044	Recall generator system - components / operating principles / characteristics
AMP045	Recall information on an Airworthiness Directive
AMP046	Recall magneto - components / operating principles / characteristics
AMP047	Recall magneto - install / inspect / repair / service
AMP048	Recall maintenance publications - service / parts / repair
AMP049	Recall piston assembly - components / operating principles / characteristics
AMP050	Recall powerplant design - structures / components
AMP051	Recall pressure type carburetor - components / operating principles / characteristics
AMP052	Recall propeller system - install / inspect / repair / service
AMP053	Recall propeller system - types/ components / operating principles / characteristics
AMP054	Recall radial engine - components / operating principles / characteristics
AMP055	Recall radial engine - install / inspect / repair / service
AMP056	Recall reciprocating engine - components / operating principles / characteristics
AMP057	Recall reciprocating engine - install / inspect / repair / service
AMP058	Recall regulations - maintenance reports / records / entries
AMP059	Recall regulations - privileges / limitations of maintenance certificates / licences
AMP060	Recall regulations - privileges of approved maintenance organizations
AMP061	Recall rotor system - components / operating principles / characteristics
AMP062	Recall sea level - standard temperature / pressure
AMP063	Recall starter / ignition system - components / operating principles / characteristics
AMP064	Recall starter / ignition system - install / inspect / repair / service
AMP065	Recall starter system - starting procedures
AMP066	Recall thermocouples - components / operating principles / characteristics
AMP067	Recall thermocouples - install / inspect / repair / service
AMP068	Recall turbine engines - components / operational characteristics / associated instruments
AMP069	Recall turbine engines - install / inspect / repair / service / hazards
AMP070	Recall turbocharger system - components / operating principles / characteristics
AMP071	Recall turbojet - components / operating principles / characteristics
AMP072	Recall type certificate data sheet (TCDS) / supplemental type certificate (STC)
AMP073	Recall welding types / techniques / equipment

GENERAL ORAL AND PRACTICAL EXAM STUDY GUIDE

This appendix of the General Study Guide has been developed to aid you in preparing for the FAA General Mechanic on how applicants from Aviation Maintenance Technician Schools (AMTS), the military, or persons applying for certification through occupational experience can best prepare, apply for, and take the exam.

The second area of the appendix includes sample oral exam questions and answers, divided by subject area. These are typical questions that an examiner is likely to ask during testing. It should be noted that, since the FAA allows DMEs the flexibility to create their own Oral questions and answers, it is impossible for this or any study guide to provide the exact questions that the examiner will use. However, if you understand these questions, you should be adequately prepared to pass the test. The answers to the questions are provided along with references that can be used as an additional source of study material concerning each question.

The final part of this appendix includes sample practical projects that an examiner may assign during your test. Since the testing facilities and equipment vary between examiners, it is impossible to cover all the projects that you may be tested on. However, if you are able to perform the sample projects presented in this test guide, you should be adequately prepared to pass the FAA Practical Exam. The projects are divided into subject areas and follow the corresponding Oral questions.

The practical projects also include a skill level that must be reached in order to satisfactorily complete the projects. The completion standards are:

- Projects that require Level 1 skills are accomplished by your showing or explaining basic principles without using any manipulative skills.
- Level 2 projects require you to have knowledge of general principles, and you must demonstrate limited practical application. For these projects, you will likely be required to demonstrate sufficient manipulative skills to perform basic operations.
- Level 3 projects require you to have a high degree of knowledge of general principles and to demonstrate a high degree of practical application. To complete Level 3 projects satisfactorily, you are required to demonstrate the ability to complete the project to simulate a return-to-service condition.

Finally, each project includes a list of materials that the examiner will make available for you to use to complete the project. The examiner must provide you with access to current publications, and also will provide you with special tools and equipment. However, you should verify what tools you will be required to provide when you schedule the test. In most cases, you will at least need basic hand tools, including an inspection mirror(s), flashlight, sockets with ratchets, screwdrivers, wrenches, and safety equipment.

Requirements For Certification

The requirements for the certification of aircraft mechanics are outlined in Title 14 of the Code of Federal Regulations (14 CFR, Part 65)

Eligibility Requirements

To be eligible for a mechanic certificate, a person must:

1. Be at least 18 years of age.
2. Be able to read, write, speak, and understand the English language (unless the applicant is to be employed outside the United States by a U.S. air carrier, in which case the certificate will have a limitation to be effective only outside the United States).
3. Have passed all of the prescribed Airman Knowledge Exams within a period of 24 calendar months. If the application is for an original issuance for a mechanic certificate, depending on the rating sought, you must have passed the General and Airframe Knowledge Exams, or General and Powerplant Knowledge Exams, within 24 calendar months of taking the Oral and Practical Exams.
4. Comply with other applicable regulations of Part 65 as detailed below.

Experience and Application Requirements

There are two ways in which an applicant may meet the FAA requirements to be eligible to obtain a Mechanic Certificate.

The first way is to present a certificate of completion from an Aviation Maintenance Technician School (AMTS) to an examiner that is affiliated with the school. If you take the Airman Knowledge, Oral, or Practical Exams with an examiner that is affiliated with your AMTS, the school will provide two copies of FAA Form 8610-2 (Airman Certificate and/or Rating Application), and authorize you to take the required tests. If you are a graduate of an AMTS and wish to complete the Airman Knowledge or Oral and Practical Exams at a facility other than the AMTS that you attended, you must go to an FAA FSDO to have an Airworthiness Inspector authorize you to take the tests. At that time, the inspector will have you fill out two copies of the FAA Form 8610-2 and will ask you for a photo identification. Before you can begin any FAA required tests, you must present both forms with original signatures and photo identification. DO NOT LOSE THE FORMS and do not allow the Airman Knowledge Testing Center personnel to keep either of the originals (although they may make a photocopy for their records).

The second way to qualify for an Airman Mechanic Certificate is to present the FAA with documentary evidence showing work or military experience applicable to the rating(s) sought. This documentation should include descriptions of the work showing that the procedures, practices, materials, and equipment generally used in constructing, maintaining, or altering airframes or powerplants has been obtained. It is helpful if the documentation includes a contact phone number for a person that served in a supervisory position in case the FAA inspector needs further verification. For applicants with military experience, military discharge Form DD-214 may be used along with any training certificates received during military service. Part 65 requires a minimum of 18 months experience maintaining airframes to qualify for the Airframe Rating, or 30 months combined experience maintaining airframes and powerplants to qualify for both an Airframe and Powerplant rating. The work experience should essentially reflect the equivalent of a forty-hour workweek, although the work does not need to be consecutive.

The Oral and Practical Exam

The FAA Oral and Practical Exam for an Aircraft Mechanic Certificate is probably one of the most difficult FAA exams to prepare for because of the large amount of material that must be learned. For this reason, test preparation plays an important role in your ability to successfully pass the exams. However, in no way do we encourage you to memorize our test preparation materials. Instead, use your test guide as an aid to gain an in-depth understanding of concepts and procedures. Ultimately, you will find that the knowledge gained will benefit you throughout your career as an Aviation Maintenance Technician.

The purpose of this section of the appendix is to help answer some of the questions you may have about the oral and practical exams. With an understanding of the testing procedures, you will likely have less apprehension during the exam, allowing you to focus on the tasks that the examiner assigns you.

Who Conducts the Oral and Practical Exams?

The Oral and Practical Exam may be given either by a Designated Mechanic Examiner (DME) or an FAA inspector. In most areas of the country, the FAA does not have the manpower to conduct the exam, in which case you will need to schedule your exams with a DME.

How Do I Locate a DME?

If you are a graduate of an AMTS, it is likely that the oral and practical exams will be conducted by a DME that is on staff with the school. If you're applying for a Mechanic's Certificate by showing occupational or military experience, you will need to locate a DME on your own to make arrangements for testing. The names and phone numbers of DMEs in your area are available by calling your local FAA Flight Standards District Office (FSDO). The phone numbers for these offices are generally found in your local phone directory under United States Government, Federal Aviation Administration, or Department of Transportation.

How Much Do the Exams Cost?

If you take your exam from a DME, they will have their own fee for each section of the exam that you take. The fees are set by the DME and vary between examiners. It is advisable for you to shop around and talk to different DMEs about their fees. Also, ask what method of payment is required. Some DMEs will only accept cash, while others will accept checks or even credit cards.

How Long Do the Exams Take?

There is no established maximum time limit for the exams. However, there is a minimum time requirement. The minimum time allocated for the General Oral and Practical Exams is 2 hours, while the Airframe or Powerplant Exams require 4 hours each to complete. If you do not already hold a Mechanic Certificate, you will be required to take both the General and Airframe or Powerplant Exams for a total minimum time of 6 hours. However, if you already hold an Aircraft Mechanic Certificate with one rating, you will not be required to retake the General Mechanic Exam to obtain the other rating. Although these minimum times have been established, the actual times vary. It is not uncommon for the exams to take two or three times longer than the minimum requirements. Ask the examiner about typical time requirements when making arrangements to take the exams, and plan your schedule to allow adequate time to complete them.

What Items Should I Bring For the Exams?

Since you and the examiner must schedule a large block of time for the exams, it is critical that you come with all the required materials. The following items should be organized and readily available to you no later than one day before your scheduled exam. If you fail to bring any of the following items with you for the exam, the examiner may not begin administering any portion of the exam, and you will have to reschedule another time with the examiner. To verify that you have the required items, use the following list to check off items before departing to take the exam. The required items include:

✓ Two copies of FAA Form 8610-2 with original signatures — if you obtained these documents from an FAA Airworthiness Inspector, the inspector's original signature must be included.

✓ Original Airman Knowledge Exam results — copies are not accepted and if the originals are lost, you must request a replacement from the FAA. The address and information that must be included with the request are given in the introduction section of this test guide. Keep in mind that the replacements may take over a week to obtain.

✓ Photo Identification — acceptable photo identifications include a state issued driver's license or photo identification, government identification card, passport, alien residency (green) card, or military identification card.

✓ Examiner's Fee — correct cash or other form of payment as arranged with the examiner.

✓ Basic Hand Tools — assorted ratchets and sockets, screwdrivers, wrenches, mirror, flashlight, and other hand tools as required by the examiner.

✓ Reference Materials — consider bringing the General, Powerplant, and/or Airframe Textbooks, AC 43.13-1B and 2A, and other reference materials that you may find useful. You can use the reference materials while taking the practical portion of the test but cannot use any references during the oral portion of the exam, except those given to you by the examiner.

✓ Calculator, pencil, black ink pen, and paper.

What Areas Will I Be Tested On?

The Oral and Practical Exam is designed so that the examiner can evaluate your performance to determine that you will be a competent and safe aircraft mechanic and that you at least meet the minimum requirements for certification. To verify that you are knowledgeable in all areas required by FAR Part 65, you will be tested in each subject area for the General Mechanic Certificate. These subjects include the following:

1. Mathematics
2. Physics
3. Basic Electricity
4. Aircraft Drawings
5. Weight and Balance
6. Aircraft Structural Materials
7. Aircraft Hardware
8. Hand Tools and measuring Devices
9. Fluid Lines and Fittings
10. Nondestructive Testing
11. Cleaning And Corrosion
12. Ground Handling and Servicing
13. Maintenance Publications, Forms, and Records
14. Mechanic Privileges and Limitations

How is the Oral Exam Conducted?

The oral exam may be conducted in different ways depending on the examiner. Some examiners conduct the oral exam first before having you do any of the practical portions of the test, while others may ask you oral questions while you perform the practical portion of the exam. In either case, the examiner will ask you a minimum of four questions that relate to each subject area. Of these four questions, you must correctly answer 3 out of 4 to pass. If you miss more than one question, at the discretion of the examiner, additional questions may be asked to further evaluate your knowledge of the subject area. If additional questions are asked, you must correctly answer 70% of all the questions to pass the subject area.

If you do not already hold an Aircraft or Powerplant Mechanic Certificate, you will also be required to take the General Mechanic oral exam. These may be administered before the General exams, or in some cases, the examiner may elect to vary the order. Regardless of the order that the exams are taken, you must pass all the oral questions in both the General and Airframe or Powerplant subject areas. This means that you B-4 General Oral and Practical Exam Study Guide Appendix B.qxd 10/19/07 1:54 PM Page B-4 will be required to answer a minimum of 48 General questions (12 subject areas) and 68 Airframe or Powerplant questions (17 subject areas).

When taking the oral exam, it is best to listen carefully to the question and formulate your answer before responding. Try to keep your answers as direct to the question as possible. This will save time and keep the examiner from feeling the need to delve further into the subject area if your explanation is confusing.

If you do not understand the question, you can ask the examiner to elaborate further. In some cases, the examiner can rephrase the question, but in others the examiner will only repeat the question if they feel you should understand what is being asked. Regardless of the examiner's response, there is no harm in asking for clarification. Also, keep in mind that in no case is the examiner allowed to teach during the exam. If they feel that further elaboration may cause them to give you more information than they should divulge, they may elect to keep the questions very specific. In most cases, the examiner will try to remain personable, but they will keep focused on the task of administering the exam.

The examiner will also use a worksheet to keep track of your results and will likely take additional notes throughout the exam. It is required for the examiner to keep these records, so don't be concerned to see them writing after each question.

How is the Practical Exam Conducted?

The examiner will assign you projects from each of the subject areas required for the rating(s) you apply for. Depending on the examiner, you may be assigned a separate project for each subject, or you may be given a project that entails an evaluation of many subjects. For example, you may be given a project to install an up-limit switch on a landing gear. This project could allow the examiner to evaluate multiple subject areas including electrical systems, landing gear, position and warning systems, maintenance publications, and others. Regardless of the actual number of assignments that you are given, you must perform at least one practical project for each subject area. In addition, you will be required to complete an FAA Form 337 (Major Alteration and Repair Form), and to calculate a sample weight-and-balance change problem.

As mentioned earlier, the examiner will have technical manuals and special tools that you will need to complete the assigned projects. However, the examiner may not make these readily available to you. Part of the exam process includes evaluating whether you know what tools, materials and technical information you will need to work on an actual aircraft. Do not hesitate to ask the examiner where you can locate these items.

What Am I Required to Do if I Fail Part of the Exam?

The examiner will normally advise you of your progress throughout the test and give you the option to discontinue the test at any time. However, you should try to complete the exam to identify all the areas that you may be deficient in. If you complete the exam and only have a few failed subject areas, you will only be tested on the failed subjects if you retest with the same examiner. However, if you go to another examiner, you will be required to repeat the entire test.

In the event you fail any subject area, Part 65 requires that you wait 30 days before reapplying for the exam, unless you receive additional instruction from an airman holding the rating that you are seeking. The person that provides you with the additional instruction should give you a written statement detailing the number of hours of instruction they provided along with a brief description of what subject areas were covered. In addition, the statement should contain the person's signature, certificate type, and airman certificate number.

When Do I Receive my Airman's Certificate?

If you pass all areas of the oral and practical exam, you will be issued a Temporary Airman's Certificate that is immediately effective. The examiner may issue the temporary certificate on the day of the exam, or depending on the arrangements between the local FSDO and the examiner, it may be issued later by mail by the FSDO. In either case, the temporary certificate is effective for 120 days from the date of issuance. If you do not receive a permanent Airman's Certificate in the mail before your temporary certificate expires, you should contact your local FSDO to track your records and make an arrangement to issue you another temporary certificate. An FSDO inspector is the only person authorized to reissue a temporary certificate.

Suggestions for Military Applicants

Applicants coming from the military typically show a lack of experience with the civil aircraft manufacturer's technical manuals and Federal Aviation Administration documents. If you are applying for certification based on military experience, it is strongly recommended that you receive supplementary instruction in the use of civil aircraft manufacturer's illustrated parts catalogs, service manuals, and service information literature. You should also review federal publications such as Type Certificate Data Sheets, Airworthiness Directives, Advisory Circulars, and Supplemental Type Certificate Data Sheets before applying for the test.

In most cases, additional practical instruction in these areas can be received at a local AMTS or a Fixed Base Operation maintenance shop where you can contract with someone to instruct you. In some cases, you might even work with the DME that will be giving you your exam. This is not objectionable since the DME will likely not teach you the exam, but instead will teach you the material needed to be a safe and competent mechanic. Once the exam commences, the examiner will not provide any instruction, and they will evaluate you solely on your ability to do the work on your own.

Aside from these areas of study, most military applicants have adequate exposure to the tools, equipment, and maintenance practices to complete the FAA exams with the same amount of preparation as applicants coming from an AMTS. Regardless of whether you are coming from a military or civil background, the best way to guarantee success is with preparation. Our General Test Guide assures that you have the most thorough and complete test preparation materials available.

NOTES

Chapter 1 — Mathematics

Oral Questions

1. Describe the result of adding a large positive number and a smaller negative number.
    Answer – The result is a smaller positive number, and is the same as ignoring the signs and subtracting the smaller number from the larger. (Page Reference: JSGT 1-4)

2. How do you convert a fraction into a decimal?
    Answer – Divide the top number (numerator) by the bottom number (denominator). (Page Reference: JSGT 1-8)

3. What is the key step that must be performed in order to add or subtract unlike fractions?
    Answer – You must find the lowest (least) common denominator. (Page Reference: JSGT 1-5)

4. How do you divide one fraction by another?
    Answer – You invert the divisor and multiply the numerators together and the denominators together. (Page Reference: JSGT 1-5)

5. How can you convert a decimal into a percent?
    Answer – (1) Multiply the decimal by 100 and add the percent sign. (2) Move the decimal point two places to the right and add the percent sign. (Page Reference: JSGT 1-9)

6. How do you convert a fraction into a percent?
    Answer – Convert it to a decimal, move the decimal point two places to the right and add the percent sign. (Page Reference: JSGT 1-9)

7. How do you change a decimal into the nearest equivalent fraction?
    Answer – Multiply the decimal by the desired denominator. The result becomes the numerator in the fraction. (Page Reference: JSGT 1-9)

8. What are two different ways that a ratio may be expressed?
    Answer – (1) As a fraction. (2) By placing a colon (:) between the two numbers. (3) By using the word "to" between the two numbers. (Page Reference: JSGT 1-10)

9. What is a proportion?
    Answer – A statement of equality between two or more ratios. (Page Reference: JSGT 1-10)

10. What is meant by the root of a number?
    Answer – A root is two or more equal smaller numbers that, when multiplied together, equal the specified number. (Page Reference: JSGT 1-10)

11. How do you find the square of a number? Give an example.
    Answer – Multiply the number by itself. Examples: 4 X 4 = 16, 7 X 7 = 49. (Page Reference: JSGT 1-11)

12. What is a common method of making computations involving very large or very small numbers more manageable?
    Answer – Convert the numbers into scientific notation by using powers of 10. (Page Reference: JSGT 1-11)

13. How is 100,000 expressed as a power of 10?
    Answer – 10^5 (10 to the 5th power). (Page Reference: JSGT 1-11)

14. What formula is used to find the area of a rectangle and of a triangle?
    Answer – For a rectangle, A = L X W, For a triangle, A = 1/2(B X H). (Page Reference: JSGT 1-27)

15. Define Pi (π).

Answer – Pi is a constant that expresses the relationship between the circumference of a circle and its diameter and is approximately equal to 3.1416. (Page Reference: JSGT 1-29)

16. Describe a trapezoid.
   Answer – A trapezoid is a closed, four-sided figure having two parallel sides and two sides that are not parallel. (Page Reference: JSGT 1-29)

17. What is the formula for computing the area of a circle?
   Answer – A = π r^2 (Page Reference: JSGT 1-29)

Practical Test

1. **Project:** Calculate the square root of the assigned numbers. (Level 2)

   Given: Reference material and charts

   Performance Standard: The applicant will calculate the square root of several assigned numbers.

2. **Project:** Locate the instructions for performing mathematical operations such as for determining square root. (Level 1)

   Given: Reference material

   Performance Standard: The applicant will locate the instructions for performing the assigned mathematical operations.

3. **Project:** Locate the formulas for calculating areas and volumes of various geometrical shapes and/or match a list of formulas with the appropriate geometrical shape. (Level 2)

   Given: Reference material, a list of various geometrical shapes and formulas.

   Performance Standard: The applicant will locate and list or match the formula used with each geometrical shape.

4. **Project:** Use the appropriate formulas to determine the surface area of a cylinder. (Level 2)

   Given: The dimensions of a cylinder and reference materials.

   Performance Standard: The applicant will compute the surface area of the given cylinder.

5. **Project:** Compute wing area. (Level 2)

   Given: The shape and dimensions of a wing.

   Performance Standard: The applicant will use appropriate formula and compute the area of a wing.

6. **Project:** Determine the volume of a baggage compartment from measurements of its dimensions. (Level 2)

   Given: The dimensions and shape of a baggage compartment.

   Performance Standard: The applicant will correctly determine the volume of the baggage compartment.

7. **Project:** Convert fractions to decimals and fractions to their percentage equivalents. (Level 2)

   Given: A list of fractions.

   Performance Standard: The applicant will convert the assigned fractions into their decimal equivalent.

8. **Project:** Determine the ratio of two numbers. (Level 2)

   Given: A list of numbers in two columns and instructions.

   Performance Standard: The applicant will determine the ratio of each pair of numbers and reduce the ratios so as to express them in the form "X to one".

9. **Project:** Compute the compression ratio of an engine. (Level 2)

   Given: A drawing of a piston and cylinder assembly with the volume of the piston at top dead center and bottom dead center specified, and reference material.

   Performance Standard: The applicant will compute the compression ratio of the cylinder to an accuracy of one decimal place.

10. **Project:** Perform addition, subtraction, multiplication and division of positive and negative numbers. (Level 2)

      Given: An information sheet with algebraic problems.

      Performance Standard: The applicant will perform the necessary mathematical operations to solve the assigned problems.

11. **Project:** Find the least (lowest) common denominator of various fractions. (Level 2)

      Given: A list of fractions.

      Performance Standard: The applicant will determine the least (lowest) common denominator for each listed fraction.

12. **Project:** Compute the change in torque value when using a torque wrench with an extension. (Level 2)

      Given: Reference materials and the desired torque value.

      Performance Standard: The applicant will compute the torque wrench setting required to produce the specified torque value with one or more extensions.

13. **Project:** Convert decimal numbers to their equivalent fractional values and reduce them to their lowest denominator.(Level 2)

      Given: A list of decimal numbers.

      Performance Standard: The applicant will perform the required conversions.

14. **Project:** Convert percentage numbers to their decimal equivalents and decimal numbers to their percentage equivalents. (Level 2)

      Given: A list of decimal numbers, percentage numbers, and writing materials.

      Performance Standard: The applicant will perform the required conversions.

Chapter 2 — Physics

Oral Questions

1. Define matter.
   Answer - Any substance that occupies space and has mass. (Page Reference: JSGT. 2-2)

2. Matter may exist in what three states?
   Answer - Solid, liquid and gas. (Page Reference: JSGT 2-2)

3. Define kinetic energy.
   Answer - Kinetic energy is the energy of motion. (Page Reference: JSGT 2-6)

4. Work is the product of what two factors?
   Answer - Force and the distance moved. (Page Reference: JSGT 2-10)

5. What are the parts of a lever?
   Answer - A rigid bar and a pivot point called the fulcrum. (Page Reference: JSGT 2-11)

6. A wheelbarrow is an example of what class of lever?
   Answer - A second-class lever. (Page Reference: JSGT 2-12)

7. Are all three states of matter affected by thermal expansion and if so, which state is affected most?
   Answer - All three states are affected, with gases being affected the most. (Page Reference: JSGT 2-26)

8. What is a British Thermal Unit?
   Answer - The amount of heat energy required to change the temperature of 1 pound of water 1 degree Fahrenheit. (Page Reference: JSGT 2-26)

9. Name the three methods of heat transfer?
   Answer - Conduction, convection and radiation. (Page Reference: JSGT 2-27)

10. What term defines the temperature at which all molecular motion ceases?
    Answer - Absolute zero. (Page Reference: JSGT 2-29)

11. Can liquids be compressed?
    Answer - No, liquids are generally considered incompressible. (Page Reference: JSGT 2-33)

12. What are the customary units used to express hydraulic or pneumatic pressure in the United States?
    Answer - Pounds per square inch. (Page Reference: JSGT 2-33)

13. Describe how pressure is transmitted when a force is applied to a confined liquid.
    Answer - Pressure is transmitted equally in all directions. (Page Reference: JSGT 2-34)

14. What formula expresses the relationship between force, pressure and area?
    Answer - Force equals area times pressure. (Page Reference: JSGT 2-34)

15. What is the approximate speed of sound at sea level on a standard day?
    Answer - 661 Knots or 340 meters per second. (Page Reference: JSGT 2-37)

16. What is the atmospheric pressure at sea level on a standard day?
    Answer - 29.92 inches of Mercury or 1013.2 millibars. (Page Reference: JSGT 2-45)

17. On a standard day at sea level, what is the value for temperature?

Answer - 59°F or 15°C. (Page Reference: JSGT 2-45)

18. What are the factors that determine density altitude?
    Answer - Temperature and atmospheric pressure. (Page Reference: JSGT 2-46)

19. What is the term used to describe the ratio between the amount of moisture actually present in the atmosphere as compared to the amount the air could hold if it were completely saturated?
    Answer - Relative humidity. (Page Reference: JSGT 2-47)

20. What are the four principle forces acting on an airplane in flight?
    Answer - Lift, drag, thrust and gravity. (Page Reference: JSGT 2-49)

21. What is the term that describes the angle between the relative wind and the chord line of an airfoil?
    Answer - The Angle of Attack. (Page Reference: JSGT 2-51)

22. What are the factors that cause an airplane wing to stall?
    Answer - Stall is caused when the angle of attack exceeds a critical value and the airflow separates from the upper surface and becomes turbulent. (Page Reference: JSGT 2-52)

23. What are the principle effects that result from lowering the flaps while in flight?
    Answer - Lift increases, drag increases and stall speed decreases.(Page Reference: JSGT 2-53)

24. What is the function of a wing mounted vortex generator?
    Answer – Vortex generators delay or keep the airflow from separating from the upper surface of a wing during high speed flight. (Page Reference: JSGT 2-72)

25. How does blade-flapping help to compensate for dissymmetry of lift in helicopter main rotor systems?
    Answer – Flapping increases the angle of attack and lift on the retreating blade and decreases the angle of attack and lift on the advancing blade. (Page Reference: JSGT 2-83)

26. How does the airflow through the main rotor of a helicopter change during the transition from normal flight to autorotation?
    Answer – During normal flight the air moves downward and during autorotation the air moves upward. (Page Reference: JSGT 2-84)

27. What is friction?
    Answer – The opposition to relative motion between two objects in contact with each other. (Page Reference: FGH)

Practical Test

1. **Project:** Compute temperature conversions. (Level 2)

    Given: Charts, graphs or formulas
    Performance Standard: The applicant will compute various temperature conversions as assigned.
2. **Project:** Calculate density altitude. (Level 2)

    Given: Charts, graphs or formula and a given pressure and temperature.
    Performance Standard: The applicant will determine the density altitude
3. **Project:** Determine the pressure altitude from an aircraft instrument. (Level 2)

    Given: A sensitive altimeter
    Performance Standard: The applicant will properly adjust the altimeter so as to determine the current pressure altitude.
4. **Project:** Compute force. (Level 2)

Given: Values for pressure and area.

Performance Standard: The applicant will calculate force.

5. **Project:** Determine standard temperature at various altitudes. (Level 2)

    Given: A standard temperature chart and a list of altitudes.

    Performance Standard: The applicant will correctly interpret the chart to determine the standard temperature for the assigned altitudes.

6. **Project:** Calculate the pressure required to produce a specified force. (Level 2)

    Given: An actuator or a drawing of an actuator with piston dimensions indicated and the force required.

    Performance Standard: The applicant will compute the pressure required to produce the specified force.

7. **Project:** Demonstrate an understanding of the means by which mechanical advantage is developed by various classes of levers. (Level 2)

    Given: A ruler, a weight, and a fulcrum.

    Performance Standard: The applicant will properly place the fulcrum and weight to produce a specified mechanical advantage using a first, second, and third class lever.

8. **Project:** Design an inclined plane to move a specified weight a given distance using a specified force. (Level 2)

    Given: An instruction sheet, data, and writing materials.

    Performance Standard: The applicant will draw an inclined plane of sufficient length to raise the given weight using the specified force.

9. **Project:** Design a rope and pulley system. (Level 2)

    Given: An instruction sheet writing materials and data.

    Performance Standard: The applicant will draw a pulley system to lift a given weight with a specified force.

10. **Project:** Determine the amount of stretch of bolts or studs. (Level 2)

    Given: Reference material and measuring equipment.

    Performance Standard: The applicant will determine the stretch at a given torque of the bolts or studs.

11. **Project:** Determine the centrifugal force applied to a rotating mass. (Level 2)

    Given: Reference material and data relating to the weight increase of a rotating object such as a rotor or propeller blade.

    Performance Standard: The applicant will calculate the centrifugal force applied.

12. **Project:** Determine the density of a solid object with a specific gravity of less than one. (Level 2)

    Given: A graduated beaker, an appropriate object, and reference material.

    Performance Standard: The applicant will find the specific gravity of the assigned object.

13. **Project:** Identify venturi pressure and velocity. (Level 2)

    Given: A venturi, or drawing of a venturi, and reference material.

    Performance Standard: The applicant will indicate the area of the venturi having the lowest pressure and highest velocity.

14. **Project:** Calculate horsepower. (Level 2)

    Given: Data on the weight moved, the time elapsed, and reference material.

    Performance Standard: The applicant will calculate horsepower.

15. **Project:** Calculate the amount of expansion or contraction in different materials due to temperature changes. (Level 2)

    Given: The length of various objects, the coefficient of expansion, and the temperature change.

    Performance Standard: The applicant will calculate the linear change in dimension.

16. **Project:** Identify the type of simple machine(s) or mechanical advantage device(s) present in the design and function of various aircraft parts. (Level 2)

Given: Samples or illustrations of aircraft parts and reference materials.

Performance Standard: The applicant will describe the type of simple machine(s) or mechanical advantage device(s) present in the specified parts.

17. **Project:** Describe the methods of heat transfer in aircraft parts or systems. (Level 2)

Given: An aircraft or examples of aircraft systems and reference material.

Performance Standard: The applicant will indicate whether the method of heat ransfer involved with specified systems is convection, conduction or radiation.

18. **Project:** Identify parts or systems in an aircraft that employ Bernoulli's principle in accomplishing their function. (Level 2)

Given: An aircraft or examples of aircraft parts or systems and reference material.

Performance Standard: The applicant will identify a specified number of parts and/or systems that utilize Bernoulli's principle in their operation.

19. **Project:** Determine which of the five stresses are acting on an aircraft or aircraft part at specific points. (Level 2)

Given: An aircraft or examples of aircraft parts or systems and reference material.

Performance Standard: The applicant will determine the type of stresses acting on the aircraft, system, or part at specified locations, while at rest and/or during operation.

Chapter 3 — Basic Electricity

Oral Questions

1. One kilowatt is equal to how many watts?
   Answer - 1,000 watts. (Page Reference: JSGT 3-5)

2. What law describes the most fundamental or basic relationships in an electrical circuit?
   Answer - Ohm's law. (Page Reference: JSGT 3-13)

3. What are the three elements of Ohm's law?
   Answer - Voltage, current and resistance. (Page Reference: JSGT 3-13)

4. How would you write Ohm's law as an equation?
   Answer - $E = I \times R$, $R = E \div I$, $I = E \div R$. (Page Reference: JSGT 3-13)

5. If the resistance in a DC circuit remains the same but the voltage doubles, what happens to the amount of current flowing in the circuit?
   Answer - It also doubles. (Page Reference: JSGT 3-13)

6. In DC circuits, what unit measures power?
   Answer – Watts. (Page Reference: JSGT 3-14)

7. What three elements are required to form an electrical circuit?
   Answer - A source of electrical energy, a load or resistance to use the electricity, and wires or conductors to connect the source to the load. (Page Reference: JSGT 3-15)

8. DC circuits can take one of three forms or types. What are they?
   Answer – Series, parallel and complex (or series-parallel). (Page Reference: JSGT 3-32)

9. A 24-volt lead-acid battery has how many cells?
   Answer – Twelve. (Page Reference: JSGT 3-66)

10. A fully charged lead-acid battery has a specific gravity that varies between what two values?
    Answer - 1.275 and 1.300. (Page Reference: JSGT 3-69)

11. You must apply a correction to the specific gravity reading of the electrolyte of a lead-acid battery when the temperature is outside of what two values?
    Answer – Whenever the temperature is less than 70°F or more than 90°F. (Page Reference: JSGT 3-69)

12. What is the reason for having separate facilities for storing and servicing nickel-cadmium and lead-acid batteries?
    Answer - The electrolyte in the two types of batteries is chemically opposite and the fumes from one type can contaminate the electrolyte of the other type. (Page Reference: JSGT 3-73)

13. The state of charge of a nickel-cadmium battery cannot be determined by measuring the specific gravity of the electrolyte for what reason?
    Answer – There is no significant change in the specific gravity of the electrolyte as the battery is charged or discharged. (Page Reference: JSGT 3-73)

14. What is the principal advantage of AC current over DC current?
    Answer – Power can be transmitted over long distances more efficiently and with smaller wires because the voltage can be easily increased or decreased by a transformer. (Page Reference: JSGT 3-81)

15. What are the three causes of opposition to current flow in an AC circuit?

Answer – Resistance, inductive reactance and capacitive reactance. (Page Reference: JSGT 3-86)

16. Define inductance.
    Answer - An induced voltage which is opposite in direction to the applied voltage. (Page Reference: JSGT 3-86)

17. What component creates capacitance in AC circuits?
    Answer - A capacitor. (Page Reference: JSGT 3-92)

18. How does a capacitor store electricity?
    Answer - The energy is stored in the form of an electrostatic charge or field that exists between two conductors separated by an insulator. (Page Reference: JSGT 3-92)

19. What property of an AC circuit is defined by the term "impedance"?
    Answer - The total opposition to current flow. (Page Reference: JSGT 3-98)

20. What are two reasons that might cause a nickel-cadmium battery to fail to deliver its rated capacity?
    Answer – Faulty cells or cell imbalance. (Page Reference: JSGT 3-74)

21. What electrical values are measured by a typical multimeter?
    Answer – Voltage, current and resistance. (Page Reference: JSGT 3-143)

Practical Test

1. **Project:** Demonstrate the ability to install wires in an electrical connector plug. (Level 3)

   Given: Electrical wires, a connector, tools and reference material.

   Performance Standard: The applicant will cut, strip and install wires in an electrical connector in accordance with the reference material.

2. **Project:** Interpret an AC electrical circuit diagram and perform the necessary mathematical computations required to compute the inductive reactance in the circuit. (Level 2)

   Given: A circuit diagram for a simple AC circuit containing inductance, the formula for inductive reactance, and the circuit values.

   Performance Standard: The applicant will accurately compute the value of inductive reactance in the circuit.

3. **Project:** Perform an analysis of the electrical power requirements for an aircraft. (Level 2)

   Given: A list of appliances and their operating characteristics.

   Performance Standard: The applicant will compute the total electrical power requirements for the listed appliances.

4. **Project:** Determine the load on an electrical generator by computation. (Level 2)

   Given: Technical data on an aircraft generator, and a list of electrical system components.

   Performance Standard: The applicant will compute the maximum allowable load on the generator and add as many electrical components as possible, while remaining within the limits specified in the technical data.

5. **Project:** Demonstrate knowledge of electrical prefixes. (Level 2)

   Given: A list of electrical quantity prefixes such as kilo, milli, mega and micro and the numerical value of each (kilowatt, millivolt, etc.).

   Performance Standard: The applicant will accurately match the various prefixes with their numerical values.

6. **Project:** Test an electrical circuit for an open circuit condition. (Level 3)

   Given: A multimeter, a mockup or an electrical system with a fault, and instructions.

Performance Standard: The applicant will test the circuit and properly identify the location of one or more faults.

7. **Project:** Test an electrical circuit for a short circuit condition. (Level 3)

    Given: A multimeter, a mockup or an electrical system with a fault, and instructions.

    Performance Standard: The applicant will test the circuit and properly identify the location of one or more faults.

8. **Project:** Measure the voltage at various locations in an electrical circuit. (Level 3)

    Given: A multimeter, an AC and/or DC electrical system, and a wiring diagram.

    Performance Standard: The applicant will accurately measure voltages at different points in the circuit.

9. **Project:** Determine the resistance of electrical system components. (Level 3)

    Given: A multimeter, various electrical components, and instructions.

    Performance Standard: The applicant will accurately measure the resistance of the supplied components.

10. **Project:** Mathematically compute the voltage in electrical circuits. (Level 2)

    Given: Drawings of simple DC electrical circuits with known current and resistance, and the formula for Ohm's Law.

    Performance Standard: The applicant will accurately compute the voltages using the known values.

11. **Project:** Mathematically compute the resistance of electrical circuits. (Level 2)

    Given: Drawings of simple DC electrical circuits with known voltage and current values and the formula for Ohm's Law.

    Performance Standard: The applicant will accurately compute the resistances using the known values.

12. **Project:** Calculate the current flowing in an electrical circuit. (Level 3)

    Given: Test equipment, an aircraft DC circuit, and reference material.

    Performance Standard: The applicant will use the test equipment and reference material to measure the voltage and resistance in the circuit. The applicant will then calculate the current flow and determine if the voltage, current, and resistance meet the specifications.

13. **Project:** Demonstrate knowledge of commonly used electrical symbols. (Level 2)

    Given: Examples of aircraft wiring diagrams, without labels, such as those commonly used in aircraft maintenance.

    Performance Standard: The applicant will label the assigned symbols.

14. **Project:** Trace an electrical circuit and locate specific circuit components or connections. (Level 2)

    Given: An aircraft wiring diagram, an electrical mockup or an aircraft electrical system, and instructions.

    Performance Standard: The applicant will trace the circuit, and locate and identify the specified components or connections.

15. **Project:** Use typical maintenance discrepancy reports of electrical malfunctions and identify the system or component at fault. (Level 3)

    Given: Examples of typical flight crew write-ups concerning electrical malfunctions, circuit diagrams of the involved system.

    Performance Standard: The applicant will analyze each report and use the circuit diagrams to identify the component or fault that caused each malfunction.

16. **Project:** Inspect an aircraft battery and connect it to a battery charger. (Level 3)

    Given: A lead-acid or nickel-cadmium aircraft battery, tools, equipment, and reference material.

    Performance Standard: The applicant will visually inspect the battery for external condition, check the electrolyte level if appropriate, and set up and connect the battery to the charger, according to the reference material.

17. **Project:** Check the state of charge of an aircraft battery. (Level 3)

Given: A battery, the necessary equipment, and reference material.

Performance Standard: The applicant will check and record the battery state of charge in accordance with the manufacturer's instructions.

18. **Project:** Demonstrate the proper procedures for removing and installing an aircraft battery. (Level 3)

Given: A battery, an aircraft, necessary equipment, and reference material.

Performance Standard: The applicant will remove and install the battery in accordance with the reference material.

19. **Project:** Inspect a battery compartment to determine its general condition including a check for spilled electrolyte, the condition of the sump jar and hose connections (if applicable), and the condition of the battery compartment venting and terminal connections. (Level 3)

Given: An aircraft with the battery removed and instructions.

Performance Standard: The applicant will inspect the compartment and record any defects found.

20. **Project:** Measure the voltage drop across a resistance. (Level 2)

Given: An electrical circuit, wiring diagram, test equipment, and reference material.

Performance Standard: The applicant will measure and record the voltage drop across the specified resistance in the circuit.

21. **Project:** Demonstrate knowledge of the proper way to connect test equipment to measure voltage, resistance and current. (Level 2)

Given: Illustrations of test meters connected correctly and incorrectly.

Performance Standard: The applicant will determine which illustrations show correct and incorrect meter connections.

22. **Project:** Use reference material to locate formulas for calculating power, voltage, current and resistance in electrical circuits. (Level 1)

Given: Reference materials

Performance Standard: The applicant will locate the appropriate formulas for each usage and properly list and label them.

23. **Project:** Demonstrate the ability to read and interpret logic circuits. (Level 2)

Given: Logic circuit diagrams, the associated truth tables, and reference material.

Performance Standard: The applicant will trace the logic circuit in the diagram and indicate correct functioning of the circuit logic gates.

Chapter 4 — Electrical Generators and Motors

There are no FAA Oral and Practical test questions regarding Electrical Motor and Generator questions in the General Mechanic Exam. These subjects are included in the Airframe and Powerplant O&Ps.

Chapter 5 — Aircraft Drawings

Oral Questions

1. How many views are required to represent the important details of most aircraft parts?
   Answer - One, two or three views are usually enough. (Page Reference: JSGT 5-2)

2. What kinds of parts can be represented by one-view drawings?
   Answer - Parts with uniform thickness such as shims, plates and gaskets. (Page Reference: FGH)

3. What is the name for a part of a drawing used to bring out important details and how is it drawn?
   Answer – A detailed view, which is usually drawn to a larger scale than the main drawing. (Page Reference: JSGT 5-2)

4. What is the purpose of schematic diagrams?
   Answer – They are primarily used for troubleshooting systems. (Page Reference: JSGT 5-8)

5. Describe an orthographic projection.
   Answer – It is a way of drawing an object using different views at right angles to each other, such as a top, front, and side view. (Page Reference: JSGT 5-10)

6. Why do manufacturers use symbols on aircraft drawings?
   Answer - Symbols are a form of shorthand and are used to convey the characteristics of a component with a minimum of drawing. (Page Reference: FGH)

7. Describe the appearance of lines used to show hidden views, alternate positions and the middle of symmetrical objects, and give their proper name.
   Answer - Hidden views are shown with hidden lines, which are short, evenly spaced dashes. Alternate positions are shown with phantom lines made up of light, alternating long dashes and two short dashes. Center lines, consisting of alternating long and short dashes, show the middle of symmetrical objects. (Page Reference: JSGT 5-15)

8. How can you determine if a drawing has been changed?
   Answer - A record of the changes is listed either in a revision block or in ruled columns, which may be in a corner of the drawing or next to the title block. (Page Reference: JSGT 5-18)

9. How are dimensions shown on aircraft drawings, and what is their purpose?
   Answer – Dimension lines are usually solid and generally broken at the midpoint for insertion of the measurement. They provide a means to accurately represent the size of an object. (Page Reference: JSGT 5-18)

10. What is the difference between an "allowance" and a "tolerance"?
    Answer - An allowance is the difference between the nominal dimension and the maximum and minimum permissible sizes. The tolerance is the difference between the extreme permissible dimensions, which may be found by adding the plus and minus allowances. (Page Reference: JSGT 5-16)

11. What is meant by "clearance" when used on aircraft drawings?
    Answer - An allowable dimension between two parts. (Page Reference: FGH)

12. What kinds of information about an aircraft drawing can be found in the title block?
    Answer – The part or assembly name, drawing size, scale, date, company name, name or initials of the people responsible for creating or approving the drawing. (Page Reference: JSGT 5-17)

13. What information is contained in a "bill of materials"?

Answer - A list of the materials and parts needed to fabricate or assemble the component or system shown in the drawing. (Page Reference: JSGT 5-17)

Practical Test

1. **Project:** Accurately interpret the lines, symbols, dimensions and other details of typical aircraft drawings. (Level 2)

   Given: Typical aircraft detail and assembly drawings.

   Performance Standard: The applicant will identify and interpret the meaning of various lines and symbols as they relate to the details of the drawing, interpret dimensions and tolerances, and describe the types of information found in title blocks, bill of materials, etc.

2. **Project:** Interpret installation diagrams and/or schematics and use either or both to determine how parts are installed or assembled, or to troubleshoot a system (Level 2)

   Given: Installation drawings and/or schematic diagrams of a specific system such as fuel, oil, hydraulic, pressurization, etc. and the maintenance manual for the airplane.

   Performance Standard: The applicant will name the components, describe their location, and/or discuss how the parts should be installed or assembled

3. **Project:** Prepare a sketch or drawing suitable for an FAA Form 337 to visually depict a major repair or alteration. (Level 3)

   Given: Appropriate drawing tools, reference material, and data describing a major repair or alteration to an aircraft structure

   Performance Standard: The applicant will create a sketch or drawing illustrating the repair or alteration, correctly positioning the views, and include appropriate dimensions, materials, etc.

4. **Project:** Interpret information found on blueprints. (Level 2)

   Given: Aircraft blueprints drawn to various scales that incorporate different title blocks and changes from the original drawings

   Performance Standard: The applicant will read and interpret the information contained in various sections of the drawing and describe the contents.

5. **Project:** Extract information from graphs and charts. (Level 2)

   Given: Graphs and charts of the type that appear in maintenance manuals and pilot operating handbooks.

   Performance Standard: The applicant will read, interpret, and plot data from various manufacturers' charts and graphs.

6. **Project:** Locate specific areas on, and identify changes to, an aircraft drawing or blueprint. (Level 1)

   Given: Drawings, blueprints and reference material.

   Performance Standard: The applicant will point out changes made to an original document.

7. **Project:** Using appropriate data, describe how an installation or modification will be accomplished. (Level 2)

   Given: Installation or modification data (i.e. STC, AD, Service Bulletin) and reference material.

   Performance Standard: The applicant will describe the steps necessary to accomplish the installation or modification in the correct sequence.

8. **Project:** Create a sketch drawing to scale. (Level 3)

   Given: An aircraft part, materials, drawing tools, and reference material.

   Performance Standard: The applicant will measure the part and create an accurately scaled three-view sketch drawing.

9. **Project:** Read and interpret a Bill of Materials. (Level 3)

   Given: A blueprint detailing an aircraft repair or alteration and reference material.

   Performance Standard: The applicant will use the bill of materials to determine the items necessary to accomplish the repair or alteration.

10. **Project:** Use typical aircraft drawings, sketches, or blueprints to perform maintenance or an inspection. (Level 3)

> **Given:** A drawing, sketch, or blueprint, tools, and reference materials
>
> **Performance Standard:** The applicant will perform maintenance or an inspection using the documents supplied, and additional reference material as necessary.

Chapter 6 — Weight and Balance

Oral Questions

1. If an aircraft is loaded so that the aft C.G. limit is exceeded, what undesirable flight characteristic is likely to result?
   Answer - The aircraft will be tail-heavy and may be unable to recover from a stall or spin. (Page Reference: JSGT 6-4)

2. If all the records for an aircraft are missing, how would you determine the empty weight and empty weight C.G.?
   Answer - The aircraft would have to be weighed, and new weight and balance records would have to be prepared. (Page Reference: JSGT 6-3)

3. Define "tare weight" and describe how it is handled when weighing an aircraft.
   Answer - Tare weight is the weight of anything on the scales that is not part of the aircraft. It must be subtracted from the scale weight reading to determine the net weight of the airplane. (Page Reference: JSGT 6-3)

4. If a piece of equipment such as a radio is added to an aircraft, how can you determine the effect on weight and balance without re-weighing the aircraft?
   Answer - If the weight and balance records are up to date, a new weight and C.G. location can be determined by computation. (Page Reference: JSGT 6-3)

5. Why is control of the weight and balance of an aircraft important?
   Answer – To provide maximum safety. (Page Reference: JSGT 6-4)

6. What is the datum of an aircraft and what is its function?
   Answer - The datum is an imaginary vertical plane at right angles to the longitudinal axis of the airplane. It is the reference point from which all horizontal measurements are taken. (Page Reference: JSGT 6-4)

7. How do you determine the moment of an item of equipment?
   Answer - The weight of the item is multiplied by its arm, which is the distance between the item and the datum. (Page Reference: JSGT 6-5)

8. What are two ways of determining the arm of an item of equipment?
   Answer - Measure the distance between the item and the datum, or use data supplied by the manufacturer. (Page Reference: FGH)

9. What should be done to obtain a positive (plus) moment aft of the datum?
   Answer - Add weight. (Page Reference: JSGT 6-6)

10. What should be done to obtain a negative (minus) moment aft of the datum?
    Answer - Remove weight. (Page Reference: JSGT 6-6)

11. What should be done to obtain a positive (plus) moment forward of the datum?
    Answer - Remove Weight (Page Reference: JSGT 6-6)

12. What should be done to obtain a negative (minus) moment forward of the datum?
    Answer - Add weight. (Page Reference: JSGT 6-6)

13. How does the category of an aircraft affect its loaded weight?
    Answer - Aircraft certificated in more than one category, such as Normal and Aerobatic, may have two different maximum gross weights and different useful loads. (Page Reference: Type Certificate Data Sheet (TCDS))

14. As you prepare an aircraft for weighing, you determine that there is equipment aboard that is not permanently installed and recorded on the equipment list. What should you do with this equipment?

Answer - All equipment not permanently installed in the aircraft or included on the equipment list should be removed from the aircraft. (Page Reference: JSGT 6-7)

15. Define the term "residual fuel."
    Answer - Any fuel that remains in the tanks, lines, and engines, after the system has been drained. (Page Reference: FGH)

16. Define the term "residual oil."
    Answer - Any oil that remains in the tanks, lines, and engines, after the system has been drained. (Page Reference: FGH)

17. How should you account for fuel when weighing an aircraft to determine weight and balance?
    Answer - Either drain the fuel system until only unusable fuel remains, or fill the tanks full and subtract out the weight of the useable fuel. (Page Reference: JSGT 6-7)

18. Where are leveling instructions found, and describe one method of leveling an aircraft?
    Answer – Leveling instructions are found in the Type Certificate Data Sheets. An aircraft may be leveled by using a spirit level at specified points, or an aircraft may be leveled by using a plumb bob from a designated point along with a leveling scale or protractor. (Page Reference: JSGT 6-11)

19. Define the term "Mean Aerodynamic Chord" or MAC.
    Answer – Mean Aerodynamic Chord is the chord drawn through the center of the wing plan area. (Page Reference: JSGT 6-14)

20. Describe the two most common ways of showing the C.G. location and/or C.G. range.
    Answer - In inches from the datum or in percent of MAC. (Page Reference: JSGT 6-14)

21. What is the purpose of an aircraft loading graph?
    Answer - It is a method for determining how to distribute the load so as to keep the C.G. within allowable limits. (Page Reference: FGH)

22. What is ballast, and why would you use it in an airplane?
    Answer – Ballast is weight added to an airplane to bring its C.G. into the allowable or desired range. (Page Reference: JSGT 6-23)

23. Installation of several new radios in the nose of an aircraft causes the forward C.G. limit tobe exceeded. How can you correct this problem without removing the new equipment?
    Answer – Ballast may be installed in the tail to move the C.G. aft. (Page Reference: JSGT 6-23)

24. How does the C.G. range of a helicopter compare to that of a fixed-wing airplane?
    Answer – Helicopters typically have a much smaller C.G. range. (Page Reference: JSGT 6-40)

Practical Test

1. **Project:** Perform the necessary calculations to determine the maximum loaded condition of an aircraft. (Level 3)

   Given: An Aircraft Specification or Type Certificate Data sheet, a weight and balance report and other reference material as required.

   Performance Standard: The applicant will compute the weight of the aircraft using standard weights with full fuel, baggage, pilot(s) and passengers, and determine if it is within the approved loading envelope.

2. **Project:** *Verify calibration and adjust aircraft weighing scales for accuracy.* (Level 3)

   Given: Aircraft scales and the manufacturer's instructions.

   Performance Standard: The applicant will check for calibration and use the instructions to check the accuracy of the scales, and adjust them, if required.

3. **Project:** *Determine the effect of an equipment change on the weight and balance of an aircraft.* (Level 3)

   Given: An Aircraft Specification or Type Certificate Data sheet, the old weight and empty weight C.G., the location and weight of removed and installed equipment

   Performance Standard: The applicant will correctly compute a new C.G. and determine if the forward or aft limits have been exceeded.

4. **Project:** *Compute the most forward and most aft loaded C.G.* (Level 3)

   Given: The necessary data to compute the C.G. of an aircraft that can be loaded in such a manner that either or both limits can be exceeded.

   Performance Standard: The applicant will compute the most forward and most aft C.G. conditions and determine what limits are exceeded and by how much.

5. **Project:** *Discuss the preparations that must be accomplished in order to weigh an aircraft(excluding jacking and leveling).* (Level 2)

   Given: Manufacturer's publications, Aircraft Specifications or Type Certificate Data sheets, weight and balance records and the equipment list, and an assigned aircraft.

   Performance Standard: The applicant will locate and interpret the information necessary to weight the assigned aircraft, list any missing equipment and the work that must be accomplished prior to weighing. (e.g., drain fuel and/or oil, position flaps, etc.)

6. **Project:** *Determine where an item of special equipment should be installed on an aircraft inorder to keep the C.G. within approved limits.* (Level 3)

   Given: Manufacturer's publications, a weight and balance report, and project information on the assigned aircraft.

   Performance Standard: The applicant will use the information provided to compute the location for installation of the special equipment so that the C.G. will remain within approved limits.

7. **Project:** *Make an appropriate maintenance record entry to record a weight and balance change.* (Level 3)

   Given: A current weight and balance report and a list of changes.

   Performance Standard: The applicant will make a maintenance record entry for the weight and balance change that meets the requirements of FAR Part 43.

8. **Project:** *Weigh an aircraft and record the scale readings.* (Level 3)

   Given: The necessary data, equipment and assistance required to weigh the aircraft.

   Performance Standard: The applicant will level and jack the aircraft, position the scales, and determine the aircraft weight in accordance with the manufacturer's instructions.

9. **Project:** *Compute a weight and balance change for a helicopter.* (Level 3)

   Given: The necessary information and manufacturer's data for an assigned helicopter

   Performance Standard: Using the information provided, the applicant will compute the weight and balance changes and determine if the approved limits have been exceeded.

10. **Project:** *Using applicable arm and moment information, compute the weight of a pieceof equipment.* (Level 2)

    Given: Aircraft weight and balance data, the distance from the datum, and the moment.

    Performance Standard: The applicant will compute the weight of the equipment.

11. **Project:** *Determine the lateral C.G. limits of a helicopter.* (Level 2)

    Given: Manufacturer's data and a helicopter weight and balance report.

    Performance Standard: The applicant will list the lateral C.G. limits and determine the distance between the limits.

12. **Project:** *Locate weight and balance information and determine the location of the datumfor one or more aircraft.* (Level 1)

    Given: Aircraft Specifications or Type Certificate Data sheets, and/or other manufacturer's data.

    Performance Standard: The applicant will locate the weight and balance information and find the datum for the assigned aircraft.

13. **Project:** *Research the requirements for a baggage compartment placard.* (Level 2)

> **Given:** Reference materials as necessary.
>
> **Performance Standard:** The applicant will determine the baggage compartment capacity in pounds and determine that placards are installed to reflect the capacity.

14. **Project:** *Prepare a revised equipment list following an equipment change.* (Level 3)

> **Given:** An aircraft equipment list and a list of items to be removed and/or installed.
>
> **Performance Standard:** The applicant will revise the equipment list to reflect the changes in aircraft configuration.

15. **Project:** *Following equipment changes that result in a requirement for adding ballast, determine the weight and location of the ballast.* (Level 3)

> **Given:** Aircraft weight and balance information and a list of equipment changes that result in the need for ballast.
>
> **Performance Standard:** The applicant will determine the weight of the required ballast and its location relative to the datum.

16. **Project:** *Make the required adjustments to the load of an aircraft to eliminate an overweight condition.* (Level 3)

> **Given:** Aircraft weight and balance data and loading information for an aircraft loaded so as to exceed its maximum certificated gross weight.
>
> **Performance Standard:** The applicant will indicate which payload items must be removed to cause the aircraft to be within its allowable weight and C.G. limits.

17. **Project:** *Compute the C.G. in percent of MAC for a swept wing aircraft.* (Level 2)

> **Given:** Aircraft weight and balance information, and reference material.
>
> **Performance Standard:** The applicant will compute the location of the C.G. in percent of MAC.

Chapter 7 — Aircraft Structural Materials

Oral Questions

1. How do you work harden a piece of metal?
   Answer - By cold working the metal. (Page Reference: JSGT 7-9)

2. Describe the primary difference between a thermosetting and a thermoplastic resin.
   Answer - A thermosetting resin doesn't soften when heated and chars or burns rather than melting. Thermoplastic resins become soft and pliable when heated, and harden when cooled. (Page Reference: JSGT 7-27)

3. Explain how thermoplastic and thermosetting resins are commonly used in modern aircraft.
   Answer - Plexiglas is a thermoplastic resin commonly used for windshields and windows. Thermosetting resins are most often used as the matrix material in composite structures. (Page Reference: JSGT 7-27)

4. Name one of the types of resin commonly used as a matrix material for aircraft composite laminates.
   Answer - Polyester resin or Epoxy resin. (Page Reference: JSGT 7-28)

5. What are some of the materials that are commonly used as the reinforcing component in a composite structure?
   Answer - Fiberglass, Aramid (Kevlar), Graphite (Carbon) fiber, linen and paper. (Page Reference: JSGT 7-29)

6. *What are the reasons that alloy steel that is responsive to heat treatment is usually less suitable for welding?*
   Answer - It may become brittle and lose its ductility in the area of the weld. (Page Reference: FGH)

7. Give one advantage of pre-preg (pre-impregnated) materials, other than saving time in the construction or repair of composite components.
   Answer - (1) Pre-preg fabrics contain the correct amount of matrix. (2) The matrix material evenly and completely permeates the reinforcing fibers. (3) The matrix has the resin and hardener in the correct proportions. (Page Reference: JSAT 3-31)

Practical Test

1. **Project:** Use the manufacturer's markings to identify different kinds of aircraft materials and/or hardware. (Level 2)

   Given: Samples of materials and hardware with visible manufacturer's markings, and reference material.

   Performance Standard: The applicant will correctly identify the assigned samples.

2. **Project:** Perform a chemical etching test. (Level 2)

   Given: Sample strips of aluminum alloy that are not coded and a chemical etching kit.

   Performance Standard: The applicant will test the samples and identify those which are weldable.

3. **Project:** Select aluminum alloy sheet for an aircraft repair and identify rivets by their physical characteristics. (Level 2)

   Given: Samples of aluminum alloy sheet, rivets, written instructions and reference materials.

   Performance Standard: The applicant will select the aluminum alloy sheet of the correct type and thickness for the designated repair and identify various rivets by type.

4. **Project:** Determine if various materials are suitable for aircraft repairs. (Level 2)

   Given: Written technical information and sample materials.

   Performance Standard: The applicant will select the proper material for the specified repair in conformance with the technical instructions provided

5. **Project:** Identify the heat treatment processes that harden, soften, and relieve stresses in steel and aluminum alloys. (Level 2)

   Given: A list of heat treatment processes and reference material.

Performance Standard: The applicant will identify which processes are used to harden, soften, and relieve stresses in steel and aluminum alloys.

Chapter 8 — Aircraft Hardware

Oral Questions

1. What is indicated by the markings on the heads of solid shank rivets?
   Answer - The material that they are made of, and indirectly, their strength. (Page Reference: JSGT 8-4)

2. How can you keep heat treated aluminum alloy rivets soft enough to install after the quenching process?
   Answer - If the rivets are stored in a freezer they will remain soft for several days. (Page Reference: JSGT 8-5)

3. What is the grip length of a bolt?
   Answer - The length of the unthreaded portion. (Page Reference: JSGT 8-21)

4. In what way are AN standard steel bolts identified?
   Answer - By the code markings on the bolt heads. (Page Reference: JSGT 8-22)

5. What is the difference between a close tolerance bolt and a general purpose bolt?
   Answer - Close tolerance bolts are machined to more accurate dimensions. (Page Reference: JSGT 8-23)

6. For what types of applications are self-locking nuts not allowed?
   Answer - Self locking nuts may not be used when either the bolt or the nut is subject to rotation. (Page Reference: JSGT 8-27)

7. If the maintenance procedures do not specify a torque value for a bolt or nut, how can you determine the proper values?
   Answer – Consult a standard torque table such as found in AC 43.13-1B. (Page Reference: JSGT 8-29)

8. What is the most commonly used type of aircraft control cable?
   Answer - Extra flexible 7 X 19 stainless steel cable. (Page Reference: JSGT 8-39)

Practical Test

1. **Project:** Select and install aircraft bolts and screws. (Level 3)

   Given: An aircraft or mockup, aircraft bolts and screws, installation tools, and reference material.
   Performance Standard: The applicant will select the correct hardware, install it, and torque in accordance with written instructions.

2. **Project:** Demonstrate two methods of safety wiring turnbuckles. (Level 3)

   Given: Turnbuckles, safety wire, tools, and reference materials.
   Performance Standard: The applicant will safety wire one turnbuckle using the double-wrap method and one turnbuckle using the single-wrap method, in accordance with the reference material.

3. **Project:** Identify samples of aircraft control cable. (Level 2)

   Given: Sample of aircraft control cable and reference materials.
   Performance Standard: The applicant will identify the assigned samples according to construction and flexibility.

4. **Project:** Fabricate a cable assembly using swaged end fittings. (Level 3)

   Given: Aircraft hardware, reference materials, and any necessary tools.
   Performance Standard: The applicant will fabricate a cable assembly that will pass the manufacturer's Go, No-Go dimensional check.

5. **Project:** Describe the proper installation procedures for various seals, backup rings, and gaskets. (Level 2)

   Given: Reference materials, tools, and samples of O-rings, packings, gaskets and backup rings.
   Performance Standard: The applicant will describe the proper installation procedures for each sample.

6. **Project:** Select and install aircraft hardware other than bolts and screws. (Level 3)

   Given: An aircraft or mockup, a variety of aircraft hardware, tools, and reference material.

   Performance Standard: The applicant will select and install appropriate hardware in accordance with the reference material.

Chapter 9 — Hand Tools and Measuring Devices

Oral Questions

1. What Type of precision measuring instruments can be used to measure the outside dimensions of aircraft parts?
   Answer – Outside micrometers and vernier calipers. (Page Reference: JSGT 9-42)

2. For what reasons should a micrometer be periodically calibrated?
   Answer – If dropped, its accuracy may be affected, OR If the spindle is over-tightened, the frame may be sprung, OR Continually sliding objects between the anvil and the spindle may wear the surfaces. (Page Reference: JSGT 9-44)

Practical Test

1. **Project:** Make precision measurements using an instrument having a vernier micrometer scale. (Level 3)

   Given: Reference material, measuring equipment, and various aircraft parts such as bearings, shafts, pistons, etc.

   Performance Standard: The applicant will measure the assigned parts and determine whether they are within limits.

2. **Project:** Check the alignment of a shaft. (Level 3)

   Given: A dial indicator, "V" blocks, a surface plate, a shaft, and reference material.

   Performance Standard: The applicant will check the alignment of the shaft and determine if it is within acceptable limits.

3. **Project:** Determine the correct torque values for various items. (Level 2)

   Given: Hardware of different types and sizes, various installations, and reference materials.

   Performance Standard: The applicant will determine the required torque values for the assigned applications.

4. **Project:** Verify that a micrometer is within calibration limits. (Level 3)

   Given: A micrometer, a standard block, and reference material.

   Performance Standard: The applicant will check the calibration of the micrometer and determine if it meets the calibration limits for aircraft use.

Chapter 10 — Fluid Lines and Fittings

Oral Questions

1. What are the two types of fluid lines commonly found in aircraft?
   Answer - Rigid metal lines and flexible hoses. (Page Reference: JSGT 10-2 & 10-17)

2. Describe the method of classifying metal tube according to size.
   Answer - Metal tubing is sized according to wall thickness and outside diameter. Outside diameter is measured in 1/16th inch increments. (Page Reference: JSGT 10-3)

3. When installing stainless steel tubing, what type of fittings should be used?
   Answer - Stainless steel fittings. (Page Reference: JSGT 10-5)

4. What is the function of the sleeve on a flared-tube fitting?
   Answer - The nut fits over the sleeve and draws the sleeve and the tubing flare tightly against the male fitting to form the seal. (Page Reference: JSGT 10-5)

5. Describe the two types of flares commonly used on aircraft tubing.
   Answer - The single flare and the double flare. (Page Reference: JSGT 10-6)

6. How can you determine if a fitting is an AN type rather than an AC type?
   Answer - AN fittings have a shoulder between the flare cone and the end of the threads, AC fittings do not. (Page Reference: JSGT 10-8)

7. What are the most significant differences between AN and AC fittings?
   Answer - Sleeve length, thread pitch, and the shoulder between the threads and the flare cone on AN fittings. (Page Reference: JSGT 10-8)

8. What are the names of the parts of a flareless tube fitting?
   Answer - The nut and the ferrule or sleeve. (Page Reference: JSGT 10-9)

9. How do you tell a flareless fitting from a flare-type fitting?
   Answer - Flareless fittings don't have a flare cone and there is no space between the threads and the end of the fitting. (Page Reference: JSGT 10-9)

10. What is the effect of over-tightening a flare type fitting?
    Answer - The sealing surface may be damaged or the flare cut off. (Page Reference: JSGT 10-10)

11. In addition to being securely clamped, what is an additional requirement for installing metal fuel, oil and hydraulic lines?
    Answer - The lines must be electrically bonded to the structure. (Page Reference: JSGT 10-11)

12. What are some of the important advantages of Teflon tubing?
    Answer - It is compatible with nearly every liquid, has a broad operating temperature range, low resistance to fluid flow and has a very long shelf and service life. (Page Reference: JSGT 10-17)

13. Describe the identification markings commonly found on flexible hoses.
    Answer - A lay line, identification such as a Mil Spec number, the manufacturer's name or symbol, the hose size and a date code. (Page Reference: JSGT 10-18)

14. How can you determine if a flexible hose has been correctly or incorrectly installed?
    Answer - The lay line will be straight if the hose is properly installed. A twisted lay line indicates an incorrect installation. (Page Reference: JSGT 10-18)

15. How are flexible hose sizes designated?

Answer - By the inside diameter, measured in 1/16th inch increments. (Page Reference: JSGT 10-19)

16. What precautions must be observed when deburring the end of a tube after it is cut?

Answer - The wall thickness must not be reduced in size or fractured. (Page Reference: FGH)

17. Describe the operation of quick disconnect couplings.

Answer - Each half has a valve that is held open when coupled and is spring-loaded closed when disconnected. (Page Reference: FGH)

18. If you fabricate a replacement for a flexible hose, what percentage of the total length must be added to allow for movement under pressure?

Answer - 5 to 8 percent. (Page Reference: FGH)

19. What happens to the tube when a flareless fitting is overtightened?

Answer - The tube is weakened when the nut drives the cutting edge of the sleeve too deeply into the tube. (Page Reference: FGH)

20. Why are quick disconnect fittings used?

Answer - To provide a quick means to connect or disconnect a fluid line without loss of fluid or entrance of air into the system. (Page Reference: FGH)

Practical Test

1. **Project:** Fabricate a replacement for an aluminum or stainless steel fluid line by making appropriate bends. (Level 3)

   Given: Project instructions, tubing, and tube bending equipment.

   Performance Standard: The applicant will use the project information to make the required bends.

2. **Project:** Form a bead on a tube (Level 3)

   Given: Project instructions, aluminum tubing, and beading tools.

   Performance Standard: The applicant will form a bead on each end of two different diameter aluminum tubes without distortion, cracks or deformation.

3. **Project:** Fabricate a single and a double flare on a section of aluminum tubing. (Level 3)

   Given: Project instructions, aluminum tubing, and flaring tools

   Performance Standard: The applicant will form the required flares, one on each end of the tube, without distortion, cracks or deformation.

4. **Project:** Fabricate a replacement for a flexible hose. (Level 3)

   Given: Project instructions, fittings, flexible hose, and necessary tools.

   Performance Standard: The applicant will identify and select the correct hose materials and fittings, fabricate a replacement hose, and proof test the hose to the specified operating pressure.

5. **Project:** Install the correct flexible hose and fittings for a specified application. (Level 3)

   Given: Reference materials, flexible hose assemblies, fittings, seals, and tools.

   Performance Standard: The applicant will select the appropriate fittings (e.g. bulkhead or banjo), seals (O-rings), and hose assembly for the system and demonstrate proper installation procedures by installing them in an aircraft or mockup.

6. **Project:** Inspect metal tubing for damage and defects. (Level 3)

   Given: Samples of metal tubing, some of which have defects that are cause for rejection.

   Performance Standard: The applicant will point out and identify each defect.

7. **Project:** Fabricate a repair to a section of damaged tubing. (Level 3)

Given: A length of damaged tubing, replacement tubing, fittings, reference material, and the necessary tools.

Performance Standard: The applicant will repair the damaged tubing and test the repair under operating pressure to verify that it does not leak.

8. **Project:** Use clamps to properly install and secure a fluid line. (Level 3)

    Given: Project instructions, a metal fluid line, support clamps, and the required tools.

    Performance Standard: The applicant will install the fluid line and properly secure it, including electrical bonding (grounding).

9. **Project:** Determine if various samples of fluid and/or air lines are suitable for installation on an aircraft. (Level 2)

    Given: Samples of flexible fluid lines and reference materials.

    Performance Standard: The applicant will explain the markings on samples of flexible tubing, identify which lines are of aircraft quality and which are not permitted to be installed on an aircraft.

10. **Project:** Plan the routing of a fluid line. (Level 2)

    Given: The starting and ending points for a fluid line, an aircraft or mockup, and reference material.

    Performance Standard: The applicant will determine an acceptable routing for the fluid line and indicate the locations of clamping points.

11. **Project:** Fabricate a metal tubing assembly. (Level 3)

    Given: Reference material, tubing, fittings, and the necessary tools.

    Performance Standard: The applicant will select the proper tubing and fittings, fabricate the assembly, and pressure check it according to the reference material.

12. **Project:** Identify various aircraft fittings and identify correct and incorrect installation of flexible and/or rigid fluid lines. (Level 2)

    Given: Reference material, various sizes and types of fittings and examples of correct and incorrect installations.

    Performance Standard: The applicant will identify the size and proper application for the assigned fittings and identify the correct and incorrect installations, and explain what is wrong with the incorrect installations.

13. **Project:** Fabricate a flareless-fitting tube connection. (Level 3)

    Given: Tubing, fittings, sleeves, nuts, tools and reference material.

    Performance Standard: The applicant will select the appropriate parts and form the connection.

14. **Project:** Fabricate a repair to a section of tubing using swaged tube fittings. (Level 3)

    Given: A length of damaged tubing, replacement tubing, swage fittings, tools, and reference material.

    Performance Standard: The applicant will repair the tubing using swaged fittings and test the repair to verify that it does not leak under operating pressure.

Chapter 11 — Nondestructive Testing

Oral Questions

1. Describe the steps involved in a dye penetrant inspection.
    Answer - The surface is cleaned, and then penetrant is applied and allowed to dwell for a specified time. The penetrant is then removed with an emulsifier or cleaner. Once removed, the part is dried and then developer is applied. The results are then inspected and interpreted. (Page Reference: JSGT 11-4)

2. Name some tools that are commonly used to assist in making visual inspections of welds.
    Answer - A magnifying glass, flashlight, mirror and, possibly, a borescope. (Page Reference: JSGT 11-2)

3. What are some of the non-destructive testing methods that may be used on aluminum parts?
    Answer – visual, dye penetrant, eddy current, ultrasonic testing and radiography. (Page Reference: JSGT 11-2, 11-13)

4. What process occurs during the preparation stage of a dye penetrant inspection when the penetrating liquid is applied, and then removed from a cracked part?
    Answer - The penetrant enters the crack by capillary action and remains there until made visible by the developer. (Page Reference: JSGT 11-4)

5. A correctly made butt weld will have what bead width and how much penetration?
    Answer - The bead width should be 3 to 5 times the thickness of the base metal and there must be 100% penetration. (Page Reference: JSGT 11-4)

6. What telltale characteristics are evidence of a cold weld?
    Answer - A cold weld has rough, irregular edges that are not feathered into the base metal and has variations in penetration amounts. (Page Reference: JSGT 11-4)

7. The penetration of a fillet weld should be what percentage of the thickness of the base metal?
    Answer - 25 to 50 percent. (Page Reference: JSGT 11-4)

8. Describe the basic steps for conducting a magnetic particle inspections.
    Answer - Magnetize the part, then coat the surface with ferromagnetic particles. If a defect or discontinuity is present, the particles align with the discontinuity forming a visible pattern. (Page Reference: JSGT 11-7)

Practical Test

1. **Project:** Visually inspect welds for defects. (Level 3)

    Given: Samples of acceptable and unacceptable welds, reference material, and a magnifying glass of at least 10-power.

    Performance Standard: The applicant will identify the defective welds and describe their undesirable characteristics.

2. **Project:** Perform a magnetic particle inspection of a steel part. (Level 2)

    Given: A steel part with a known flaw, magnetic particle inspection equipment, and reference material.

    Performance Standard: The applicant will locate the flaw in the part using the magnetic particle equipment.

3. **Project:** Inspect an aircraft part using the dye penetrant method. (Level 2)

    Given: A dye penetrant kit, written instructions, and an aircraft part with a known, invisible surface crack.

    Performance Standard: The applicant will prepare the part for inspection, use the dye penetrant kit, and identify cracks.

4. **Project:** Use an eddy current tester to locate defects in aircraft parts. (Level 3)

Given: A part with known defects, eddy current equipment, and reference materials.

Performance Standard: The applicant will use the test equipment to locate the defect(s) in the part.

5. **Project:** Identify the non-destructive testing method that is most appropriate for use on a specified aircraft part. (Level 2)

Given: An aircraft part and reference material

Performance Standard: The applicant will identify the appropriate nondestructive test procedure(s) that may be used on the part.

Chapter 12 — Cleaning and Corrosion

Oral Questions

1. Is there any requirement for cleaning an aircraft prior to an annual or 100 hour inspection?
    Answer - It is not only good, common sense, but it is a legal requirement as specified in FAR Part 43, Appendix D. (Page Reference: JSGT 12-2)

2. Discuss the general precautions that should be observed when washing an airplane.
    Answer - Avoid or protect areas, which may be damaged or contaminated,such as: Pitot and static ports, hinges, sealed areas, and bearings. (Page Reference: JSGT 12-2)

3. What are some of the more common light-duty cleaning agents?
    Answer - Soap or detergents and water. (Page Reference: JSGT 12-2)

4. What materials are commonly used as heavy duty cleaners?
    Answer - Solvents and emulsions. (Page Reference: JSGT 12-2 & 12-3)

5. What are the preferred cleaners for plastic surfaces such as windshields?
    Answer - Mild soap and water or a manufacturer approved cleaner. (Page Reference: JSGT 12-4)

6. What type of cleaning agents should be used to remove grease, oil or fuel from aircraft tires?
    Answer - Soap and water. (Page Reference: JSGT 12-3)

7. Give at least three examples of the factors that cause or influence corrosion.
    Answer - (1) The environmental conditions (2) The presence of dissimilar metals. (3) The type of metal. (4) The presence of electrolytes and/or contaminants. (5) The condition of protective coatings. (Page Reference: JSGT 12-6)

8. Name at least three forms of corrosion.
    Answer - (1) Surface. (2) Intergranular. (3) Filliform. (4) Dissimilar metal (or galvanic). (5) Oxidation. (6) Pitting. (7) Stress. (8) Fretting.(Page Reference: JSGT 12-9)

9. Name at least one cause of filliform corrosion.
    Answer - (1) Improper or incomplete curing of a wash primer prior to painting. (2) Failure to completely wash off acidic surface contamination. (Page Reference: JSGT 12-12)

10. What are the visible signs of filliform corrosion?
    Answer - Blistered paint surfaces or worm or thread-like tracks or patterns under the paint. (Page Reference: JSGT 12-12)

11. What are the two primary factors that may cause development of stress corrosion cracks?
    Answer - A corrosive environment and sustained tensile stress. (Page Reference: JSGT 12-14)

12. What are the visible signs of fretting corrosion?
    Answer - The corrosion residue has a dark, smoky appearance and often appears around and streaming back from rivet heads. (Page Reference: JSGT 12-14)

13. Why are piano-type hinges prime spots for corrosion?
    Answer - The steel pin and aluminum hinge material are dissimilar metals and he hinge design tends to trap moisture and contaminants. (Page Reference: JSGT 12-24)

14. What is the best way to protect piano hinges from corrosion?
    Answer - Keep them clean and properly lubricated. (Page Reference: JSGT 12-24)

15. Provide at least four examples of procedures used to prevent corrosion.
    Answer - (1) Cleaning (2) Lubrication (3) Treatment (4) Sealing (5) Inspection (6) Installing protective covers (7) Keeping drain holes free and clear (Page Reference: JSGT 12-30)

16. Describe the tools that should be used to remove corrosion from anodized aluminum surfaces.
    Answer - Nylon scrubber pads such as Scotch-Brite™, bristle brushes, aluminum wool or aluminum wire brushes. (Page Reference: JSGT 12-32)

17. Describe the effects of using steel brushes or steel wool to remove corrosion from aluminum surfaces.
    Answer - Steel brushes or steel wool must not be used to clean aluminum because steel particles can become embedded in the aluminum and cause corrosion. (Page Reference: JSGT 12-32)

18. What is the purpose of Alodine?
    Answer - Alodine® is a chemical process that deposits a protective film on aluminum alloys. This film improves corrosion resistance and paint adhesion. (Page Reference: JSGT 12-34)

19. For what reason should you avoid cleaning anodized aluminum surfaces with aluminum metal polish?
    Answer - It should not be used on anodized surfaces because it will remove the oxide coat. (Page Reference: FGH)

20. Why should aircraft fabrics and plastics be cleaned only with recommended cleaners?
    Answer - Recommended cleaners cause the least amount of deterioration or damage. (Page Reference: FGH)

21. List at least five examples of areas in an aircraft that are prone to corrosion.
    Answer - (1) Battery compartments (2) Exhaust trail areas (3) Bilge areas (4) Vent areas (5) Landing gear and wheel wells (6) Fuel tanks (7) Wing flap recesses (8) Around and below galleys and lavatories (9) Piano Hinges (10) Any area that can trap water (Page Reference: JSGT 12-20)

Practical Test

1. **Project:** Identify and explain damage caused by caustic cleaners. (Level 2)

    Given: Samples of cleaner-damaged aluminum and/or magnesium.

    Performance Standard: The applicant will identify cleaner-damaged metal(s) and explain the effects of improper use of caustic cleaners.

2. **Project:** Clean aluminum and/or magnesium with caustic cleaners. (Level 3)

    Given: One or more aircraft parts, caustic cleaner, and instructions.

    Performance Standard: The applicant will mix a solution, apply it to the part(s), and use proper removal techniques. The solution will be the proper strength and the proper soak time will be used to prevent damage to the part(s). Proper safety precautions will be observed to prevent personal injury.

3. **Project:** Identify and select cleaning agents. (Level 2)

    Given: Manufacturer's information, manuals, and product catalogs.

    Performance Standard: The applicant will use reference material to select the correct cleaning materials for steel, aluminum, and magnesium parts.

4. **Project:** Clean an assigned area of an aircraft. (Level 3)

    Given: An aircraft, a cleaning assignment, cleaning supplies, appropriate equipment, and reference material.

    Performance Standard: The applicant will select the proper cleaning supplies and equipment, and use them to clean an assigned area of an aircraft without damage to the finish or components.

5. **Project**: Identify corrosion. (Level 2)

> **Given:** Samples of aircraft parts or materials with and without corrosion.
> **Performance Standard:** The applicant will select the corroded samples and identify the type of corrosion.

6. **Project:** Remove rust and/or corrosion. (Level 3)

> **Given:** Corroded steel and/or aluminum part, cleaning materials, equipment, and reference materials.
> **Performance Standard:** The applicant will select the proper cleaning agent, use the instructions, and remove the corrosion from the part without unnecessary removal of solid metal.

7. **Project:** Demonstrate the procedures used to apply protective coatings to aircraft parts and/or metallic surfaces. (Level 3)

> **Given:** Aircraft parts, protective paint or organic coatings, and reference material.
> **Performance Standard:** The applicant will properly prepare the part for coating, then select and apply paint or an organic coating to the part.

8. **Project:** Clean rubber parts. (Level 3)

> **Given:** An aircraft rubber part in need of cleaning, access to cleaning agents, and reference material.
> **Performance Standard:** The applicant will select the proper cleaning agent and clean the part.

9. **Project:** Remove paint from a corroded aircraft part and determine the extent of corrosion. (Level 3)

> **Given:** A painted aircraft part that has been corroded, paint stripper or paint removing equipment, and reference material.
> **Performance Standard:** The applicant will remove the paint without damaging the part and identify the extent of the corrosion.

10. **Project:** Demonstrate the procedures used to prepare aircraft parts for extended storage. (Level 3)

> **Given:** Aircraft parts, materials, and instructions.
> **Performance Standard:** The applicant will prepare and properly preserve one or more parts for extended storage.

11. **Project:** Demonstrate the procedures used to clean and protect plastics and/or composite materials. (Level 3)

> **Given:** Plastic or composite materials, access to cleaning agents, and reference materials.
> **Performance Standard:** The applicant will select and use the appropriate materials to clean and preserve the assigned materials.

12. **Project**: Locate the instructions and safety information for use with various aircraft cleaning agents. (Level 3)

> **Given:** Access to Material Safety Data Sheets (MSDS) and instructions provided by the manufacturers of cleaning agents.
> **Performance Standard:** The applicant will use the MSDS and manufacturer's instructions to properly clean a part or area of the aircraft.

Chapter 13 — Ground Handling and Servicing

Oral Questions

1. Name at least three possible hazards that may be encountered during typical ground operations, such as during engine run-up or taxiing?
   Answer - The possibility of fire, especially during engine starting. Turning props, rotors, prop or jet blast and inlet areas. Other aircraft, vehicles, people and obstacles. Foreign objects such as rocks, gravel, rags, or loose hardware. High noise levels that might cause hearing damage. Hydraulic lock in radial engines. Weathervaning of tailwheel aircraft. (Page Reference: JSGT 13-16)

2. What is the most generally used knot for tying down small aircraft?
   Answer - The bowline (although other anti-slip knots may be used). (Page Reference: JSGT 13-17)

3. Describe the precautions that should be taken to protect life and property while starting and running an aircraft engine.
   Answer - Study the procedures in the Airplane Flight Manual. Be sure the propeller or inlet area is clear and check for loose stones, gravel, etc. that could be sucked into the prop or engine. Also ensure that the prop or jet blast doesn't blow into hangars or other airplanes, and have a fire guard nearby. (Page Reference: JSGT 13-21)

4. If an engine induction fire occurs while starting a reciprocating engine, what procedure should be followed to extinguish the fire?
   Answer - Continue cranking the engine to start it and suck the fire into the engine. If the engine doesn't start and the fire continues to burn, discontinue the start attempt and extinguish the fire with a suitable fire extinguisher. (Page Reference: JSGT 13-22)

5. What safety procedures must be observed when hand-propping a small aircraft engine?
   Answer - Become thoroughly trained. Have a qualified person in the cockpit, check the brakes, call "SWITCH OFF" before moving the prop, and make sure you have solid footing. When ready to start, call 'CONTACT" and listen for the reply. Swing the prop with the flat of your hand and move back from the prop arc. (Page Reference: JSGT 13-22)

6. What procedure should be followed prior to starting a large radial engine to detect and/or prevent a hydraulic lock in the cylinders?
   Answer - Pull the propeller through by hand for three or four complete revolutions. Resistance to the prop turning indicates a possible hydraulic lock in at least one of the cylinders. (Page Reference: JSGT 13-22)

7. What is the cause of hydraulic lock in large radial engines?
   Answer - Oil seeps by the piston rings and accumulates in the combustion chamber of lower cylinders. When a piston comes up on its compression stroke, the incompressible liquid seizes it. (Page Reference: JSGT 13-22)

8. What is meant by the term "Hot Start" when starting a jet engine?
   Answer - Ignition occurs with an excessively rich mixture, leading to a rapid temperature rise that can exceed the exhaust gas temperature limit. (Page Reference: JSGT 13-23)

9. When towing an aircraft, should you use the tow vehicle or aircraft brakes to stop the aircraft?
   Answer - The tow vehicle brakes should be used except in an emergency - then the aircraft brakes may be used. (Page Reference: JSGT 13-26)

10. Why should an aircraft technician become familiar with standard light signals?
    Answer - Light signals may be used when taxiing an airplane without a radio or when a radio becomes inoperative on a tower controlled airport. (Page Reference: JSGT 13-26)

11. If a mixture of aviation gasoline and jet fuel is used in a reciprocating aircraft engine, what are the possible results?

Answer - Avgas contaminated by jet fuel must not be used in piston engines - the engine may be damaged or destroyed. (Page Reference: JSGT 13-31)

12. What does the number 100 signify in 100LL aviation gasoline?
    Answer - It refers to the lean mixture performance number (or octane rating) of the fuel (Page Reference: JSGT 13-33)

13. Is it permissible to use avgas in a turbine engine?
    Answer - Limited operation may be allowed by the manufacturer. Continued use may reduce efficiency due to lead deposits on the turbine blades. (Page Reference: JSGT 13-33)

14. What are some of the possible outcomes of using a lower grade of avgas than the specified grade?
    Answer - An increased chance of engine damage due to detonation, loss of engine power, and an increased probability of overheating. (Page Reference: JSGT 13-32)

15. Part 23.973 of the FAA regulations specifies that certain markings must be placed adjacent to fuel filler openings. What markings are used for reciprocating engine-powered airplanes?
    Answer - The filler openings must be marked with the fuel grade and the word "AVGAS." (Page Reference: JSGT 13-39)

16. Describe the important precautions that should be observed when fueling an aircraft.
    Answer - Be certain you are using the correct fuel, properly ground the aircraft and refueling unit, and protect the aircraft surfaces from hose and nozzle damage. (Page Reference: JSGT 13-38)

17. The marking requirements for oil tank filler openings are specified by FAR 23.1157. What markings are required for a piston engine powered airplane?
    Answer - The word "OIL" and the permissible grades and/or types or a reference to the appropriate Airplane Flight Manual for permissible grades and/or types. (Page Reference: FGH)

18. Where can the standard aircraft taxi hand signals be found?
    Answer - In the Aeronautical Information Manual (AIM). (Page Reference: FGH)

19. Under what conditions should a reciprocating engine be pre-oiled?
    Answer - Prior to starting a new engine or one that has been preserved for storage. This ensures adequate lubrication on initial startup. (Page Reference: FGH)

20. Under what conditions may automobile gasoline be used in an aircraft engine?
    Answer - Only if approved by the FAA, usually by the issuance of a Supplemental Type Certificate (STC). (Page Reference: FGH)

21. What are the indications of water in aircraft fuel after draining a sample from the fuel sumps?
    Answer - The sample may have a cloudy or hazy appearance or a solid slug of water. (Page Reference: JSGT 13-36)

Practical Test

1. **Project:** Start and operate an aircraft piston engine installed in an aircraft or test cell. (Level 3)

    Given: An aircraft with a fuel injection system, or either a float-type or pressure-injection carburetor, and engine operating procedures

    Performance Standard: The applicant will start the engine, operate the engine through its normal operating range and shut down the engine according to the operating instructions.

2. **Project:** Start and operate an aircraft turbine engine. (Level 3)

Given: An aircraft turbine engine installed in an aircraft, simulator or test cell, and operating limitations and procedures.

Performance Standard: The applicant will start the engine, operate the engine through its normal operating range and shut down the engine according to the operating instructions.

3. **Project:** Prepare an aircraft for a full power run-up. (Level 3)

    Given: An aircraft, tiedown equipment, towing equipment, and an auxiliary power source.

    Performance Standard: The applicant will properly position the aircraft relative to the prevailing wind, secure the aircraft for the engine run, connect a source of external electrical power, clear the blast area, and secure a fireguard.

4. **Project:** Demonstrate the procedures for tying down and securing an aircraft on an outdoor ramp area. (Level 3)

    Given: An aircraft, storing procedures, and tiedown equipment.

    Performance Standard: The applicant will tie down and secure the aircraft so as to prevent damage when stored outside under normal weather conditions.

5. **Project:** Connect a towbar and prepare an aircraft for towing. (Level 3)

    Given: An aircraft, a towbar, and towing procedures.

    Performance Standard: The applicant will properly connect the towbar to the aircraft and prepare for towing according to the procedures provided.

6. **Project:** Demonstrate the hand signals used to direct the movement of aircraft. (Level 3)

    Given: Hand signal charts and live or simulated aircraft movement.

    Performance Standard: The applicant will provide directions using acceptable aviation hand signals.

7. **Project:** Demonstrate the procedures used to locate and clear a hydraulic lock in a piston engine. (Level 3)

    Given: An aircraft or mockup with a piston engine, tools, and instructions.

    Performance Standard: The applicant will locate and remove a simulated hydraulic lock using the procedures that would drain trapped oil from a cylinder.

8. **Project:** Demonstrate the proper procedures for fueling an airplane (Level 3)

    Given: An aircraft, fueling equipment, fueling procedures, and a specified fuel load.

    Performance Standard: The applicant will fuel or simulate fueling of an aircraft using the fueling equipment provided. The aircraft will by fueled to a specified fuel load and fuel location.

9. **Project:** Determine the amount of fuel on board an aircraft. (Level 2)

    Given: An aircraft, a specified fuel load, fuel loading charts, a dipstick, and instructions.

    Performance Standard: The applicant will measure the amount of fuel previously loaded on the aircraft and determine the amount in each tank.

10. **Project:** Identify aviation fuels and describe how to determine the proper fuel grade for different types of aircraft. (Level 2)

    Given: Samples of aviation fuels, a list of aircraft requiring different types and grades of fuel, and appropriate reference materials.

    Performance Standard: The applicant will identify aviation fuel samples by color and select the proper fuel for each aircraft, according to the reference materials supplied.

11. **Project:** Inspect an aircraft fuel system for water contamination. (Level 3)

    Given: An aircraft with fuel on board, fueling procedures, and fuel samples with and without water contamination.

    Performance Standard: The applicant will drain the fuel sumps and check to determine if the fuel system is contaminated with water. The applicant will also identify fuel samples contaminated with water.

12. **Project:** Demonstrate the procedures for extinguishing a fire that occurs in an engine induction system during starting. (Level 3)

    Given: An aircraft, fire extinguishing equipment, and reference material.

> **Performance Standard:** The applicant will demonstrate the proper procedure for extinguishing the fire without discharging the extinguisher.

13. **Project:** Connect an external ground power unit to an aircraft. (Level 2)

> **Given:** An aircraft, ground power unit, and reference material.
>
> **Performance Standard:** The applicant will connect the ground power unit to the aircraft.

14. **Project:** Start and operate a turbocharged aircraft engine. (Level 3)

> **Given:** An engine with a turbocharger, and operating instructions.
>
> **Performance Standard:** The applicant will start the engine, operate it through its normal operating range, and shut down the engine according to the operating instructions.

15. **Project:** Secure a helicopter on an outdoor ramp in anticipation of windy conditions. (Level 3)

> **Given:** A helicopter, ramp tie-down equipment, and the manufacturer's instructions.
>
> **Performance Standard:** The applicant will demonstrate the procedures used to secure the helicopter according to the manufacturer's instructions.

16. **Project:** Secure a turbine-powered aircraft after engine shutdown. (Level 3)

> **Given:** A simulator, mockup, or turbine-powered aircraft, and reference material.
>
> **Performance Standard:** The applicant will demonstrate the proper procedures for securing the engine depending on type (turboprop, turbofan or turbine). The propeller and/or the engine inlets and exhausts will be secured according to the manufacturer's instructions.

17. **Project:** Identify different types of shop and/or flightline fire extinguishers, and discuss their suitability for use on different classes of fires. (Level 2)

> **Given:** One or more fire extinguishers, and reference material.
>
> **Performance Standard:** The applicant will identify the different classes of fires and he extinguishers that may be used to fight them.

18. **Project:** Determine the condition of shop and/or flightline fire extinguishers. (Level 3)

> **Given:** One or more fire extinguishers, and reference material.
>
> **Performance Standard:** The applicant will determine the condition of the extinguishers according to the reference material.

Chapter 14 — Maintenance Publications, Forms, and Records

Oral Questions

1. What federal aviation regulation prescribes the requirements for issuance of a type certificate?
   Answer – FAR (14 CFR) Part 21. (Page Reference: JSGT 14-3)

2. What part of the FARs describes the airworthiness standards for Transport Category airplanes?
   Answer - FAR Part 25. (Page Reference: JSGT 14-2)

3. What part of the FARs describes the performance characteristics that a small aircraft must demonstrate in order to be airworthy?
   Answer - FAR Part 23. (Page Reference: JSGT 14-3)

4. Who is responsible for ensuring that only the most current information is used when performing maintenance on an aircraft?
   Answer - The person performing the maintenance. (Page Reference: JSGT 14-3)

5. Why are Airworthiness Directives issued?
   Answer - To correct unsafe conditions found in aircraft, engines, propellers, or appliances. (Page Reference: JSGT 14-4)

6. How does the FAA notify aircraft owners of unsafe conditions that must be corrected?
   Answer - By issuing Airworthiness Directives. (Page Reference: JSGT 14-4)

7. How do you determine the timeframe within which AD compliance is required?
   Answer - The AD contains the compliance time or period for completing the corrective action. (Page Reference: JSGT 14-4)

8. If a mechanic wishes to develop a checklist for an annual or 100-hour inspection, what publication contains the guidelines for the required inspection items?
   Answer - FAR Part 43, Appendix D contains the scope and detail of an inspection checklist. (Page Reference: JSGT 14-4)

9. How can you determine if the repair of damage is a major or minor repair?
   Answer - FAR Part 43, Appendix A defines major and minor repairs as well as preventive maintenance. (Page Reference: JSGT 14-4)

10. What publication might you consult for guidance when maintaining an old aircraft for which no maintenance manual exists?
    Answer - AC 43.13-1B or its latest revision. (Page Reference: JSGT 14-7)

11. What are Advisory Circulars?
    Answer - Non-regulatory information of interest to the aviation public. (Page Reference: JSGT 14-7)

12. What publication would you consult to determine an aircraft's (or engine's or propeller's) type design and its limitations?
    Answer - The Type Certificate Data Sheets and/or Aircraft Specifications. (Page Reference: JSGT 14-8)

13. In what FAA publication could you find a list of engines approved for use in a specific make and model of airplane?
    Answer - In the Type Certificate Data Sheets and/or Aircraft Specifications. (Page Reference: JSGT 14-8)

14. What reference material can be used to determine if an aircraft is certificated in more than one category?
    Answer - The Type Certificate Data Sheets and/or Aircraft Specifications. (Page Reference: JSGT 14-8)

15. What is the name of the manual that the manufacturer provides to technicians who normally perform work on the systems and components of an aircraft?
    Answer - The aircraft maintenance manual. (Page Reference: JSGT 14-14)

16. Under what circumstances is compliance with a manufacturer's service bulletin mandatory?
    Answer - When the service bulletin is incorporated into an AD (or other approved data). (Page Reference: JSGT 14-14)

17. What kinds of publications are used by aircraft manufacturers to notify owners of design defects and product improvements?
    Answer - Service Bulletins, Service Letters and Service Instructions. (Page Reference: JSGT 14-14)

18. If you need to determine the serviceable dimensional limits for an engine part, what publication would you consult?
    Answer - The current engine manufacturer's overhaul manual. (Page Reference: JSGT 14-14)

19. How often is the summary of ADs published?
    Answer - Every two years. (Page Reference: AIM)

20. As a certificated mechanic, will you automatically receive all ADs?
    Answer – No. ADs are automatically sent only to registered aircraft owners. (Page Reference: AIM)

21. How are AD updates issued to subscribers to the Summary of Airworthiness Directives?
    Answer – Through biweekly supplements. (Page Reference: AIM)

22. Where do you find the minimum scope and detail requirements that a 100-hour inspection checklist must contain?
    Answer - FAR Part 43, Appendix D. (Page Reference: JSGT 14-20)

23. Records of a major alteration must be made in what two places?
    Answer – The aircraft maintenance records and FAA Form 337. (Page Reference: JSGT 14-20)

24. When completion of FAA Form 337 is required, how many copies are normally prepared and what is their distribution?
    Answer – Two signed copies. One is given to the aircraft owner and one is sent to the local FAA Flight Standards District Office within 48 hours of the approval or return to service. (Page Reference: JSGT 14-20)

25. When an aircraft is sold, what do the regulations require regarding the disposition of records that contain the current status of Airworthiness Directives?
    Answer – The seller must transfer the records to the buyer at the time of sale. (Page Reference: JSGT 14-26)

26. For what period of time must an aircraft owner maintain the records of a 100-hour inspection?
    Answer - Until the work is superseded or for one year after the inspection. (Page Reference: JSGT 14- 27)

27. In what publication may a mechanic find an example of a maintenance record entry for a 100-hour inspection?
    Answer - FAR Part 43.11. (Page Reference: JSGT 14-27)

28. Where should a 100-hour inspection be recorded?
    Answer - In the appropriate maintenance record for the airframe, powerplant, propeller or appliance. (Page Reference: JSGT 14-27)

29. What items must be entered into the aircraft records after maintenance is performed?
    Answer - (1) A description of the work performed and/or reference to acceptable data. (2)The date the work was completed.

(3)The signature, certificate number and type of certificate of the person approving the aircraft for return to service. (Page Reference: JSGT 14-27)

30. What person makes the final maintenance record entry after a 100-hour inspection is completed?
    Answer - The person approving the aircraft for return to service. (Page Reference: JSGT 14-27)

31. What documents must be prepared when a required inspection is performed and defects are found which render the aircraft or engine unairworthy?
    Answer - The required maintenance entries must be made and a list of discrepancies and unairworthy items must be furnished to the owner. (Page Reference: JSGT 14-27)

32. What maintenance record entries are required to contain the aircraft total time in service?
    Answer - Only records of inspections require the total time. (Page Reference: JSGT 14-29)

33. What regulation authorizes a certificated mechanic who holds an Inspection Authorization to approve or disapprove a major repair or alteration?
    Answer - FAR 65.95. (Page Reference: JSGT 15-3)

34. Who has the authority to rebuild an aircraft engine and return the operating time to zero?
    Answer - Only the engine manufacturer or an overhaul facility approved by the manufacturer. (Page Reference: FAR-M)

35. Are there any circumstances when more than two copies of Form 337 are required, and if so, when?
    Answer – Yes. Three copies are required when a fuel tank is installed in the passenger or baggage compartment. The third copy must be kept aboard the aircraft. (Page Reference: FAR-M)

36. How do the regulations define "time-in-service" in regard to maintenance record entries?
    Answer - With respect to maintenance entries, "time-in-service" begins when the aircraft leaves the surface of the earth until it touches it at the next point of landing. (Page Reference: FAR-M)

37. What are the penalties for making fraudulent or intentionally false entries in any required record or report?
    Answer - The applicable airmen certificate(s) can be suspended or revoked. (Page Reference: FAR-M)

38. What persons are authorized to make the required maintenance entry approving the return to service after a progressive inspection is performed at a location other than the aircraft's home base?
    Answer - An applicable certificated mechanic. An appropriately rated repair station. The aircraft manufacturer. (Page Reference: FAR-M)

39. What is the difference between the terms "overhaul" and "rebuilding" as they pertain to aircraft engine maintenance records?
    Answer - "Overhauled" engines must be tested to approved or acceptable current standards and technical data. "Rebuilt" engines must be tested to the same tolerance and limits as a new engine. (Page Reference: FAR-M)

40. When performing an inspection required by FAR Part 91, what rotorcraft systems must be inspected in accordance with the manufacturer's maintenance manual or instructions for continued airworthiness?
    Answer -The drive shafts or similar systems. The main rotor transmission gearbox for obvious defects. The main rotor and center section. The auxiliary rotor on helicopters. (Page Reference: FAR-M)

41. How can you determine that an aircraft part or appliance you receive is serviceable?
    Answer - By an approval for return to service in the maintenance record for the part or appliance. With a completed Form 337. (Page Reference: FAR-M)

Practical Test

1. **Project:** Find the Type Certificate Data Sheets or Aircraft Specifications for various aircraft specified by make, model and serial number. (Level 1)

    Given: A list of aircraft with serial numbers and the appropriate FAA publications.

    Performance Standard: The applicant will list the Aircraft Specification or Type Certificate Data Sheet for the assigned aircraft.

2. **Project:** Use the Type Certificate Data Sheets or Aircraft Specifications to determine the C.G. range of an aircraft and/or the maximum allowable gross weight limit. (Level 2)

    Given: FAA publications and a list of aircraft by model and serial number.

    Performance Standard: The applicant will locate the appropriate Type Certificate Data Sheets or Aircraft Specifications and find and list the C.G. range and or maximum allowable gross weight.

3. **Project:** Use the manufacturer's maintenance information to determine the flight control travel limits for a specified aircraft. (Level 2)

    Given: The manufacturer's maintenance information for a specific aircraft make and model, and written instructions.

    Performance Standard: The applicant will list the flight control travel limits as printed in the current manufacturer's manual.

4. **Project:** Locate the Service Bulletins applicable to a particular aircraft component. (Level 1)

    Given: Access to the component and the manufacturer's service bulletins.

    Performance Standard: The applicant will list the service bulletins applicable to the assigned component.

5. **Project:** List the Airworthiness Directives applicable to a specific aircraft and/or engine, appliance, or propeller. (Level 2)

    Given: The make, model and serial number of the aircraft, engine appliance or propeller, and the Summary of AD's.

    Performance Standard: The applicant will locate all relevant AD's that apply to the assigned item and list them.

6. **Project:** Inspect an aircraft to determine if an AD is applicable to that aircraft and whether or not the aircraft is in compliance. (Level 3)

    Given: Access to an aircraft and an AD applicable to that make and model.

    Performance Standard: The applicant will review the AD, inspect the aircraft, and determine the applicability and compliance status.

7. **Project:** Determine which part of an Instructions for Continued Airworthiness is FAA approved. (Level 1)

    Given: A manufacturer's Instructions for Continued Airworthiness and/or a copy of the Code of Federal Regulations, Part 23 or Part 27

    Performance Standard: The applicant will locate and point out the FAA approval of the Airworthiness Limitations sections.

8. **Project:** Determine the correct replacement part number from a manufacturer's illustrated parts catalog. (Level 2)

    Given: The name and location of a specific part, the appropriate parts catalog, and the aircraft serial number.

    Performance Standard: The applicant will use the illustrated parts catalog to locate the specified part, list the correct part number, and verify the units per assembly and useable on code.

9. **Project:** Determine if an STC has been issued for a specific modification to an aircraft. (Level 1)

    Given: An aircraft make, model and serial number that has an STC listing for a specific modification.

    Performance Standard: The applicant will use the STC listings to determine if an STC for the specified modification has been issued for the assigned aircraft.

10. **Project:** Interpret technical information. (Level 2)

Given: Technical references such as AC 43.13-1B, ADs, service instructions, an STC, etc.

Performance Standard: The applicant will review the reference material to select acceptable repair procedures and/or write a short description of the work to be accomplished.

11. **Project:** Verify that instrument range markings and/or placards are correct. (Level 2)

> **Given:** An aircraft flight manual (AFM) or pilots operating handbook (POH), Type Certificate Data Sheets, and a specific aircraft make, model and serial number
>
> **Performance Standard:** The applicant will use the information supplied to determine if the assigned instrument range markings and/or placards are correct and installed as required.

12. **Project:** Select the correct size and ply rating of tires for installation on an aircraft. (Level 2)

> **Given:** The appropriate aircraft specifications or parts manual and a specific aircraft make, model and serial number.
>
> **Performance Standard:** The applicant will use current data to select the proper size and ply rating for the specified aircraft.

13. **Project:** Determine the proper lubricant and lubrication procedure for an aircraft part or system. (Level 2)

> **Given:** An aircraft or engine manufacturer's service manual and a specified aircraft part or engine.
>
> **Performance Standard:** The applicant will locate the proper grades of lubricating oil and the method for lubricating the part or the servicing procedure for the engine.

14. **Project:** Locate and apply technical information contained in a maintenance manual in the performance of maintenance or inspections. (Level 3)

> **Given:** Manufacturer's maintenance manual.
>
> **Performance Standard:** The applicant will use the data to determine how often, what type(s) of lubricants, and the method(s) of application is/are specified for use on the part or system.

15. **Project:** Locate and apply technical information contained in an AD in the performance of maintenance or inspections. (Level 3)

> **Given:** Access to AD's, an aircraft, mockup, or aircraft part or appliance, necessary tools and equipment, and a specific task to perform.
>
> **Performance Standard:** The applicant will locate and apply the information contained in the AD in the performance of a specific maintenance or inspection task.

16. **Project:** Determine conformity by locating and applying the technical information contained in an Aircraft Specification or Type Certificate Data Sheet. (Level 3)

> **Given:** Aircraft Specification or Type Certificate Data Sheets, an aircraft, mockup, or aircraft part or appliance, and necessary tools and equipment.
>
> **Performance Standard:** The applicant will locate and apply the information in the Aircraft Specification or Type Certificate Data Sheet to perform a conformity inspection.

17. **Project:** Prepare a condition report following the inspection of an aircraft, or a portion thereof. (Level 3)

> **Given:** An aircraft or aircraft parts, service or inspection information, and written instructions.
>
> **Performance Standard:** The applicant will use the service or inspection information to inspect the aircraft or part, and produce a written report of the status and condition at the time of inspection.

18. **Project:** Prepare the appropriate maintenance record entries for an actual or simulated repair or alteration. (Level 3)

> **Given:** Information on a completed repair or alteration.
>
> **Performance Standard:** The applicant will prepare an aircraft maintenance record entry to describe the work accomplished in a manner that will comply with the requirements of FAR Part 43.

19. **Project:** Prepare the appropriate maintenance record entries for an actual or simulated routine maintenance operation (Level 3)

> **Given:** Information on a completed routine maintenance operation.

Performance Standard: The applicant will prepare an aircraft maintenance record entry to describe the work accomplished in a manner that will comply with the requirements of FAR Part 43.

20. **Project:** Prepare the appropriate maintenance record entries for an actual or simulated 100-hour inspection. (Level 3)

> **Given:** Information on a completed 100-hour inspeciton.
>
> **Performance Standard:** The applicant will prepare an aircraft maintenance record entry to describe the work accomplished in a manner that will comply with the requirements of FAR Part 43.

21. **Project:** Prepare the appropriate maintenance record entries for an actual or simulated annual inspection. (Level 3)

> **Given:** Information on a completed annual inspeciton.
>
> **Performance Standard:** The applicant will prepare an aircraft maintenance record entry to describe the work accomplished in a manner that will comply with the requirements of FAR Part 43.

22. **Project:** Prepare the appropriate maintenance record entry to indicate compliance with an Airworthiness Directive. (Level 3)

> **Given:** An AD, an instruction sheet, and the method of compliance.
>
> **Performance Standard:** The applicant will prepare an aircraft maintenance record entry to describe the work accomplished in a manner that will comply with the requirements of FAR Part 43.

23. **Project:** Complete an FAA Form 337. (Level 3)

> **Given:** An instruction sheet and a blank FAA Form 337.
>
> **Performance Standard:** The applicant will complete the Form 337 in accordance with FAR Part 43, Appendix B and AC 43.9-1.

24. **Project:** Perform an evaluation of actual or simulated aircraft records. (Level 3)

> **Given:** Samples of aircraft record entries.
>
> **Performance Standard:** The applicant will examine the records and prepare a list of those entries in compliance with FAR Part 43 and a list of entries not in compliance, along with the reasons for non-compliance.

25. **Project:** Evaluate a completed FAA Form 337. (Level 3)

> **Given:** One or more completed Form 337's and AC 43.9-1
>
> **Performance Standard:** The applicant will examine the assigned Form 337's and determine if they contain the required information.

26. **Project:** Research the Summary of AD's and determine which AD's are applicable to a specific airframe, engine and/or propeller. (Level 3)

> **Given:** FAR Part 39, AD summary, current biweekly AD listings, and a specific aircraft and equipment.
>
> **Performance Standard:** The applicant will prepare a list of all AD's applicable to the specific airframe, engine and/or propeller by make, model and serial number.

27. **Project:** Prepare an aircraft maintenance record entry for an actual or simulated minor repair performed by an individual and supervised and approved for return to service by an appropriately rated mechanic. (Level 3)

> **Given:** A description of a minor repair and FAR Part 43.
>
> **Performance Standard:** The applicant will prepare a maintenance record entry that complies with FAR Part 43.

28. **Project:** Prepare a sample of the documents required to record an actual or simulated 100-hour or annual inspection for an aircraft that is not approved for return to service. (Level 3)

> **Given:** A report of the work performed and a list of discrepancies and unairworthy items.
>
> **Performance Standard:** The applicant will prepare the appropriate maintenance record entries and supporting documents in compliance with FAR Part 43.

29. **Project:** Prepare a sample of the maintenance record entry required to indicate compliance with a manufacturer's service bulletin, service letter, or service instruction. (Level 3)

Given: An instruction sheet, a service bulletin, letter or instruction, and instructions on the method of compliance.

Performance Standard: The applicant will write the maintenance record entry for the assigned service bulletin, letter or instruction so as to comply with the requirements of FAR Part 43.

30. **Project:** Prepare an updated equipment list for an aircraft. (Level 3)

    Given: Aircraft records, Type Certificate Data Sheets, and other information as required.

    Performance Standard: The applicant will update the equipment list, show added and removed equipment, and keep the list in compliance with applicable Federal regulations.

31. **Project:** Prepare an aircraft maintenance record entry for approval for return to service after a major repair or major alteration. (Level 3)

    Given: Appropriate instructions, FAA Form 337, and copies of FAR Part 43 and AC 43.9-1.

    Performance Standard: The applicant will prepare the maintenance record entry and complete a Form 337.

32. **Project:** Prepare an aircraft maintenance record entry documenting the installation of a serviceable part. (Level 3)

    Given: A serviceable part tag, maintenance information, and an instruction sheet.

    Performance Standard: The applicant will prepare a maintenance record entry that complies with applicable Federal regulations.

33. **Project:** Complete the proper part or component tag for a part of known condition. (Level 3)

    Given: An instruction sheet, a selected component with pertinent information, and a selection of blank parts tags.

    Performance Standard: The applicant will select an appropriate parts tag and fill in the correct information.

34. **Project:** Prepare a list of discrepancies and unairworthy items following a 100-hour inspection. (Level 3)

    Given: An instruction sheet and the results of an actual or simulated 100-hour inspection.

    Performance Standard: The applicant will prepare a list of discrepancies and unairworthy items in accordance with FAR Part 43.

35. **Project:** Complete a Form 337 for the major repair or alteration of an engine or component that will not be immediately installed (i.e. a spare) (Level 3)

    Given: FAA Form 337, AC 43.9-1, and an instruction sheet.

    Performance Standard: The applicant will complete the FAA Form 337 and identify the proper distribution of copies in accordance with FAA Regulations.

36. **Project:** Locate the applicable regulations pertaining to the requirements for mechanics making maintenance record entries showing approval for return to service for maintenance satisfactorily performed and for inspections other than progressive inspections conducted under Part 91. (Level 2)

    Given: A copy of the Code of Federal Regulations containing multiple parts including Part 43.

    Performance Standard: The applicant will locate and identify the requirements of Part 43.9 and 43.11.

37. **Project:** Complete an FAA Form 8010-4, Malfunction or Defect Report. (Level 3)

    Given: A blank Form 8010-4, and information about a malfunction or defect.

    Performance Standard: The applicant will correctly complete the form.

Chapter 15 — Mechanic Privileges and Limitations

Oral Questions

1. What publication should a mechanic consult to determine if a repair is considered major or minor?
    Answer – 14 CFR (FAR), Part 43, Appendix A. (Page Reference: JSGT 14-4)

2. Where in the FARs will you find the certification requirements for mechanics?
    Answer - FAR Part 65. (Page Reference: JSGT 15-2)

3. What are the ratings issued under a mechanic's certificate?
    Answer - Airframe and Powerplant. (Page Reference: JSGT 15-2)

4. What types of work may a certificated mechanic perform?
    Answer - A mechanic may perform or supervise maintenance, preventive maintenance, or alterations. (Page Reference: JSGT 15-3)

5. Is a certificated airframe mechanic allowed to perform maintenance on engines?
    Answer - Not unless they are supervised by a certificated powerplant mechanic. (Page Reference: JSGT 15-3)

6. What are the limitations to a mechanic's privileges with regard to propellers?
    Answer - A mechanic may not perform or supervise major repairs to, or major alterations of, propellers. (Page Reference: JSGT 15-3)

7. Is a mechanic allowed to repair or alter an aircraft instrument?
    Answer – No. Mechanics may not perform any repairs or alterations on instruments. (Page Reference: JSGT 15-3)

8. What are the requirements for recent experience in order to exercise the privileges of your mechanic's certificate or rating?
    Answer - You must have worked as a mechanic or technically supervised other mechanics for at least 6 months out of the past 24 months. (Page Reference: JSGT 15-3)

9. What authority does a mechanic have regarding approval for return to service?
    Answer - A mechanic may approve an aircraft, airframe, engine, propeller, or appliance for return to service in accordance with the provisions of FAR Part 65. (Page Reference: JSGT 15-3)

10. What are the privileges of an A & P mechanic regarding inspections?
    Answer - A mechanic may perform and approve for return to service an airframe or engine following a 100-hour inspection (Page Reference: JSGT 15-3)

11. What is the duration of a mechanic's certificate?
    Answer - The certificate is valid until surrendered, suspended or revoked. (Page Reference: JSGT 15-3)

12. What are the privileges and limitations of an A & P mechanic regarding major repairs and alterations to airframes and engines, and their approval for return to service?
    Answer - A & P mechanics may perform major repairs and alterations but may not approve them for return to service unless they hold an Inspection Authorization. (Page Reference: JSGT 15-3)

13. In addition to performing maintenance, what other privileges are granted to a powerplant mechanic?
    Answer - A powerplant mechanic may perform a 100-hour inspection on an engine and approve the engine for return to service. (Page Reference: JSGT 15-3)

14. When may a mechanic perform an annual inspection and return the aircraft to service?

Answer - When the mechanic holds an Inspection Authorization. (Page Reference: JSGT 15-3)

15. May a mechanic supervise an inspection (or a portion of an inspection) and then approve the aircraft for return to service?
Answer – No. The mechanic approving the aircraft for return to service must actually perform the inspection. (Page Reference: JSGT 15-3)

16. What is the duration of a temporary airman's certificate?
Answer - 120 days. (Page Reference: FAR part 65)

17. If a mechanic's certificate is revoked, how long must he/she wait before applying for a new certificate?
Answer - One year unless the revocation order states otherwise. (Page Reference: FAR part 65)

18. What should a mechanic do if his or her temporary certificate is about to expire?
Answer – Contact a local FAA office and seek assistance. (Page Reference: FAR part 65)

19. Is a person with a private pilot's certificate allowed to perform maintenance and, if so, what are his/her limitations?
Answer - A pilot may perform preventive maintenance in accordance with FAR Part 43.3, 43.7 and Appendix A on an airplane owned by the pilot. He or she can also approve the aircraft for return to service following that maintenance. (Page Reference: FAR part 43)

20. What are your requirements as an aircraft mechanic when you have a change of address?
Answer – You must notify the FAA in writing within 30 days of any change to your permanent address. (Page Reference: FAR part 65)

Practical Test

1. **Project:** Determine if an aircraft repair or alteration should be classed as major or minor. (Level 2)

    Given: FAR Part 43 and a list of major and minor repairs and alterations.

    Performance Standard: The applicant will use Part 43 to classify the listed repairs and alterations.

2. **Project:** Prepare a change of address notification. (Level 2)

    Given: FAR Part 65

    Performance Standard: The applicant will write a change of address notification that complies with the requirements of Part 65.

3. **Project:** Interpret the privileges and limitations of an airframe or powerplant mechanic. (Level 2)

    Given: A list of maintenance functions such as repairs, alterations, 100-hour inspections and annual inspections with reference to airframes, engines, propellers, appliances, and parts, and FAR Parts 43 and 65.

    Performance Standard: The applicant will review the maintenance functions and list those that may be performed by a mechanic with only the airframe rating OR a powerplant rating.

4. **Project:** Locate the FAR(s) that stipulate the privileges and limitations of a mechanic's certificate. (Level 1)

    Given: FAR Part 65

    Performance Standard: The applicant will locate and list the privileges an limitations of the mechanics certificate.

5. **Project:** List the persons authorized to demand that a certificated mechanic show them his/her certificate. (Level 1)

    Given: FAR Part 65

    Performance Standard: The applicant should list the FAA, NTSB, Federal, State, and local law enforcement personnel.

6. **Project:** List the technical data needed to exercise the privileges of a certificated mechanic with an airframe rating OR a powerplant rating. (Level 2)

   Given: A list of job assignments, FAR Part 65, and reference material.

   Performance Standard: The applicant will determine which rating a person must hold to perform and return to service each job assignment and select the publications needed to perform each assignment.

7. **Project:** List the types of inspections (excluding approved aircraft inspections programs) that a certificated mechanic with both an airframe and a powerplant rating may perform and the FAR reference for each one. (Level 1)

   Given: FAR Parts 43, 65, and 91.

   Performance Standard: The applicant will list the inspections permitted by FAR 65.85, 65.87 and required by Part 91.

8. **Project:** Identify the items and/or operations that are classified as "maintenance" and "preventive maintenance." (Level 1)

   Given: FAR Part 43 with Appendices.

   Performance Standard: The applicant will list the items that are included in the definition of "maintenance" and authorized as "preventive maintenance."

9. **Project:** List the maintenance functions that a certified mechanic may NOT supervise. (Level 2)

   Given: FAR Parts 43 and 65.

   Performance Standard: The applicant will determine those maintenance functions he/she may not supervise as a mechanic.

10. **Project:** List the functions in preparation for a 100-hour inspection that a certified mechanic may NOT supervise. (Level 2)

   Given: FAR Part 43

   Performance Standard: The applicant will indicate that removal of all necessary inspection plates, access doors, fairings, and cowlings, as well as cleaning the aircraft and engine(s), must be accomplished personally by the appropriately rated person performing the inspection.